D1272413

LIFTOFF!

...THE STORY OF

Liftoff!

AMERICA'S SPACEPORT

L. B. Taylor, Jr.

E. P. DUTTON & CO., INC.   NEW YORK   1968

This book is for Norma, a patient and understanding wife . . .
And for Cindy, Chris and Tony, who were born into the Age of Space.

Other books by L. B. Taylor, Jr.

PIECES OF EIGHT: Recovering the Riches of a Lost Spanish
Treasure Fleet (with Kip Wagner)

THAT OTHERS MAY LIVE: The Aerospace Rescue and Recovery
Service

CONTENTS

ILLUSTRATIONS

"This spot appears to me by its rocky and barren character to offer all the conditions requisite for our experiment. On that plain will be raised our magazines, workshops, furnaces, and workmen's huts; and here, from this very spot," said he, stamping his foot on the summit of Stone's Hill, "hence shall our projectile take its flight into the regions of the Solar World."

—*Impey Barbicane,* on the selection of the launch site for the first manned lunar landing mission. (Jules Verne —*From the Earth to the Moon,* 1865)

Chapter 1

DESTINATION: MOON

"On my mark the countdown is at T minus 15 minutes and counting. Three . . . two . . . one . . . mark."

"Close first stage lox interconnect valves."

"Booster lox dome and fuel injector purge on."

"Note launch support ready for forward retract."

"Verify guidance reference release."

"Note launch support ready for ignition."

The voices ringing off the above commands are those of test conductors and stage engineers in firing room one of the Launch Control Center at the National Aeronautics and Space Administration's John F. Kennedy Space Center in Florida.

They are completing the countdown for the greatest adventure in the history of civilization, the first manned lunar landing flight. Three and a half miles from the Control Center, atop the 363-foot-tall Saturn V space vehicle, three astronauts are strapped tightly in their contoured couches inside the Apollo spacecraft. In a few minutes they will attempt to fly Apollo to the moon, explore the lunar surface, and return home.

"T minus 10 minutes and counting," a voice announces over one of the 109 communications circuits monitored by launch crew members. "There will be no smoking in the firing room until further notice."

This is the mission Americans have been working toward since the late president of the United States, John F. Kennedy, made it a national goal on May 25, 1961. Now the flight is less than 10 minutes from beginning.

The count continues. Over the past dozen hours or so, thousands of items have been checked off a master list, the bible of rocketry, the three-inch-thick countdown manual. More than 450 men are in the firing room, each a specialist. They monitor a vast array of electronic panels, checking, inspecting, measuring, testing. The huge launch status board shows all green. There are no problems.

"T minus eight minutes and counting." The words are unnecessary to those in the room. Instinctively, they glance at the winking countdown clock as it silently flicks off the seconds.

"Engine control power—on."

"Telemetry tape recording—on."

A rundown on the prelaunch commentary is broadcast to a site just north of the Control Center. This is the press area. More than 2,000 newsmen, representing television, radio, and papers around the world, stare, transfixed, at the immense "bird" on the pad. The TV commentators are on live, coast to coast and across the oceans via satellite. Reporters have telephones over their shoulders, holding lines open to their editors as they await the moment of liftoff.

"T minus five minutes. T minus five and counting."

"Note instrument unit and spacecraft ready for launch."

"Verify all stages ready for power transfer on."

Long plumes of a white, mistlike substance hang off the 36-story-tall rocket. This vapor is boiling off from the Saturn V's propellants, being vented before the vehicle is pressurized during the last minute or two prior to engine ignition.

At liftoff, it will be like a hundred jet liners screaming at the same instant, but now it is quiet on the pad. There is no one within three miles, save the three spacemen in Apollo. They make last-minute checks of their instrument panels. All is still go.

"T minus three minutes 10 seconds and counting."

"Initiate firing command and verify."

A button is pushed. It triggers an automatic sequencing system. The rest of the countdown will be done automatically. Computers take over. If any trouble develops past this point, machines will electronically shut down the operation. Man mostly monitors the series of final events now taking place.

"T minus two minutes."

A million people have driven down the Florida coast to see this launch; to view this moment of history. They have jammed the beaches from Daytona, 60 miles to the north, to Vero Beach, 70 miles to the south. Cars have clogged highways, sideroads, and cause-

A 363-foot-tall Apollo/Saturn V facilities vehicle in position at Launch Complex 39 of the John F. Kennedy Space Center. This test vehicle will not itself make the actual journey to the moon, but was used to verify launch facilities, train launch crews, and develop test and checkout procedures. (NASA Photo)

ways. Most people have camped overnight. Many have been waiting a week, some longer. They have come from every state and dozens of foreign countries. They have come to see what newspapers have headlined "the greatest story since Columbus sailed to the New World."

"T minus 60 seconds and counting."

Final checks are made with NASA's Manned Spacecraft Center halfway across the country in Houston, Texas. The lunar flight will be controlled from there after launch. The word is "go."

"T minus 30 seconds."

In the large glassed-in booth overlooking the firing room there is a group of distinguished-looking gentlemen. They are U.S. Senators and members of the House of Representatives. Many rank high on Congressional space committees. In the center of the group is a distinguished-looking man wearing a dark suit. He is the President of the United States. He landed at Cape Kennedy's jet strip barely two hours ago. He stands and looks to the east, to the great white rocket. Everyone in the viewing room is looking eastward. The white plumes of vapor have disappeared. The rocket is undergoing final pressurization.

"T minus 15 seconds . . ."

Firing room at the Launch Control Center of the Spaceport during the first flight test of the Apollo/Saturn V lunar launch vehicle, November 9, 1967. (NASA Photo)

All attention is now centered on the launch pad. On the beaches, binoculars are raised to eye level; at the VIP bleachers, everyone stands. Newsmen, with direct phone lines open to their papers and radios in New York, London, Tokyo, and a thousand other cities around the world, repeat the words: "T minus 15 seconds." Network telecasters turn from facing the cameras to view the massive moon rocket. Fingers are crossed, rosaries kissed, handkerchiefs gnawed, breaths held, tiptoes stood upon. Everywhere, for 75 miles surrounding Complex 39, hundreds of thousands of people strain their eyes for a clear view.

In the Launch Control Center there is silence. No one is talking. On the main floor, everyone eyes overhead television monitors. They won't be able to pick up the rocket through the windows until it has cleared the pad and is on its way. Too, they must monitor its movements, measure its heartbeat. Tension works through subconsciousness. Lucky coins are rubbed, lucky neckties are tugged at; more fingers are crossed.

Then the lone voice again breaks the silence: "T minus 10 seconds and counting . . . nine . . . ignition! We have ignition!"

Within milliseconds of one another, the five Saturn V engines erupt like inverted volcanoes, spewing fire and smoke down the huge flame deflector at the base of the pad. In an instant, all five are roaring simultaneously, whipping thunderous shock waves across the flat oceanfront. The towering rocket vibrates violently under the tremendous strain. Huge sheets of ice that have formed on its metallic skin chilled by the super-frigid propellants within, flake off and crash to the ground in an avalanche of whiteness.

"Seven . . . six . . . five . . . four . . ."

Rivers of flame gush down the scorched deflector and funnel out on both sides of the pad for several hundred feet. For nearly nine seconds the rocket remains locked on its mobile launcher. The ground for miles around rumbles as if an earthquake were taking place. One is, a man-made earthquake! As the throbbing shock waves roll across the flatlands, thousands of birds take wing, darkening the skies. Rabbits, raccoons, opossums, and armadillos scamper through the undeveloped scrub brush. The nearest human observers, more than three miles away, squint at the brilliant fireball under Saturn V, then shield their eyes. Others instinctively clasp hands over their ears to shut out the near-deafening roar. The seconds seem like an eternity.

"Three . . . two . . . one . . ."

High in the Apollo cockpit the three astronauts grip hard on their couch armrests. Though their spacecraft is built to withstand heat and shock, the vibrations set off by the flaming niagaras of power at the base of the booster are bone-rattling.

Precisely at 8.9 seconds after the cry of ignition, the powerful steel holddown arms that had been clamping the straining giant to the pad during engine thrust buildup are released.

"Liftoff! We have liftoff!"

The rocket is free. Slowly, ever so slowly, it begins to rise. A 36-story-tall cylindrical building in flight. The behemoth engines bellow under the 6.2-million-pound load they must lift. The 7.5 million pounds of thrust the five F-1 engines are now generating equals 180 million horsepower, or the equivalent power of nearly 3,000 diesel locomotives.

Ominously, standing by at special roadblocks are teams of doctors, nurses, safety officials, ordnance experts, and recovery specialists. If there is a launch site explosion, they are ready to move in. Should the moon rocket blow up on the pad it would shatter with the force of more than 1.2 million pounds of TNT, creating a monumental fireball.

Specially trained firemen in asbestos suits also stand by, in heavily armored vehicles. If the Apollo spacecraft is trapped in an on-site fire, they will brave the flames and push the capsule free. In thick underbrush and along the beachfront, amphibious Larc vehicles patrol. Overhead, helicopters manned by pararescuemen hover at points surrounding the complex. If, after engine ignition, the astronauts sense trouble in the rocket, they can trigger the launch escape tower atop Apollo. This would pull them free of the Saturn V, shooting them up for several hundred yards, where they would then float back to earth under large parachutes. The helicopters and amphibious vehicles, each carrying firemen and medical specialists, would speed to the crash-landing scene.

An instant after liftoff, when the rocket is but three quarters of an inch off the ground, a switch is tripped, disconnecting the umbilicals carried by five of the nine swing arms on the mobile launcher. The other four arms had been retracted earlier in the countdown. The Saturn V has now been fully committed to flight. If something goes wrong from this point on, the mission will have to be aborted. Once liftoff has occurred, the engines cannot be shut down.

One by one, the disconnected umbilical cables and fuel lines quickly withdraw, snatching back like plugs pulled from wall sockets. Heat inside the engines runs between 5,000 and 6,000 degrees

As a niagara of searing flame beats down on the launching pad, the first Apollo/Saturn V lunar space vehicle lifts off from Complex 39 at Kennedy Space Center. On this test mission in November, 1967, the launch vehicle third stage and Apollo spacecraft twice orbited the earth. The third stage then reignited to place the Apollo spacecraft into a new orbit, during which the spacecraft reached an apogee of 11,234 miles before reentering the earth's atmosphere to splash down in the Pacific Ocean. (NASA Photo)

Fahrenheit. Fire perhaps half this hot beats back down on the pad, peeling paint and scorching cables and other exposed materials on the mobile launcher as Saturn V begins its climb to destiny.

The enormous bulk of the rocket slows its ascent. Ninety percent of the weight is propellants. There are 534,000 gallons of kerosene and liquid oxygen in the booster tanks alone: enough to fill 48 fuel tank cars. But the load rapidly decreases. The F-1 engines have a gargantuan thirst. They gulp 3,500 gallons a second. Saturn V begins to move more swiftly now. It clears the mobile launcher, over 400 feet above the pad. Still, the torturing flames spew to the ground in a dazzling fireworks display. Tons of water are pumped onto the pad and mobile launcher to cool them.

At the press site and all along the beaches, hundreds of thousands of proud Americans scream and squeal in delight at the spectacular sight. "Go, baby, go!" they cry. Some pray, some shout; others stand silent, in total awe. In the Launch Control Center, technicians turn from watching the pad to the maze of electronic instruments before them. Dials and meters and plotting boards tell them how the bird is flying. Five miles away, inside the Range Control Center at Cape Kennedy, an alert Air Force Range Safety Officer eyes instrumentation in front of him, telling him if Saturn V is following its scheduled flight plan; if it is on course. If it is not, this man must trigger switches to blow the bird out of the sky, a second or two after the astronauts have been pulled free by the launch escape tower.

Inside the cockpit, the crushing forces of the liftoff press the three pilots deep into their couches. There is an extraordinary sight just outside their windows, but they have no time now to see the shrinking earth. There are more than 450 switches, lights, dials, knobs, meters and other instruments they must monitor and record. They are too busy to enjoy the view . . . or worry about how well the rocket is functioning.

Saturn V rises straight up for several seconds, until it has cleared the mobile launcher. Then it performs a roll maneuver to align with the desired launch azimuth. About a minute and a half into the flight, the rocket is eight miles high and passing through one of its most critical phases: the region of maximum dynamic pressure on the vehicle, known as "Max Q." If there is a structural flaw in any stage of the vehicle it could literally shake apart at this altitude. There are "oohs" and "ahhs" from the onlookers as a long vapor or contrail plumes in the icy thin air high over the Florida coast.

One hundred and fifty-five seconds after liftoff, the inboard en-

Apollo/Saturn V after liftoff on its first and highly successful test flight in November, 1967. (NASA Photo)

gine shuts down. The four outboard engines cut off four seconds later. Their job is done. They have shoved the rocket 38 miles up and 65 miles downrange to the southeast. It is now moving at 6,000 miles per hour. Tracking of its movements has been continuous, as have communications between the flight crew and the ground. Now, personnel stationed on Grand Bahama Island, 180 miles southeast of the launch site, have picked up the bird.

Second-stage ullage rockets and first-stage retrorockets are fired, separating the spent booster from the still-live upper stages and spacecraft. The S-IC booster tumbles free, and plummets into the ocean. At this point the five J-2 engines of the second stage roar to life, and in seconds they are revved to full steam—more than one million pounds of thrust.

This remarkable sight is still visible to the masses back on the Florida coast. But the 363-foot rocket is now only a tiny speck in the sky; one that is disappearing fast. Approximately 25 seconds after second stage ignition, the S-IC-S-II forward interstage is jettisoned. This is followed, five seconds later, by the jettisoning of the launch escape tower. If serious trouble develops now, Apollo's service propulsion system has the capability to separate the spacecraft from the launch vehicle. The escape tower thus becomes excess weight and can be expended.

The second stage burns for a little more than six minutes, and then its engines shut down. The rocket is now out of visible sight from earth observers. Electronic eyes continue to follow its every move, however, and communications with the astronauts are never broken. The S-II has reached a peak acceleration of 16,000 mph, just a little short of the speed needed to inject the third stage and Apollo into earth orbit. Saturn V is now about 100 miles up and 950 miles downrange. The second stage separates from the third stage and drops off. It, too, has completed its task.

The single third stage J-2 engine now fires, and soon reaches the necessary 17,500 mph speed to obtain orbit. When word comes that this has been accomplished, 11 minutes after liftoff, there is another cheering roar from the crowds watching the launch in person and on television. The first leg of the flight has been covered without incident. So far so good.

After burning for only two and a half minutes, the third stage engine shuts down. Its job is only half over. As the Apollo-Saturn V S-IVB stage combination sails into its first orbit of earth, contact with ground stations is temporarily lost. But the spacecraft has been acquired by tracking instrumentation aboard a ship some 1,600 miles southeast of Cape Kennedy, in the Atlantic. The ship confirms that Apollo is in a safe orbit, and speeds 100 miles up the command to continue the mission.

For the next three hours there is time to relax a little. Apollo swings around earth twice as the astronauts and the mission controllers on the ground check and recheck every system. The craft is circling in what is known as a parking orbit. If anything goes wrong during this time, the pilots will be called back to earth and the lunar mission will be cancelled. The men can circle the globe three times if necessary to complete the final checks.

Computers at the Manned Spacecraft Center calculate trajectory and orbit, and determine the exact instant when to refire the third stage engine. It comes on the second pass over the Pacific Ocean. The go signal is given to aim for a translunar injection, to aim not

Facing Page: Course of Apollo's manned lunar landing and return to earth. (Courtesy of NASA)

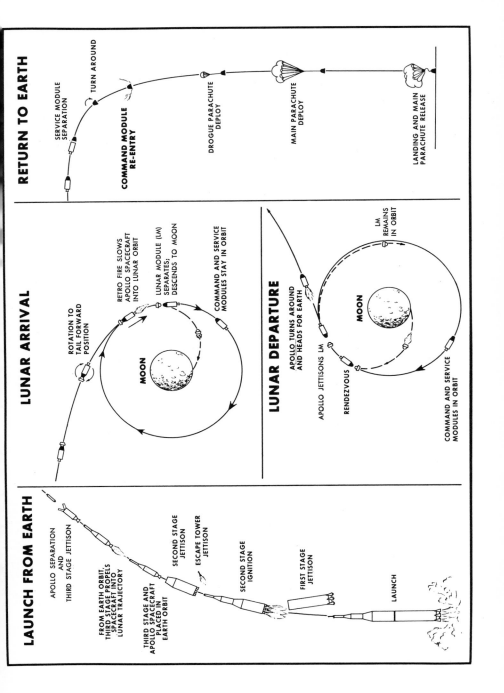

RETURN TO EARTH

SERVICE MODULE SEPARATION

TURN AROUND

COMMAND MODULE RE-ENTRY

DROGUE PARACHUTE DEPLOY

MAIN PARACHUTE DEPLOY

LANDING AND MAIN PARACHUTE RELEASE

LUNAR ARRIVAL

ROTATION TO TAIL FORWARD POSITION

RETRO FIRE SLOWS APOLLO SPACECRAFT INTO LUNAR ORBIT

LUNAR MODULE (LM) SEPARATES; DESCENDS TO MOON

COMMAND AND SERVICE MODULES STAY IN ORBIT

MOON

LUNAR DEPARTURE

APOLLO TURNS AROUND AND HEADS FOR EARTH

LM REMAINS IN ORBIT

APOLLO JETTISONS LM

RENDEZVOUS

MOON

COMMAND AND SERVICE MODULES IN ORBIT

LAUNCH FROM EARTH

APOLLO SEPARATION AND THIRD STAGE JETTISON

FROM EARTH ORBIT, THIRD STAGE PROPELS SPACECRAFT INTO LUNAR TRAJECTORY

THIRD STAGE AND APOLLO SPACECRAFT PLACED IN EARTH ORBIT

SECOND STAGE JETTISON

ESCAPE TOWER JETTISON

SECOND STAGE IGNITION

FIRST STAGE JETTISON

LAUNCH

at where the moon is now but where it will be in 70 hours, when the astronauts will reach it.

The moon is a satellite itself. It orbits earth and is constantly moving, as earth is, around the sun. This presents a complex but solvable problem to navigators in space. The earth's speed at 67,000 mph relative to the sun must be planned for, as well as the speed of the moon, at 2,300 mph relative to the earth. Add to this Apollo's coasting speed between the two orbiting spheres, about 3,300 mph, and the complexity of hitting the moving target from a moving base with a moving projectile becomes more readily apparent.

The actual commit point for translunar injection is at least seven minutes before the S-IVB third stage engine is fired up for the second time. The restart sequence takes this long. The spacecraft continues in earth orbit once this sequence begins. It crosses the South Pacific, flies over Hawaii, and approaches the west coast of the United States.

Then the 200,000-pound-thrust engine reignites and burns for five and a half minutes, ramming the speed to a velocity of about 25,000 mph. Apollo frees itself of earth orbital bonds and coasts in space, toward its legendary target, the moon. Communications with earth are lost, but are regained within eight minutes of the translunar injection. All is still okay. The signal comes through.

"Proceed."

The astronauts now detach the command and service modules as one unit from the lunar module and S-IVB third stage. In an intricate maneuver, they rotate 180 degrees until the nose of the spacecraft is head to head with the top of the LM. Then, ever so gently, they nudge Apollo into a docking position at this angle. It is difficult, but astronauts have practiced this for years, on the ground and in earth orbit, first with Gemini, and later with early Apollo missions. Now the command and service modules are again linked with the lunar module, locked tightly in place by 12 latches.

Upon completion of the transposition, the used Saturn V third stage and the lower part of the lunar module adapter become excess luggage and are jettisoned. At this point, Apollo is more than 9,000 miles above earth, sailing toward the moon. It has been on the translunar trajectory for an hour. The spacecraft is being listened to by some of the world's most sensitive "ears," the deep space tracking stations at Goldstone, California, Canberra, Australia, and Madrid, Spain. Eighty-five-foot antennas at these sites will follow the entire flight. Apollo's flight path is accurately determined by extensive ground tracking. Meanwhile, the crew makes a series of star-landmark sightings to check out their space mode of navigation, which is a backup to the ground navigation.

About three to five hours after the translunar injection has been made, a critical phase of the mission arrives—the midcourse correction. Though the craft may be only a fraction off the line it needs to follow to go into orbit around the moon, the distance it must travel through space is so vast that this fraction would be greatly multiplied if nothing were done, and Apollo could fly past the moon and into the eternities of space. Thus, it is necessary to correct the flight direction toward its moving lunar target. The service module's reaction control system is used if the midcourse maneuver is minor; if more power is needed, the service module propulsion system fires.

For key events in the mission such as midcourse, all three astronauts participate. At other times only one or two are active. The astronaut seated on the left is the spacecraft commander. He is in charge of the flight. The man in the center seat is the command module pilot, who doubles as a systems engineer, and has a general knowledge of all onboard systems. The third astronaut, on the right, is the navigation specialist, and is designated as lunar module pilot. All three are cross-trained to the point where any one man can do another's job if necessary.

Following midcourse correction, the crew settles back for an earned rest. Their spaceship is dead on the mark, and they will coast along for another two and a half days before nearing their destination. There is relaxation now for the first time on earth, too. Flight controllers have done all they can for the time being. Periodically, pilots make status checks of all equipment, and of their position and velocity, which is also continually monitored from the ground. One crew member uses a specially designed sextant from time to time to take star sightings and check Apollo's in-flight alignment.

About one hour after entering the moon's sphere of influence, a second midcourse correction is made. The astronauts then rest again, the last time before they land. Understandably, sleep comes hard. When they awake, one of the three men slips through the tunnel connecting the command and service modules with the lunar module. He checks all LM systems to verify that they are still able to function properly for the landing. Should he discover any trouble areas, the mission may be called off.

From earth, now more than 200,000 miles away, the astronauts get word they are indeed on the proper course. They get the "go" sign to proceed to lunar orbit insertion. They are now together again in the command module. The moon's gravitational pull becomes stronger than distant earth's, and Apollo plunges swiftly toward the surface. A few minutes later, the craft passes out of earth's line of sight, the service module propulsion system ignites for about six minutes, and Apollo slows down and is neatly inserted into a circular orbit around the moon, 80 miles above its pocked face. Another major step has been successfully taken. There are more cheers on earth, and for a brief time, some relief from the ever-mounting tensions of the flight.

For the next five and a half hours the astronauts sail around the moon, making three passes over its front side, where Apollo's movements can be watched by ground trackers. The crew scans the mountains and craters below and makes a series of landmark sightings in the vicinity of the landing area. Again the word comes through.

"Apollo, you are go for lunar module descent."

The green light is what the astronauts have been waiting for. There are joyous whoops in the cockpit. Two crewmen embrace the third pilot. He wishes them well as they crawl, feet first, through the connecting tunnel to the LM. The third man will not land with them. He will remain with the command and service modules in lunar orbit until they have landed, explored, and then flown back to rendezvous with him. His is a lonely scouting task, but one that is vital to the success of the mission.

A short five-second burn of the LM's reaction control system's small thrusters is all that is needed to separate the men and their machines. The astronauts maneuver the lunar module as a driver handles an old-fashioned milk truck. There are no seats. They stand. By standing, they can also lean forward and get a better view of their landing site. Gradually, the two vehicles drift apart. They coast in orbit for 30 minutes. Then, behind the moon, the LM's descent engine is fired.

All earth is awake now . . . listening. Every word, every signal is relayed a quarter million miles through space to an anxious audience. The descent engine burns for 32 seconds; not long, but enough to exit from lunar orbit and coast toward the surface. For an hour it slowly descends until it reaches to within 10 miles of the moon. Here, the pilots receive a final source of navigation data from earth, which has been tracking their descent. If, for some reason, the decision is made not to initiate powered descent, the LM is in a safe orbit. It can still rendezvous with the command and service modules, or, if necessary, the third astronaut could perform a rescue.

Surface of the moon photographed from the Lunar Orbiter 3 unmanned spacecraft, which was then about 160 miles south of Galilei, largest crater shown in the background, and about 38 miles above the lunar mountains and craters. (NASA Photo)

However, once the landing has been committed, should anything go wrong with the lunar module, there is no return. There is no way to get back. That is why so many checks and rechecks have been made before this commitment was okayed. That is why tens of thousands of skilled workmen put their best efforts into the construction of the bug-like device the astronauts have entrusted their lives to. A failure now could be fatal. And it would be a colossal fiasco before the eyes of the world. But the crewmen have absolute faith in the vehicle, complete confidence in the flight controllers who have guided them this far. They know they are flying a ship that is the best man can make, and they harbor no fears. Failure, in fact, is the farthest thing from their minds.

The decision flashes through space.

"Go!"

The astronauts fire the descent engine again. They are now totally committed to a lunar landing. The LM brakes for almost eight minutes, until it is about a mile and a half above the surface. Phase two of the descent, the final approach phase, is then reached. At 11,000 feet, the pilots see the planned landing site through the bottom of their triangular window. Though they view it for the first time, it is a familiar scene. They have studied close-up photos taken earlier by unmanned Ranger, Surveyor, and Lunar Orbiter spacecraft.

At an altitude of 500 feet the landing phase is entered. The men make a detailed assessment of the touchdown point. Over the last 100 feet down, they hover slowly, much as a helicopter does on landing. The command pilot controls the vertical descent. The moon's surface comes closer . . . 50 feet . . . 20 feet . . . a whirlwind of dust kicks up. There are no familiar landmarks, like trees or houses, to help the astronauts judge their altitude and distance. The dust storm, caused by the descent engine's torrent of flames, fools normal radars. The men rely, instead, on their eyes. They reach 10 feet . . . five feet . . . *touchdown!* The podlike feet of the lunar module sink slightly, then hit rock and settle onto the new environment after digging a few inches into the terrain.

Apollo has landed!

The astronauts restrain their emotions. They begin a systematic checkout of all instruments to see whether their craft has suffered any damage on impact. After everything is inspected and okayed, they ask—through hundreds of thousands of miles of space—for permission to step out of their cabin and onto the lunar surface. Permission is granted. Each man dons an extravehicular mobility unit—a veritable life pack that will feed him oxygen to breathe. They depressurize the cabin and open the forward hatch, an hour and three quarters after landing.

The commander crawls through the hatch and lowers himself down a 12-foot ladder. Carefully, he steps upon the surface of the moon!

In so doing, he instantaneously becomes the most famous explorer in the history of mankind. Marco Polo, Leif Ericson, Christopher Columbus, Magellan, Sir Francis Drake, Balboa, Ponce de León, John Smith, the Pilgrims, Lewis and Clark, the Wright Brothers, Admiral Peary, Sir Edmund Hillary and Tenzing—collectively, their accomplishments pale by comparison with the technological miracle that has just been performed. One man has set foot upon the moon. Hundreds of thousands of fellow earthlings helped him there.

It is the most spectacular feat man has ever accomplished. In New York, Los Angeles, Houston, Detroit, all over America, there is riotous cheering. There is joy, celebration, and deep pride. The President conveys his congratulations through space. Sirens blare, flags fly, parades are formed, schools are let out. A national holiday is declared. It is one of the few truly epic moments of history. This day, this hour, this minute will live forever. It is Washington at Valley Forge, Lincoln at Gettysburg. It is VE- and VJ-day in one. It is momentous, overpowering, unifying. It is the crowning culmination of more than a decade of hard work, pressure, tensions, failures, and frustrations. It is a memorial to Gus Grissom, Ed White, Roger Chaffee, and the other astronauts who did not live to see this day of days. Books will be written about this man, movies made, parades will be held, medals pinned on him, audiences will clamor to hear him, the nation's youth will idolize him. With a single footstep he has become *the* hero. He is the first to realize and point out that he only carried the ball across the goal line, the team deserves the real credit. But it is the way of his countrymen to single him out for individual idolation.

But his is not merely a national accomplishment. This sole astronaut is representing all the peoples of the world. In London, Paris, Rome, Moscow, Tokyo, Melbourne, Buenos Aires, Mexico City, Cairo, Johannesburg—everywhere—the feelings are the same. Everyone has hoped and prayed and pulled for this brave team of astronauts. Everyone. For this minute, for this occasion, the world has forgotten its troubles. They now seem such petty troubles. One man has banded together the earth's billions; its colors, creeds, and differ-

Artist's conception of an astronaut on the moon using a hand TV camera to send close-up views of lunar scenery to the world. Beyond him is the Apollo lunar module. (Courtesy of NASA and North American Rockwell)

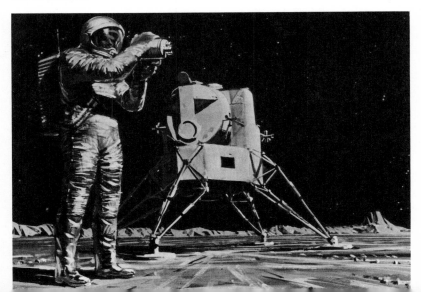

ences, for this instant, vanish. For this man has transcended earthly concerns. He has opened a new horizon, a new frontier.

Man is on the moon!

That man is oblivious to the cheers, the shouting, the celebrating. He is busy. It has taken more than 10 years to get him to the lunar surface. He knows he must leave in a few hours and there is much work to do. He has not a moment to waste. He first inspects the outside of the lunar module for any possible damage incurred upon landing. Measurements are made of the landing gear stroke, and of the depression made by the foot "pods" of the LM. This information may prove invaluable for future flights. He erects an antenna, to relay TV photos to his home planet.

Meanwhile, the LM pilot makes a detailed description and photographic record of the lunar terrain from his vantage point on the module's forward boarding platform. Then he, too, descends to the surface. Together, they unload equipment, including the lunar surface experiments package. Their first scientific task is to gather lunar samples. They fill sterilized plastic containers with nearby specimens of the surface materials.

Man moves easily on the moon. Its gravitational field is only one sixth that of earth's, and there is a sensation of buoyancy. The 150-pound astronauts now effectively weigh only 25 pounds each. Overhead, stars are double in number, size, and brightness. Earth is a hazy bluish ball veiled partly in white. It glows with an eerie brilliance that bathes the crater valleys and peaks in a strong light.

For three hours the astronauts explore this strange world, gathering more samples farther from their landing point and setting out experiments, seismometers, and radiation detectors, among other equipment, which will be left behind to continue relaying data back to earth. Then they reenter the lunar module, pressurize it, eat, and sleep—or try to—for six hours.

Following the rest period and another meal, they leave their craft again. This time they venture farther afield, 1,000 feet out, walking, observing, photographing, sampling, examining, leaving footprints in virgin terrain with every step. For three or four hours they wander, alone, a quarter million miles from home.

All too quickly, their time is up. Reluctantly, they trek back to their machine. They have been on the surface 18 hours. They face a long voyage. Inside the lunar module, they check all systems thoroughly and prepare for launch. This is another critical point in the mission. The ascent engine must fire perfectly or the astronauts will

The first view of the earth ever taken by a spacecraft from the vicinity of the moon. The photo was transmitted by Lunar Orbiter 1, which was then about to pass behind the moon. The crescent earth is at left, the moon at right. (NASA Photo)

remain forever marooned. Now, they have no team of scientists and engineers available to help them as they did when they began their trip. They are alone and are solely dependent upon the reliability of this one small engine. There are no rescue crews standing by.

When their teammate, the astronaut still orbiting the moon in the command module, is properly aligned, they fire the LM's ascent engine. The vehicle lifts off! They rise vertically for 12 seconds. Soon, they have attained orbital velocity. The main ascent burn takes about six and a half minutes. Once in lunar orbit, the LM acquires and tracks the CSM with the rendezvous radar to determine its position. The two craft are about 350 miles apart. Both are also being tracked by earth stations.

Slowly, the astronauts maneuver the LM toward the leading command module, guided by radar, across the moon's face and around its back side. It closes in on an intercept trajectory. Visual sighting of the lead spacecraft is made, and the LM is jockeyed into position for docking. Again, long hours of actual, in-space rendezvous and docking practice are used to fullest advantage. Flick firings of small thrusters inch the lunar module forward until the two vehicles are joined.

In the next hour or a little longer, the LM is deactivated and the history-making astronauts crawl back through the tunnel and greet their companion. Its job completed in excellent fashion, the lunar module is jettisoned into space. The command and service modules remain in lunar orbit for another pass while the astronauts carry out systems readiness checks and exchange data with earth. Proper alignment is then made for the next crucial phase of the mission: transearth injection—the long flight home.

This occurs on the back side of the moon, in darkness. The service module propulsion system burns for about two minutes, eating four tons of propellants. The bonds of lunar orbit are broken. Apollo is now on its long coast toward earth. The crew members, weary from excitement and work, go to sleep.

For the next two and a half days, they sail through the vast ocean of space, making midcourse corrections similar to the ones executed en route to the moon. The first is made about 10 hours after injection into the transearth coast, and the second one comes about two hours before reentry. About 15 minutes before this, at an altitude of more than 2,500 miles above earth, the service module has been jettisoned, its last job having been completed with the final midcourse correction engine firing.

Apollo left the Spaceport on a 363-foot-tall, 6.2-million-pound vehicle. All that remains now is the comparatively tiny cone-shaped command module. To regain the earth, the astronauts must guide their craft into a narrow corridor, 300 miles wide and 40 miles deep. If they miss, there are two gruesome alternatives. (1) by hitting it too steeply, abrupt deceleration in the thickening air will crush them like "ants under a boot"; (2) if their angle of descent is too high, they will miss the reentry altogether and skip off into the horizon, eventually winding up in a permanent circuit of the sun, sealed in the most expensive coffin ever built!

Dr. Hugh L. Dryden, the late deputy director of NASA, once described how difficult it is to hit this corridor upon reentry. "Indeed, the accuracy requirement seems fantastic, equivalent to shooting the nap off a tennis ball, but not hitting the ball, from a distance of 100 yards."

Despite the gloomy analogies, the astronauts correctly orient Apollo to the entry attitude, using its reaction control jets. They begin their return into the earth's atmosphere over the western Pacific at about 400,000 feet altitude. The guidance system does its job well. They enter the corridor on target. But the dangers are not over. Tremendous heat enwraps the blunt end of the spacecraft as it plunges back into earth's atmosphere at seven miles a second. Flames lap at the heatshield. Temperatures soar to an unbelievable 5,000 degrees Fahrenheit—twice the reentry heats Mercury capsules were subjected to. But the shield has been tested on previous flghts to withstand such heat-force, and it absorbs the fire, protecting the passengers and equipment inside.

The reentry phase of the mission is not in line of sight to a regular ground station, but an Australian tracking site picks up Apollo, then ships in the mid-Pacific follow it, and the astronauts guide it in for landing. Their every move, every heartbeat is followed now. Live television cameras whir aboard Navy carriers in the prime recovery area of the Atlantic Ocean, several hundred miles east and south of their point of origin at the Spaceport. Electronic eyes scan the horizon for the first report of sighting.

For two minutes, the world holds its breath. The astronauts pass through a zone of ionization where all communications are blacked out. There is absolutely no word from the crew during this period, and though there is no reason for concern—it is a natural physical phenomenon that is expected on all manned reentries—there *is* anxiety. For this moment, the spacecraft has been lost.

Suddenly, with dramatic flair, an announcement is made aboard Apollo that is instantaneously beamed around the globe.

"Apollo Control, the drogue chutes have deployed." Then, seconds later, comes the follow-up everyone has been waiting to hear: "We have main chute deployment at 10,000 feet. What a beautiful sight!"

From the prime recovery carrier comes another exclamation: "We have sighted the parachutes. We can see Apollo!"

With this, there is a tumultuous chorus of cheers aboard the huge ship, its decks lined with sailors, recovery specialists, doctors, debriefing officers, photographers, and press representatives. Also aboard to greet the returning heroes is the Vice President of the United States and several members of the Congressional space committees.

Helicopters have been in the air for 30 minutes. Now they converge on the landing area. Apollo glides toward the water under three billowing, brilliant red and white parachutes. It hits the surface of the ocean with the same force a swimmer encounters when diving off a 12-foot board, and the chutes drag it sideways for an instant, but its wide bottom quickly uprights the craft again, and the chutes are automatically cut loose. Frogmen leap from hovering helicopters and swim to the pioneer spacecraft. As the astronauts complete their final reading of instruments and check their gear inside, the team of divers affix a flotation collar around Apollo to guard against the possibility of sinking.

Minutes later a hatch opens and one of the pilots pops his head out. A broad grin on his face, he raises his right thumb high in the air to indicate that all is well with the crew. This scene, photographed from a low-hovering chopper directly overhead, is to become one of the most famous news pictures of all time.

One by one, the three astronauts are hauled into a helicopter and flown to the nearby carrier. As they step upon the deck, pandemonium breaks loose. The Navy band, playing the National Anthem, can barely be heard above the whistles and cheering. The moon conquerors are home safely. Admirals and seamen, scientists and senators cry unashamedly. The Vice President runs to the crewmen and embraces each one as a thousand shutters click. No words can adequately describe the emotions of everyone on the carrier.

Never again will these three men ever step foot in public without instant recognition. Parades will be held for them, joint sessions of Congress called, streets and schools named for them, scholarships awarded in their honor, memorials built. They are not mere national heroes. Their fame is international. They are now ambassadors of the world, for they have represented earth in man's greatest adventure, man's greatest exploration, man's greatest conquest. Their journey began but eight days before. It will be relived for the rest of their lives, for all recorded history.

Man has landed on the moon and returned home safely.

This is how it will be when astronauts actually do make the first manned lunar landing. It has not happened yet. It will happen one day soon. Perhaps in 1969, 1970, 1971. Perhaps, depending upon the solution of the vast technological problems to be solved enroute, it will be later. The specific date, be it December 31, 1969, or January 1, 1970, or any other, is not all that important. The significant fact is that the date is fast approaching.

America's space exploration program is still in its infancy. We are only on the threshold of a new era. For a number of practical reasons, that era began at a remote, undeveloped spit of land midway between Miami and Jacksonville, Florida, in July, 1950, when the first missile was launched from an obscure place called Cape Canaveral.

This is the story of man's advances in this incredible new age. It is the story of America's Spaceport.

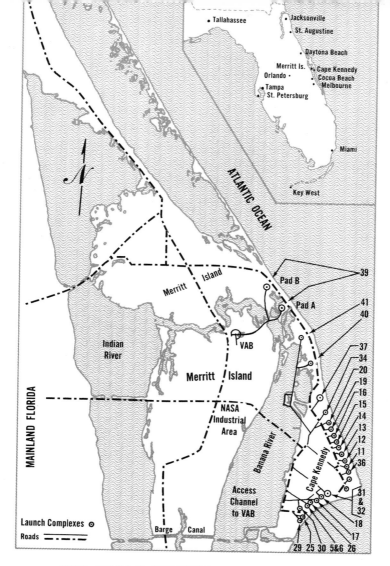

THE JOHN F. KENNEDY SPACE CENTER

The first launches took place on the arrow-shaped point of the Cape between Launch Complex 36 and Launch Complexes 31 and 32. Space vehicles launched from various launch complexes are as follows: 5, 6: Mercury Redstone. 11: Atlas. 12, 13: Atlas & Atlas Agena. 14: Mercury Atlas. 15, 16, 20: Titan. 17: Thor Delta. 18: Vanguard and Blue Scout. 19: Gemini Titan. 25, 29: Polaris. 26: Site of Explorer I. 31, 32: Minuteman. 36: Atlas Centaur. 39: Apollo/Saturn V. 40, 41: Titan III C.

Chapter 2

THE FIRST LAUNCH

The prime launching site for United States space programs today is located halfway down Florida's east coast primarily for one principal reason: its geographical uniqueness. Cape Kennedy is a 17,000-acre, 25-square-mile wedge of land that stabs into the Atlantic Ocean like the tip of a blunted spear; the only obviously protruding thorn of land in an otherwise smooth 400 miles of beachfront that stretches from the Georgia state line to Miami.

Its destiny to become the springboard for man's greatest explorations was determined over the latter stages of World War II. The U.S. Government had become intrigued with the fascinating military potential of guided missiles during the war, but until peace was won, we had been too busy fighting with more conventional weapons to develop a missile program.

Early postwar testing and experimenting with captured German rockets and with the first small American missiles was started at existing facilities in New Mexico and California. By October, 1946, however, it was clearly recognized that the fiery products under study would soon outgrow these limited ranges. At the time, the longest facility in the country was the 135-mile stretch of the combined ranges at Holloman Air Force Base and the Army's White Sands Proving Ground in New Mexico. The Navy's two ranges at Point Mugu and Inyokern, California, were also restricted to less than 150 miles, and could not economically be lengthened.

The Guided Missile Committee on New Weapons was thus created under the Joint Chiefs of Staff, and given the job of finding a suitable long-range launch area. It had a mission "to establish a Joint Long Range Proving Ground for guided missiles, and to operate and maintain this Proving Ground in furtherance of the National Guided Missiles Program, with the view to meeting, to the maximum extent possible, the requirements of the Army, Navy and Air Force for static and flight testing in connection with their research and development program, operational experimentation, and operational training."

The search lasted for months. Possible sites around the world were carefully analyzed, then either crossed off or marked for more detailed study. Finally, the choice was narrowed to two prime locations, one on each coast of the U.S.: Point Mugu, California, and Cape Canaveral (now Kennedy), Florida.

The El Centro-Gulf of California range was, in fact, the committee's first choice, but Mexico was reluctant to sign an international agreement allowing flights over its land. The British Government, on the contrary, was agreeable to negotiations for such overflights involving islands in the Bahamas, the Lesser Antilles, and other beads of land further south. C714206 CO. SCHOOLS

The physical makeup of the Cape appeared ideal. The terrain jutted far enough into the ocean so missiles could pitch southeastward almost immediately after liftoff without endangering any populated areas. The Canaveral region was relatively uninhabited and undeveloped. It would not be difficult to acquire and clear. Its relative isolation also would make safety and security possible at not too high a cost. And flight paths could be traced close enough to the Florida mainland to allow tracking stations to follow the missiles' movements until they reached the Bahamas, where other instrumentation could pick up the action.

There was also room for expansion. The range, in fact, could be extended almost without limit far into the broad South Atlantic between Africa and South America. An additional plus was the availability of existing facilities at the mothballed Banana River Naval Air Station, 15 miles south of the Cape, which had been active during the war but was closed shortly afterward.

The committee had made its selection by June 20, 1947, but the decision was not made public until nearly two years later. With the site selection taken care of, President Harry Truman signed Public Law 60 on May 11, 1949, allocating $75 million for initial development of the new missile range. This was $125 million less than asked for.

The official government announcement on the establishment of the new Joint Long Range Proving Ground (JLRPG) was made June 2, 1949. It said, in part: "The Cape Canaveral area was selected because (1) the climate was suitable for year-round operation, and (2) that area was relatively uninhabited and undeveloped and hence it would not be difficult to acquire and clear those portions of the area within about five miles of the launching points on the Cape proper, and because the nearby Banana River Naval Air Station could be utilized as a headquarters base for supporting technical, logistical and administrative facilities."

One of the first tasks undertaken was the initiation of negotiations with the British Government and the Government of the Bahamas, so no delays would effect the contruction of instrumentation or missile-tracking stations to be built on various islands. By February, 1949, an agreement had been reached, and that May the necessary Congressional legislation was passed.

In the summer of 1948, the Navy transferred to the Air Force the shuttered Naval Air Station on the Banana River, and work was begun on renovating the base. On October 1, 1949, the Joint Long Range Proving Ground was activated, and was operated jointly by the Army, Navy, and Air Force under executive control of the Air Force chief of staff. Ground was broken for Canaveral's construction.

When the committee picked the Cape area, it selected a site already steeped in history. In fact, the first missile was launched at Canaveral over 3,000 years ago! It was a flint arrowhead used by primitive Indians to kill wildlife. The first Indians to inhabit this section of Florida lived before 1,000 B.C., possibly as far back as 2,000 or 3,000 B.C.

The Spaceport is sprinkled with sites that have been traced to the preceramic period of Indian life. Most of them are located a few miles north of the moon launching pads, and are composed of mounds called "middens"—mealtime refuse piles of clamshells. Archeologists assign these particular middens to the period prior to 1,000 B.C. because there was no pottery made then and none was found in the middens. These Indians exploited the rich environment of the ocean coast and the brackish waters of the Indian and Banana rivers. For food, they fished, hunted game of many varieties in the marshes and woods, and sought the ducks and other waterfowl that still abound today. Diet staples included oysters, clams, coquina, and other shellfish. Tools were made of shell, and spear joints were chipped out of flint.

Orange Period Indians lived about the year 1,000 B.C. and there is at least one site near Launch Complex 39's Pad A that is directly associated with this specific era. Fragments of crude pottery, made by mixing clay with Spanish moss, have been uncovered there. More Indians moved from inland to the coast during the next 1,000 years, and their culture apparently became more complex; at any rate they left behind a number of large burial mounds. One, at what is now the north end of the Spaceport, was explored by members of the Florida State Museum in 1963. They found skeletons at varying levels. Evidence showed there were at least 40 separate burials in a small portion of the mound.

Indians continued to thrive in the area for more than 15 centuries after the birth of Christ. The first recorded arrival of white men was probably in 1513, when Ponce de León is believed to have cruised by the mouth of the nearby St. Johns River and then come back to the Cape and anchored off shore. Some historians claim, however, that Europeans sailed by Canaveral's point earlier.

The Spanish found Florida's Indians to be hostile and the land around the Cape nearly inpenetrable, and they virtually declared it off limits until 1564, when the French built Fort Caroline near Jacksonville. This renewed Spanish interest in the east coast and they promptly attacked and killed most of the French garrison. A handful of survivors journeyed south to Canaveral, but they were soon driven inland and disappeared in the wilderness.

It was also in the year 1564 that the French artist Le Moyne, accompanying a Huguenot expedition to Florida, recorded the name Cape Canaveral on a map he made of the peninsula. It is one of the oldest place names in the United States. Ponce de León had named the now famous landmark "Cape of Currents," but history does not accurately record how the name became changed between then and 1564 to Canaveral, which in Spanish means a field of cane or a canebrake. Translated freely, Cape Canaveral means Reedy Point.

The Ais and Surruque tribes dominated the future Spaceport area in the 16th century, and were hostile to the Spanish until the early 1700's. Physical evidence of the Spanish—olive jar fragments and pieces of mirrors—has been found near Pad A at Saturn V Launch Complex 39 and along the Banana River bank near the Air Force Titan III rocket facilities.

By 1763, disease and raids by the Spanish had decimated the Ais and Surruques, and what Indians didn't move inland were captured and held as slaves. A few attempts at establishing white settlements in the area were made during the latter part of the 18th century, but most of these failed. Things were quiet during this period, and there is little recorded history relating to it.

In 1847, a team of hardy construction workers fought mosquitoes, snakes, and alligators at the Cape to build a lighthouse. Prior to its erection, several ships had foundered or run aground on the treacherous shallows off the Cape's tip of land. It wasn't until six years later, however, that Canaveral's first permanent white settler arrived. Thirty-six-year-old Captain Mills Olcott Burnham of Jacksonville came to tend the lighthouse. He brought a wife and two small children, and he stayed for 33 years, founding a small community of tough pioneers around a 15-acre orange grove he planted.

During the Civil War, Burnham was ordered by the Secretary of the Confederate Navy to dismantle the lighthouse tower and hide the light and clock mechanisms. New equipment was installed in 1868, but despite Burnham's dedication as light tender, ships continued to run afoul of the offshore shallows. In 1870, for instance, a vessel carrying a cargo of shoes went under. Only one lucky settler found a matching pair of shoes washed up on the beach, and for years afterward, Cape residents wore the oddest assortment of footware imaginable.

The lighthouse remained the dominant Cape landmark through the turn of the century. Burnham died in 1886, but he was succeeded by other determined settlers, including many hunters and commercial fishermen. The waters and woods of Canaveral teemed with wildlife. Deer, Florida panther, bobcats, raccoons, opossums, rabbits, armadillos, alligators, and snakes were plentiful, and fishing—in the Atlantic to the east or the Banana River to the west—was excellent. There were no bridges to the mainland until the 1920's, and supplies and mail were delivered by boat.

In 1926, the Canaveral Inn, a two-story structure with 14 rooms on the second floor, complete with barber shop and billiard parlor, was built at the Cape. Later, a fishing pier, stretching over 100 yards into the ocean, was added. Winter tourists and weekend visitors from the center of the state found the sun, sand, fishing, and peace and quiet attractive. But the Florida land bust and the following national depression made Canaveral all but a forgotten name until World War II and the resulting development of missilery changed things.

Once the selection of the area as site of the new missile range was made in June, 1949, the transition of a sleepy, quiet, peaceful community into one of the world's most exciting landmarks was quickly begun. Congress charged the Air Force with responsibility for running the new test range, and crews of airmen and officers were immediately sent in to begin repairing the decaying wooden quarters that had been used during the war at the Banana River Naval Air Station, south of the Cape.

Legal proceedings also got under way for government purchase of more than 12,000 acres at Cape Canaveral. There was need for fast removal of area residents. Plans were already being developed for the launch of the first missile at the new range.

The vehicle chosen to inaugurate the Spaceport was a 56-foot-tall, two-stage, international hybrid. It was called the "WAC-Bumper." The first stage was a modified German V-2 that had been confiscated at the end of World War II and shipped to the United States. The V-2 was teamed with a U.S.-Army-developed WAC-Corporal second stage. Two V-2's and two WAC-Corporals, Bumpers 7 and 8, were trucked across the country from the White Sands Proving Grounds in New Mexico in June, 1950. It was a strange-looking caravan.

The first launchings from the Florida coast were to be under the direction of Army Colonel Harold R. Turner, who, on December 15, 1949, had been designated deputy commander of the advanced Joint Long Range Proving Ground Command. General Electric managed the Bumper program for the Army. Objectives of the firings at Canaveral were to program the two-stage Bumpers to vertical flight, a feat that had never been accomplished. The Army and GE had to achieve this to complete the Bumper phase of Project Hermes, a postwar missile feasibility study. The Cape was chosen as the launch site because the flight schedule at Point Mugu, California, had become too crowded. The White Sands range was too limited for such a mission.

As the trucks wound their way slowly across the southern half of the nation, the first launch pad at the Cape, such as it was, was beginning to take shape, at a point three quarters of a mile north of the lighthouse. It consisted, simply, of a 100-square-foot layer of cement poured atop the sandy terrain. Roads leading to the area were nothing more than wide sand paths. After a dozen or so jeeps and trucks got stuck up to their axles while delivering supplies to the pad, it was decided to top the sand with a surface layer of gravel.

For a gantry, or service support tower, $6,000 of steel scaffolding used by painters was bought and erected to surround the dart-shaped WAC-Bumper. At best, it was a plumber's nightmare. Plywood was used for work platforms at various levels of the scaffolding. When 10 or more workers climbed the piping at the same time, hand over

View from the Cape Canaveral lighthouse in 1951. The first launch from the Cape took place from the pad circled at upper right, on July 24, 1950. The missile, called Bumper, consisted of a captured German V-2 rocket with an Army WAC Corporal rocket as a second stage. (U.S. Air Force Photo)

hand, the rickety framework squeaked, swayed, and shook. Some feared it would collapse into a heap of debris.

The blockhouse from which the launches would be controlled was no better. It was a shack that had once served as a bathhouse, built of one-inch pine and tar paper, surrounded by sandbags, and located a scant 300 feet from the pad. By today's stringent safety standards, it unquestionably would have been condemned.

Central Control, where countdown information would be coordinated with reports from tracking sites set up to gather data on the flights, was also, to put it mildly, inelegant. It featured some long trailers in a row, distinguished by their reeking smell of dead fish, a carry-over from some old shacks used by commercial fishermen.

Other support facilities were equally as crude. For instance, wires leading from the blockhouse to the pad were in an open wooden trough. Water for fire protection was pumped in from a nearby pond. The only semblance of a permanent structure on the Cape, except for a few houses, was the 164-foot-tall lighthouse.

It took a dedicated missileman to stick to the job. Working conditions were deplorable. First, it was unbearably hot. As one engineer remembered, "it seemed as if we were firing from the middle of a desert." The ocean was only a few hundred feet away, but the underbrush was so thick and tall that no one could see it or benefit from the sea breeze.

Mosquitoes caused a very serious problem to the first launch crews at the Cape. The sheer abundance of them often drove workers to complete distraction. Surrounded by marshes, swamps, lagoons, stagnant ponds, and other bodies of water, Canaveral, in addition to being a missile firing site, was also, in effect, a gigantic mosquito-breeding grounds. Pioneering fishermen can recall the times when the pesky insects were so thick they actually extinguished kerosene lanterns. Spray trucks were dispatched from the motor pool to fog the launch area, but even this proved ineffective. There were days when workers had to take shelter in hastily rigged net tents. Inside, a person could put his hand on the screen covering for only a minute or two, pull it away, and see his entire hand imprinted on the screen—in mosquitoes!

There were other hindrances and hardships. In the days leading up to the first scheduled launch date, July 19, some support personnel (firemen and safety inspectors included) were on call 24 hours a day. They slept in tents, bathed in a nearby pond, and shaved about every third day. During the nights, snakes crawled through their tents to get to the water holes. The men finally had to resort to squirting them with fire extinguishers to discourage these sleep-disrupting nightly rituals.

The concrete apron of the pad was surrounded by thick palmetto underbrush, and diamondback rattlesnakes found the steaming concrete an ideal place to sunbathe. At times the reptiles were so thick, in fact, that one man was given the job of driving a jeep around the edges of the pad during key tests, just to keep them from slithering into working areas!

The environmental conditions alone were enough to discourage the most dedicated technicians, even if everything had gone well with the launch preparations. It hadn't. Despite the frustrating problems and delays that bugged Bumper Number 7, it was finally readied for flight on the morning of July 19. For the historic occasion, invitations were extended to the press, and about 100 newsmen showed up. Curious area residents took picnic luncheons to the beach to witness this newfangled phenomenon that was soon to change drastically their entire way of life.

Not all Cape families had been moved off the land by the 19th, and security guards were kept busy evacuating reluctant-to-leave homeowners. Bedridden persons had to be removed by ambulance. But this was no problem at all compared to the official who was met at the door of one home by an elderly woman brandishing a double-barreled shotgun. She didn't care what they were going to launch, she informed him, and she said she would shoot anyone who tried to evict her. It finally took the persuasive, and physical, efforts of Cape fire chief Norris C. Gray, a personal friend of the woman, to move her. Gray knew the shotgun was not loaded, but even his pleadings did not sway her. Finally, in desperation, Gray carried the protesting resident over his shoulders and off the Cape.

To insure that all offshore waters, over which Bumper 7 was programmed to fly, were clear of fishermen and boaters, six airplanes were dispatched from an airfield 15 miles away. The countdown had already been halted once, when several merchant ships unknowingly steamed into the launch corridor, and officials didn't want a repeat. As liftoff time neared, one of the search planes' pilots embarrassingly radioed that he was running out of fuel and would have to land. By the time he had gassed up and was back on post, the other planes were in the same dilemma. It was decided to postpone the flight until afternoon.

A blocked fuel line and trouble with electronic equipment further delayed the operation. Propellants were loaded via gravity flow from a barrel of oxidizer—red fuming nitric acid—suspended from the scaffolding. Firemen feared the fuel-loading operation because they were totally unfamiliar with the acid's explosive properties. But launch team members were even more terrified when they found the firemen intended to pour water on the nitric acid in the event of a mishap. This would have caused it to splatter in the same manner as water poured into a frying pan of hot grease.

Finally, everything was patched up and the countdown clicked off down to zero. Everyone held his breath as fire funneled out of the rocket's tail. But it didn't budge. It just sat there on the concrete pad sputtering and spitting flame.

Engineers, near panic, closed off the fuel valves and shut down the missile, their first launch try a frustrating fizzle. A local newspaper described the abortive action as follows: "An attempt will be made again next week to launch a reluctant rocket which never got off the ground in nine trying hours today. Just about everything that could go wrong with the first experiment in low-angled firing of a guided missile did. When they finally got around to pulling the firing switch on the giant device, it produced only a popping noise, hardly worthy of a champagne cork."

A postfiring autopsy on the balky Bumper Number 7 revealed that some of its key working components had become corroded in the salt air. The disheartened and overworked launch crew had no choice but to take down Number 7 and put up its replacement, Bumper 8. Five days later they were ready for another try. The press was invited again, but most newsmen declined. Only a handful showed up early on the morning of July 24. This time there was a radical difference in the countdown. It proceeded smoothly, almost without a hitch.

Bumper 8, with a WAC Corporal second stage, successfully lifts off on July 24, 1950. (U.S. Air Force Photo)

At 9:29 A.M. the final 10 seconds were counted off, and again a hot tongue of flame licked back onto the concrete. This time, however, the missile rose steadily and swiftly into the air, sending a thundering roar rolling across the Cape. For those who hadn't given up and had come back for the second try, it was a spectacular sight as the white-and-black-striped vehicle soared into the sky, its bright orange tail of fire providing a sharp contrast against a milk-white layer of cirrus clouds. Fifteen miles out and 51,000 feet over the ocean, after slightly more than a minute of flight, the WAC-Corporal second stage ignited and separated from the spent booster, initiating the first horizontal two-stage rocket firing. Ten miles up, Bumper 8 pitched over perfectly and followed its flight path over the Atlantic at speeds up to 2,700 miles per hour before impacting into the sea. The mission was scored as a complete success.

The Spaceport had been christened.

There was no wild, shouting celebration, however, despite the triumph. General Electric project engineer Bob Haviland summed up the launch team's feelings: "We were too tired to celebrate. We just went back to the motel and slept."

On July 29, the rewired Bumper 7 made it two in a row as it lifted off at 6:44 A.M., scoring a second on-target success. By the time the pad had cooled, the launch crew was already packing its gear and preparing to head for points west. These were the only two Bumpers to be fired at the Cape. They were also the last two ballistic missiles to be launched there for several years and were the last shots "open" to the press until years later.

Chapter 3

ISLAND STATIONS

Now that Canaveral's first pad had been scorched by the fire of a rocket, officials decided it was time to dedicate formally their administrative headquarters at the revamped Banana River Naval Air Station, 15 miles south of the Cape. At ceremonies presided over by the new Joint Long Range Proving Ground Commander, Air Force Major General William L. Richardson, the complex of wooden buildings and barracks was renamed Patrick Air Force Base in honor of Major General Mason M. Patrick, Chief of the Army Air Corps from 1921 to 1927.

It was almost three months before another missile was fired at the Cape. Like its Bumper predecessors of V-2 extraction, the Lark had first been launched during World War II, as an interceptor missile against Japanese aircraft. A pygmy by today's standards, its program at Canaveral was designed primarily as a training course, leading up to the later launchings of a more advanced interceptor vehicle, the Bomarc. The first Lark flight from the Cape occurred October 25, 1950. For it, the blockhouse was switched from the tarpaper shack to a more secure facility—an army tank. The finned, narrow, cylinder-shaped Lark scooted 18,850 yards, reaching an altitude of more than a mile and a half during its 105-second flight. When the second stage failed to ignite, it unceremoniously plunged into the Atlantic. The next day a second Lark burned for only 39 seconds before fizzling. Failure, or more accurately, apparent failure, was, in fact, quite common to early-day launches at Cape Canaveral. But it must be clearly understood that this was expected. The launch site was an outdoor testing laboratory.

An M4-A4 Army tank with four-inch bulletproof glass in the turret window served as the blockhouse for the launching of Air Force Lark surface-to-air missiles from the Cape. (U.S. Air Force Photo)

No bird flown from the Cape was ever a complete waste. Surprisingly, in fact, a test version of a new missile that explodes in flight may even be more successful in some ways than one that flies perfectly—because it provides more information to the engineers measuring its performance. To understand this point better, it must be reemphasized that rockets are unbelievably complicated. Some contain three or four hundred thousand parts, all of which must function perfectly in flight. When something goes wrong, it becomes a process for a detective, in which electronic equipment sifts through reams of data for possible clues, to find out what happened. It is only via such a procedure that missiles can be perfected and then declared operational. Of course, no one can predict ahead of time what is likely to malfunction, just as no motorist can tell when and where he will have a flat tire. But it is essential, when something does happen, to pinpoint that source of failure, analyze it, and make proper corrections. Thus, even if a new bird barely clears the Cape and plops down into the shallow offshore waters of the Atlantic, chances are that much will be learned from its abbreviated flight, and before the next launch the necessary improvements will have been made to prevent a similar occurrence.

Such an explanation, however, failed to satisfy many pioneer Cape employees. To them, the Lark was a streamlined menace which they felt must have been created to destroy the missile base rather than enemy aircraft. And for a while it began to look that way. Larks took off like the poet's arrow shot into the air: "it fell to earth, I knew not where." Several of the vehicles shot up, loop-the-looped high overhead, and then came screaming back down onto the Cape like runaway buzz bombs. One pad maintenance man ran for the woods everytime a Lark lifted off, convinced the missile was alive and chasing him.

But, as in any laboratory, as the testing continued, the product improved. By June 7, 1951, the Lark had advanced to the point where two of them were fired on the same day, both successfully. It was the Cape's first multiple launching.

By the end of June, the Joint Long Range Proving Ground was redesignated the Air Force Missile Test Center (AFMTC), under the exclusive jurisdiction of the USAF. This change was brought about by action of the Department of Defense, which redelegated management and operational responsibilities for guided missile test centers to the separate services: Point Mugu, California, for the Navy, and White Sands, New Mexico, for the Army. However, this change did not preclude the joint use of all test centers for any guided missile activity of the Army, Navy, or Air Force.

Ten days before this announcement, on June 20, the maiden flight of another missile took place, and its launching signalled an important transition in the type of vehicles tested. The Bumpers had been ballistic rockets, powered only for the short, early portion of flight. They then traveled most of their trajectory, or flight path, in a free-fall ellipse. For example, a thrown rock is a ballistic missile, as were the arrowhead-tipped spears hurled by Canaveral Indians centuries ago. If guided, a ballistic missile will ordinarily be controlled only during the powered phase of flight. The transition was to aerodynamic, or cruise type missiles; aircraftlike vehicles that required the use of aerodynamic forces to maintain their flight path. In effect, these were pilotless aircraft.

The first missile of this particular class was the Air Force Matador. It was a sleek, surface-to-surface bomber, programmed to take off horizontally, fly at subsonic speed, and then dive vertically to a target. The Matador launched on June 20, 1951, from Canaveral was the first of 286: of these flights, 154 were for research and development, while 132 of the missiles were fired as training vehicles for Air Force crews. In fact, on December 7, 1951, a decade to the day after the Japanese attack on Pearl Harbor, the Air Force's 6555th Aerospace Test Wing performed the first all-military launch at the Cape, using the Matador vehicle.

The 39-foot-long bird, which had a wingspan of 28 feet, and was about the size and weight of a jet fighter, became the Air Force's first operational missile. Capable of carrying either a nuclear or conventional warhead and of cruising at 650 miles per hour, it was deployed at strategic sites in Germany, Taiwan, and Korea as early as 1954. Matador was the first missile to prove the early functional purpose of the Spaceport as a research and test site for the development of such weapons.

The initial launching of a Matador from Canaveral was highly significant from another aspect also. It was the first flight to be tracked by a down-range island station. On new aircraft, tests can be flown again and again until they are perfected. But a missile flies only once. Therefore, it becomes imperative to obtain as much data as possible on that single flight. Every moment of the vehicle's performance is critical.

The entire flight cannot be tracked from Canaveral alone, for soon after launch each missile disappears over the earth's curvature and

Matador in flight. (U.S. Air Force Photo)

is out of view and reach of instrumentation on the Cape. Thus, it was necessary to install additional equipment at convenient points along the missile's route, so the coverage would be overlapping and total performance could be measured.

The fact that a string of islands ran southeast from the Cape, almost as if they had been placed there for such a purpose, was one of the prime reasons for locating the nation's largest and most important missile test base at Canaveral in the first place. Site selectors had foreseen the time when intermediate and intercontinental ballistic missiles would fly for hundreds, then thousands of miles. Such long-distance flights could be made only over an ocean range, one with island stepping-stones along the way for the essential tracking sites.

But before a missile reaches islands along the range, it first flies parallel to the Florida coast. Taking advantage of this, small "satellite" stations, consisting mostly of high-powered cameras and radar equipment, were set up at several points as far as 150 miles south of Canaveral. These included small bases at Melbourne Beach, Vero Beach, and Jupiter Inlet, among other places.

Most of the islands selected as the most advantageous sites were under foreign flags, but negotiations had been under way long before Matador took off from Canaveral to secure these for the test operations. By December, 1950, construction had begun at Grand Bahama Island, largest of the Bahamas, located 65 miles east of Palm Beach, and about 180 miles southeast of the Cape.

As at Canaveral, construction workers had to start from scratch, clearing a base from the thick scrub brush of the tropical isle under a searing sun. The task force of builders was to be kept busy for the next six years as they island-hopped through the Bahamas southward. By late 1956, the range had been extended to 1,500 miles— intermediate ballistic missile range.

Grand Bahama Island in 1950 was a far cry from the plush, tourist gambling mecca it has boomed into today. But even that early in the development of the Spaceport, it was predestined to become one of the most important stations on the range, for it was the first fully instrumented island over which the big birds would sail. As at the other sites, radar and telemetry equipment, high-powered cameras, and other key tracking instruments were built at the GBI base. Smaller support stations were also positioned on some cays, tiny dots of land in the turquoise sea, surrounding Grand Bahama.

Next came Eleuthera, 300 miles out of Canaveral; a long finger of land due east of Nassau that many feel is one of the most beautiful islands in the world. It has fine white sand beaches and splendid scenery, and has become, in recent years, an exclusive resort with sea-front property selling at stateside prices.

The third major tracking stop, 132 miles southeast of Eleuthera and 500 miles from the Cape, was made at historic San Salvador, where Columbus supposedly first landed in the New World in 1492. At least if he didn't land here, many people will be disappointed. There are three separate monuments on the island to honor the occasion, each staked out at the exact point where the explorer reportedly set foot. He named the island in honor of the Savior. Unlike GBI and Eleuthera, Sal has not caught up in the tropical resort boom, and outside the tracking base and a few small native villages, it remains virtually an undeveloped, sparsely populated, and not particularly attractive island.

For a while, in the early launch days of such cruise-type missiles as Matador, a tracking station was in use on Mayaguana, 100 miles southeast of San Salvador. It was off this island that Franklin D. Roosevelt loved to fish. But Mayaguana had a short life as a useful base.

About 770 miles from Canaveral is tiny Grand Turk Island, part of the Turks and Caicos group. It is the next link in the tracking chain. Barely 12 miles square, Turk was discovered by Ponce de León in 1512. Little happened to it down through the years until construction of the instrumentation site began in January, 1952.

A tracking and telemetry base was originally active on the northeast coast of the Dominican Republic, near the city of Sabana de la Mar, but it has long since been phased out of operations.

The only down-range station on U.S. property is found in Puerto Rico. Initially, a major base was built on the side of a mountain overlooking the city of Mayagüez, on the western coast of the island. Later, additional equipment, primarily for satellite and space probe tracking, was added at a site on the opposite coast, near the capital city of San Juan.

Antigua, largest of the Leeward Islands, was also discovered by Columbus, on his second voyage in 1493, and named for the church of Santa Maria la Antigua in Seville, Spain. Though there was little activity here during the earliest missile launchings, Antigua de-

The U.S. Air Force Eastern Test Range

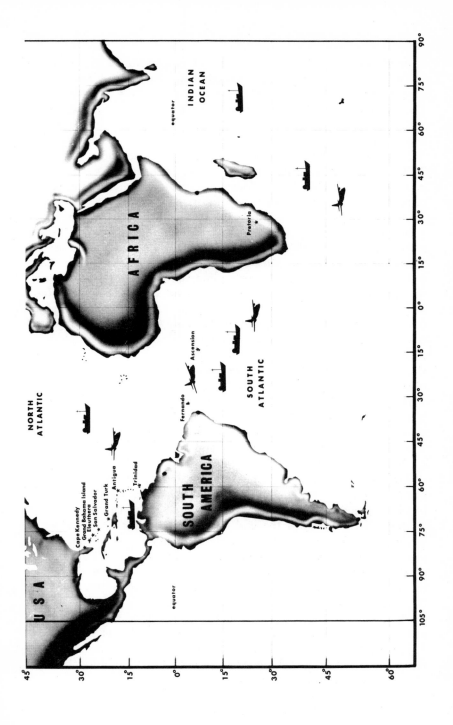

veloped into one of the most important down-range stations during testing of ballistic birds. Intermediate-range vehicles impacted into the sea off its scenic coastline, 1,250 miles from their point of origin. Today, of course, this island is one of the most popular resorts in the Caribbean, and is served by several major airlines. It is also still one of the key tracking sites.

South of Martinique, more than 1,600 miles from Canaveral, is St. Lucia, second largest of the Windward Islands. It was discovered in 1502 by Columbus on his fourth voyage. The station here, set up principally to follow the flight performance of long-range, cruise-type missiles in the mid-1950's, was soon after reduced to caretaker status.

Between St. Lucia and the next tracking site, the island of Fernando de Noronha, off the coast of Brazil, is a stretch of almost uninterrupted ocean that runs for 2,400 miles. To span this long, watery gap, over which missiles of intercontinental range would fly, the Air Force went into the maritime business. A fleet of 339-foot-long picket ships, converted World War II cargo vessels, was taken out of mothballs and outfitted with many of the same kinds of tracking instruments found on land-based stations, mainly telemetry equipment. Often, the ships would steam out of port and remain on site in the South Atlantic for weeks at a time, supporting several tests.

Home ports for these ocean range tracking vessels were at Chaguaramas, Trinidad, and in Recife, Brazil, a metropolitan city on the eastern coast. Also at Trinidad is a huge scanner-type radar screen, which helps interpret ICBM flights and follows the orbital paths of earth satellites.

Aircraft, too, are used to help gather data. Like the ships, these planes, Air Force JC-54's, JC-131's and JC-130's, are uniquely outfitted with delicate electronic gear. Airborne instrumentation is particularly critical toward the end of a ballistic shoot. Ground-based equipment is inadequate for accurate telemetry reception during the last few seconds of flight, due to signal distortion caused by reflection off the water. Also, if the nose cone of the spacecraft remains afloat, the aircraft's sensitive electronic countermeasure apparatus can trace its exact location on the ocean.

Modified C-135 jet transports and cargo carriers. with an external photographic instrumentation system known as ALOTS (Airborne Lightweight Optical Tracking System) are used on the Air Force range today. ALOTS is designed to provide high resolution tracking photographic coverage of rockets and spacecraft throughout early minutes of launch, staging, and then reentry where cloud cover extends up to 35,000 feet.

The JC-130 "Hercules" is used down range to receive midcourse and terminal telemetry, to search electronically for objects to be recovered from the ocean, to relay astronaut voice communications from spacecraft to ground stations, to make at-sea aerial pickup of ship data, and to return data collected down range for analysis at Patrick Air Force Base.

The Air Force also used JC-131 planes primarily in the up-range area for frequency control aerial photography, refractometry and data pickup. Other planes used include the C-118, U-3 and T-39. These are used for various logistic, administration, and training flights. There are about 30 aircraft operating on the range at all times.

One of the loneliest stations was at Fernando de Noronha, the mysterious island lying off the coast of Brazil. Named for its discoverer in 1503, Count de Noronha, it was, for many years, a penal colony. But at least it was green, verdant, and colorful. The last island base on the range, Ascension, cannot boast even those advantages. In fact, should astronauts want a realistic training ground on which to practice their lunar landings, Ascension would be an appropriate place to go. Its deeply scarred face, ravaged eons ago by volcanic action, is reminiscent of the moon's dead surface. Cinder cones and soot are everywhere. Only at the 2,817-foot peak of Green Mountain, in the dead center of the island, is there any evidence of flourishing plant life.

Discovered on Ascension Day, 1501—whence the name—by Portuguese explorer João da Nova, the craggy island was occupied by the British early in the 19th century after Napoleon had been exiled on neighboring St. Helena, 700 miles south. For many years, Ascension has been in the center of missile development operations, for it is the terminal point in the flights of intercontinental birds, both cruise types and ballistics. It is a spectacular sight to see the nose cone from a big ICBM reenter the earth's atmosphere in the predawn skies with a blinding flash of fire.

As the birds at Canaveral grew longer legs in later years, the range was eventually extended to reach around the tip of South Africa into the Indian Ocean, giving it a 10,000-mile-long capability. A small range station was established at Pretoria, South Africa, 30 miles north of Johannesburg, and additional tracking ships are positioned in the Indian Ocean when such long-range flights are scheduled.

A typical station is a compact, self-sufficient community, with its own power and water, its own food supplies and other supporting facilities. Each base has a complement of men, depending upon how active it is, averaging from 80 to 220. Most of the base personnel have jobs directly related to tracking the high-flying birds that soar over their island. Men not directly involved are mostly assigned to base maintenance and operations jobs.

The average base has a pair of tracking radars, to follow each missile and maintain and record its position in flight. There is also a telemetry receiver station on each site. This picks up the bulk of intelligence from the bird's pass. Timing signal generators on the islands enable sites to coordinate all instrumentation within a split second.

Weather is just as important down range as it is in the launch and recovery areas. For this reason, there are meteorological stations, staffed by experts, on ships and land bases. They provide upper atmospheric data for the full distance the missile is to travel. And, if the tracking site is in an area where vehicles will impact in the near vicinity, it is equipped with special and extensive optical devices for photographic purposes.

Engineers and technicians generally begin to tool up for a scheduled launch a couple of days in advance. Classified documents describe objectives of the upcoming flight, and spell out what tracking equipment will be needed, and how it is to be used. Down-rangers then ready their cameras, radar dishes and other instrumentation. They test it, calibrate it, and perform whatever maintenance is necessary, for once the countdown begins this instrumentation could be critical to the test.

If a vital piece of tracking gear goes out at a station, the entire shot could be delayed, or if the trouble is severe enough, the launch could be scrubbed. Any "hold" in a countdown is understandably expensive. There are hundreds of men with millions of dollars of finely tuned instruments standing by. Everything is powered up and ready to support the mission. Thus, each station checks and rechecks all its areas of responsibility so everything will be prepared when the time comes.

Countdowns are piped to the bases over a special radio frequency. Each site knows when its cameras must be turned on, at what angle its radars must be aiming. After liftoff, as the speeding bird approaches, the tracking systems pick it up and lock on during the time it is within their range, gathering valuable flight data on the pass.

One of the Cape's most colorful birds followed Matador to the launch pad. The first Northrop-built Snark was fired August 29, 1952. A surface-to-surface, cruise-type missile, the 67-foot-long Snark weighed 30 tons, and over the next eight years it set a number of dramatic firsts in American missilery.

It was, for example, the first U.S. missile with a ballistic nose configuration which separated in flight and fell in a supersonic trajectory to its target, impervious to conventional fighter aircraft or ground fire. This type of payload delivery was later to be incorporated in intercontinental ballistic missiles, and was a marked improvement over the Matador, with its comparatively slow and vulnerable descent to the target.

Snark was also the initial bird to use a stellar guidance system; that is, one which picks out certain celestial bodies and uses them for navigational aids. Today, many deep probing spacecraft such as the Mars Mariner and Mariner Venus use this method of selecting their course of flight on extended interplanetary missions.

Snark, too, was the first Cape-launched missile that could be re-

A Snark surface-to-surface missile thunders off the launching ramp at the Cape. (U.S. Air Force Photo)

covered and reused after a flight. It had the capability of being programmed back to an asphalt landing area, the "skid strip" at Canaveral. Many fell short of the return landing area and plummetted into the ocean, inspiring newsmen to call them "Snark-infested waters." But several also made it all the way home to the skid strip, bringing back important flight data in their electronic brains.

But perhaps Snark's most important credit in the Spaceport story was the fact it became America's first intercontinental missile. The tracking range of island bases had, by late fall of 1957, been extended past Antigua to Ascension Island. Construction work there had run at fever pace to get ready for the first 5,000-mile flight attempt by any U.S. missile, and when Ascension base manager Russ Reed radioed the Cape in late October, "Shoot, you're faded," he was signifying that the full range was ready to track its first comer. On October 31, 1957, a Snark inaugurated flights over the 5,000-mile range. It was a momentous milestone in the Spaceport's development.

Snark left its indelible mark on Canaveral in more dubious ways too. The best-known story concerned a 1956 flight that went haywire. The missile, streaking southeastward at more than 600 miles per hour, veered far off course, and instead of staying over the ocean, headed directly toward the continent of South America. A Range Safety Officer inside Central Control at the Cape, pushed a destruct button that ordinarily would have ripped the bird into millions of bits of metallic confetti long before it endangered land. But nothing happened. A faulty generator was supplying just enough power to keep the missile flying, but not enough to transmit the destruct signal.

It was tracked to a point about 50 miles west of Trinidad, and mathematicians quickly calculated it should hit somewhere south of Bélem, Brazil. The State Department was alerted for a possible international crisis, and everyone crossed his fingers. At this point there was nothing else to do. To this day, however, nothing has ever been heard of that errant Snark. It apparently plowed down deep in the Brazilian jungles. As one engineer put it, "maybe someday a missionary or an explorer will run into a tribe of bush Negroes cooking with orange aluminum pots and pans, and we'll find out where the darn thing landed."

On September 10, 1952, another important newcomer to the Cape scene was introduced. Its name was Bomarc, and it was an interceptor missile; one geared to zip aloft on instant notice and knock

Launch of a Bomarc interceptor missile at Cape Canaveral. (U.S. Air Force Photo)

enemy aircraft or rockets from the air before they could strike their targets. Unlike the Lark, Snark, and Matador, Bomarc was launched vertically, and had fast acceleration right from liftoff. Built by the Boeing Company, its statistics included 47-foot height, 18-foot wingspan, 15,000-pound weight, and a speed of 2,200 miles an hour.

From Canaveral, Bomarcs were launched to track and destroy drone or dummy rockets. They were guided from the ground by a SAGE (Semi-Automatic Ground Environment) system computer to the target area. Once there, their own mechanisms plotted the enemy course and speed, sending internal signals to the flight controls which steered them onto collision courses.

On one flight, for example, a Bomarc scored a direct hit on a Regulus II supersonic target missile 160 miles down range at 40,000 feet, a scant seven minutes after the interceptor had been launched from the Cape. Following its development flights, the Bomarc was positioned at military sites along the east and west coasts of the United States.

Chapter   *4*

IN ORBIT

On an unseasonably hot day, January 7, 1952, two men in a car with Alabama license tags turned east off U.S. Highway One in Cocoa, Florida. They drove over a "dreadful" wooden bridge spanning the Indian River, and followed a narrow, potholed causeway to the Atlantic Ocean. To them, Cocoa Beach consisted only of traffic lights; houses were few and far between. The two men were not on vacation. They were in the area to see Cape Canaveral for the first time. Over the next several years they would do much to change the face and the nature of the Spaceport.

In the car were Dr. Kurt Heinrich Debus and Dr. Hans F. Gruene. Both were expert, experienced German rocket scientists who had helped develop the V-2 program at Peenemuende during World War II. Debus, schooled in mechanical, electrical, and high voltage engineering, was recruited into the rocket research program at the secret Baltic missile test site from Darmstadt University, where he had been an assistant professor. Gruene was assigned as a research engineer at Peenemuende in 1943, two years after receiving his doctorate.

Work had begun on the V-2, then called the A-4, in 1939. The first one was successfully launched three years later, on October 3, 1942—15 years and one day before Russia's *Sputnik I.* By January, 1945, however, despite the reign of terror and destruction to which the deadly missile had subjected Londoners, the increased momentum of the Allied military offensive in Europe and the rapidly decreasing German defensive resources made it evident that Hitler's capitulation was close at hand.

German rocket scientists and engineers, faced with the realization that further experimentation was impossible, evacuated Peenemuende, most of them moving to locations in the Harz mountain region of Bavaria. There, they had to decide to surrender to either the Americans or the Russians. Many of the top men, led by a youthful Dr. Wernher von Braun, chose to give themselves up to American forces who occupied the area. Among them was Debus, who carried two long, deep scars on his left cheek, "marks of distinction" from his college duelling days. He had been in charge of the principal experimental V-2 launching site during the latter months of Peenemuende's operations. Later, Debus was transferred to the British occupied facilities near Cuxhaven, where he served as test engineer for Operation Backfire, a series of V-2 firings conducted by the British.

In March, 1945, the U.S. Army Ordnance Technical Intelligence received approval to initiate Operation Paperclip; the transfer of Germany's outstanding rocket scientists and engineers and the shipping of 300 boxcars of V-2's and spare parts, and over 40 boxes of guided missile documents, to the United States. The first seven Germans, including von Braun, arrived the following September, to assist in the sorting and cataloging of the documents.

Debus and more than 100 others came over in December, 1945. A month later they were organized at Fort Bliss, Texas, as a guided missile research team, and were assigned to provide technical assistance in sorting and identifying the V-2 components; to work with Americans in assembling, handling, and launching techniques peculiar to the V-2's; and to design for construction the critical parts not included in the shipments, or which had been damaged beyond use. On April 16th, the first V-2 was launched from American soil, the forerunner to Bumper Number Eight and all the hundreds of missiles and rockets that were to follow it. The project under which the Germans worked was known as Hermes.

The Paperclip specialists were given another assignment at Fort Bliss: to begin research and design studies for a long-range guided missile. The Germans had actually begun such developmental studies during the latter stages of World War II. Their A-10 configuration was to be an ocean-spanning missile. Had it gotten from the drawing boards to the launch pad, the outcome of the war might have been considerably affected.

On May 29, 1947, a modified V-2 was successfully launched at the White Sands Proving Ground in New Mexico. It soared 49 miles into the atmosphere, but went out of control. It impacted, with near-disastrous results, near Juárez, Mexico, and as a direct result, further launches were suspended until adequate instrumentation systems could be installed to provide a complex but effective range safety system. Some historians believe this incident stimulated actions to establish a long-range proving ground.

By October, 1950, 130 German scientists and more than 800 military, civil service, and contractor personnel moved from Fort Bliss to the Army's reactivated Redstone Arsenal in Huntsville, Alabama.

Debus and Gruene had driven to Canaveral to look over the launching site for a new bird they were working on in Huntsville—the Redstone ballistic missile. Sixty-nine feet tall, and capable of generating 75,000 pounds thrust at liftoff, Redstone was the Army's main hope for a new Sunday punch weapon, one that could deliver a nuclear strike dead on target 200 miles away. Unknown to anyone at that time, Redstone was also destined for even more important roles in the nation's yet-to-be-born peaceful space exploration programs.

But on that day in 1952, as Debus and Gruene turned north on the ocean road and headed for Canaveral, such future accomplishments must have seemed far off indeed. They were bewildered at how desolate and undeveloped the Cape was.

In June, 1953, the two men returned, this time with their launch crew, about 30 versatile engineers and technicians, some German, some American, all of whom could fill a variety of different jobs when needed. Their arrival in the area was reminiscent of that of a traveling circus troupe. The men came in car caravans, the Redstone components and supporting equipment were shipped in eight railroad flatcars.

Working conditions had improved little by mid-1953. Facilities had to be shared with the Bomarc and Snark launch crews, and the roof of the main building leaked. After every rain, desks and other equipment were soaked. Noise was even more of a problem. Whenever the Snark was fired up for a static or ground test of its engines, nothing could be heard above the ear-splitting roar.

All delicate Redstone tracking instrumentation was housed in trailers, and the Army's motor pool at the time consisted of one jeep, an ambulance, a two-and-a-half-ton truck, and a five-ton tractor. Because the Redstone was the largest vehicle yet to be tested at Canaveral, a new service structure, or gantry, was needed, to allow workmen access to it at any point of its seven-story height. The rickety pipe scaffolding of bygone Bumper days wouldn't do. For $360,000, an old oil derrick was requisitioned and assembled in two weeks at new Launch Complex 5-6. Today, that much is spent just for the design of a new service structure.

Despite the intense summer heat and the inevitable invasions of legions of mosquitoes, Debus and his overworked associates had readied Redstone I for launch on the morning of August 20, 1953. They had worked through the night of the 19th without rest, aiming for a liftoff time of 7 A.M. Surprisingly, the countdown went rather smoothly, particularly for such a large, new, and complex machine as the Redstone. There were a couple of minor delays—"holds"—for equipment failures at tracking sites down range.

The launch procedure was primitive by today's standards; now, gigantic automatic computers practically take the human element completely out of the operation once the countdown reaches a certain point. For instance, Albert Zeiler, another of the Peenemuende veterans, had a unique job on Redstone I and its successors. He was positioned in the blockhouse, a few hundred feet from the pad, where he could look through a couple of mirrors mounted in such a manner that he could see the Redstone at liftoff. When engine ignition occurred, Zeiler carefully scrutinized the flames funneling down on the concrete pad from the big bird's powerful engines. If the first flames were a yellowish-orange, Zeiler knew, from long experience of past V-2 launches in Germany, that the kerosene-type fuel and liquid oxygen oxidizer were mixing properly. He would then yell "Main stage," and the Redstone would be released from restraining mechanical holddown arms on the pad. If there wasn't enough fuel getting through the injector, the flames would be white. If there was too much fuel and not enough oxidizer, the color would change to bright red. In either case, Zeiler would order an immediate shutdown of the engine.

On August 20, however, the flame color met with his approval, and the Redstone kicked off on its first voyage. For at least one man in the blockhouse, it was a frightening experience. Electrical cables ran in a tunnel from the pad to the blockhouse. There was a little hole where the cables entered the building, and it had been stuffed with cotton and wadded-up paper. When the bird lifted, a concussion wave rolled down the tunnel and blew the stuffing smack into the face of veteran missile engineer Grady Williams. He thought for a terrifying minute the Redstone had scored a direct hit on the blockhouse.

Actually, its powered flight lasted only 76 seconds, and it fell short of its programmed 160 miles. Still, most of the important test objectives were satisfactorily met. Perhaps most significantly, the missile's structure was proved sound and the propulsion system worked well. To many, Redstone I was an instant success when it cleared the pad, for they feared the vehicle was so bulky compared to other Cape birds in those days that it would never get off the ground.

There were some subsequent launches that barely did. One of the earliest Redstones, in fact, shot straight up, did a somersault in mid-air, and then crashed back down onto the Cape with a shattering explosive force that blew out the doors and windows of the Number Two fire station. Like virtually all rockets launched at Canaveral, Redstone had its share of growing pains, which were to be expected. For the next few years, the Army team commuted regularly between Huntsville and Canaveral, building and launching the 30-ton missile.

On February 1, 1956, the German-American launch crew became known as the Missile Firing Laboratory group of the newly organized Army Ballistic Missile Agency (ABMA), and the Redstone was well on its way to development as an operational weapon of super size, strength and range. More important, the team was gaining invaluable experience and skill that would, in the years to come, be applied to the greater, more difficult challenges ahead.

As the missile programs began to develop at the Cape in the early 1950's, facilities started to rise and the work force steadily increased. A new Central Control Building was erected. From the electronic consoles inside it, all launches were coordinated with tracking stations down range. Propellant storage areas were set up, and fleets of trucks were purchased to transport fuels and oxidizers to pad areas. Security police and fire department personnel rosters were beefed up. Cafeterias were opened and medical dispensaries built. More suitable working areas were needed for the receipt, inspection, assembly, and checkout of missiles brought in from manufacturing plants across the nation. Aircraft-type hangars were erected in a complex of support buildings that came to be known as Canaveral's industrial area. Water pump stations, supply warehouses, sewage plants, power houses, and maintenance shops began to rise.

Pad facilities, too, were carved out of the Cape wilderness. Armies of construction workers, carpenters, electricians, welders, plumbers, sheet metal, steel and iron workers, mechanics and dozens of other tradesmen began molding together structures at Canaveral that would eventually make it virtually a self-supporting entity, a city in itself.

The Air Force realized early that it would be all too difficult to marshal enough trained personnel from military and civil service ranks to maintain and operate such a vast installation. Most Air Force personnel were either directly involved or in direct support of launch operations. So, in the spring of 1952, private companies were invited to make proposal bids describing their recommendations for running the day-to-day activities at the Cape and on stations down range.

In July, 1953, the contract was awarded to Pan American World Airways, and their Guided Missiles Range Division was born. The handful of employees who came to Patrick Air Force Base with new Pan Am Vice President Richard S. Mitchell grew, over the years, to a versatile, competent task force several thousand strong. Pan American subsequently subcontracted tracking and instrumentation responsibilities at the Cape and on the range to the Radio Corporation of America.

One of the principal reasons for selection of the airline for this contract, which was to increase to more than $100 million annually, was its years of experience in operating bases around the world. The Air Force felt this would be uniquely beneficial to the running of the tracking stations. Pan American neither builds nor flies missiles, but at the Cape and on the islands it does about everything else, from fueling the rockets to feeding the launch personnel, from providing fire, security, supply, and medical support, to countdown coordination, pad safety, and engineering help.

Division strength reached a peak of 7,000, and RCA's Missile Test Project, under G. Denton Clark, numbered almost 3,000 engineers and technicians. Today, these figures have been reduced somewhat with the phasing out of many ballistic missile test programs.

Following the flight of Redstone I on August 20, 1953, it was almost two years to the day before another new missile was introduced at Canaveral. On August 19, 1955, the first X-10 experimental, pilotless, sweptwinged aircraft was launched. The X-10 was followed in 1955 by the X-17, Lockheed Aircraft Corporation's three-stage rocket-powered missile. Over the next two years it was fired to high altitudes and then programmed to plunge at tremendous speed through the earth's thick atmosphere to gather information on how such reentry would affect the warheads of ballistic missiles. X-17 nose cones were subjected to temperatures of 3,000 degrees and more during their short, six-minute flights, but the data gained was to be put to good use in the future design of missile and space nose cones.

On August 1, 1954, Major General William L. Richardson, who had commanded first the Joint Long Range Proving Ground, and from April 10, 1950, the Air Force Missile Test Center, was succeeded by Major General Donald N. Yates as chief of the AFMTC. A West Point graduate, Yates later earned a Master of Science degree from the California Institute of Technology. A command pilot and a top-flight meteorologist, he came to Florida after serving as Air Force Director of Research and Development. Yates guided the growth of the center for the next six years, during a period which would see missilery mature from a field of uncertainty and indecisiveness, to a well-founded one upon which modern military and peaceful rocket and space programs were built.

Not all test programs at Canaveral were successful. One of the least fortunate vehicles was the Air Force's Navaho, built by North American Aviation. Its development problems were many, and its launches, the first on November 6, 1956, included frequent failures. Planned to be a long-range weapon with a speed of 2,200 miles per hour and a liftoff thrust of 270,000 pounds, Navaho actually became obsolete before its test program could be completed. High-performance intercontinental ballistic missiles were already on Cape launch schedules in 1957, when the Navaho project was cancelled.

But the ill-fated bird did make some contributions. It successfully tested a new high-powered thrust concept and an inertial guidance system that was later adapted for the world's first nuclear-powered submarine, the *Nautilus*. This guidance system was also useful in designing the more advanced components of the ICBM's that followed Navaho to the pads.

The year 1957 was one of the most eventful in the young Spaceport's history. It was to be 12 months of triumph and failure, joyousness, and heartbreak. It was the year when the age of space was dramatically opened with the October 4th launch of Russia's *Sputnik I*, the world's first man-made satellite. And, it was the year when America's initial attempt at orbiting a spacecraft, Vanguard, on December 6, ended in a catastrophic explosion on the pad that shattered United States prestige.

The year at Canaveral began as it ended, in frustration. On January 25th, the first Air Force Thor was ready for launching, just 13 months after a contract had been awarded for its development to the Douglas Aircraft Company. Though Thor was to become one of the most reliable birds ever built, its first flight attempt was a total wipe-out. The liquid oxygen start tank ruptured seconds after liftoff and the Thor crashed back onto its pad apron and exploded. Emergency crews stood by for hours before a special ordnance team, a bomb squad, was allowed into the area to disarm loaded explosive devices.

Under Douglas leaders Bill Duval and Bill Stitt, two of Canaveral's most noteworthy pioneers, launch crews literally worked around the clock in shifts to correct early test flaws and get the 90,000-pound, 65-foot-tall Thor off the ground. That they were successful in their efforts is reflected in the Cape's long logbook of "firsts." Thor became the first ballistic missile to travel more than 2,000 miles; the first operational ballistic missile to be fired; the first bird to carry a camera which photographed the earth from outer space; and it was the first to propel a recoverable nose cone over long distances down range.

It wasn't until the fifth Thor launching, on September 20, 1957, that a complete research and development flight was made without problems, but after that it was fairly smooth going. Thor became operational less than 14 months later.

"In addition to testing and proving the missile and allied equipment," Stitt recalls, "we also were trailblazing launch procedures." Thor's booster was so versatile and adaptable, and became so reliable, that it evolved into a workhorse rocket for both the Air Force and the National Aeronautics and Space Administration. Following its qualification as an operational, Intermediate Range (1,700-mile) Ballistic Missile, Thor was strategically deployed with Royal Air Force squadrons in the United Kingdom.

While the Air Force was initiating Thor firings at Launch Complex 17, a mile or so to the south the Debus-Army crew were unwrapping their Jupiter Intermediate Range (up to 1,850 mile) Ballistic Missile. It was first test-flown May 31, 1957. Like its IRBM counterpart, Thor, Jupiter was quickly developed into an operational weapon in 29 R&D launches from the south end of Canaveral. It also chalked up its own series of key "firsts." In May, 1958, the first full-scale, heat-protected IRBM nose cone was launched and recovered, demonstrating a practical solution to the aerodynamic reentry heating problem.

On December 13, 1958, a Jupiter with a nose cone containing special instrumentation and a live squirrel monkey, in addition to a warhead, was launched. And a month later, the first operational Jupiter was successfully fired. Air Force crews trained on launch methods when the operational responsibilities of Jupiter transferred from the Army. Squadrons of the 60-foot-long, 110,000-pound missile were deployed in Turkey and Italy as deterrents to war.

During the mid- and late 1950's, the Army launch team fired a third vehicle from its busy pads. It was a Jupiter C, a four-stage rocket adaptation springing from the Redstone missile. The first stage was, in fact, a modified Redstone booster with three solid propellant upper stage rockets mounted atop it in a "spinning tub" placed in the nose of the first stage. It had originally been conceived as a space vehicle, one that could be made capable of launching satellites into orbit, in 1954. On its initial flight, September 19, 1956, it carried an inert, 84-pound payload more than 600 miles up and 3,000 miles down range, setting new altitude and distance records. Less than a year later, SCUBA divers recovered a nose cone from a Jupiter C that had been launched several thousand miles down range. It marked the first such recovery of a reentry body at long range, another major milestone. The fire-blackened cone was later shown to the nation on television by President Dwight D. Eisenhower.

It is now a well-established fact, particularly among those involved directly or indirectly with missiles and rockets, that the United States of America could have been the first country to crack the space barrier by placing a satellite into orbit. Serious discussion began in the fall of 1954, a full three years before *Sputnik I*, when Army and Navy scientists met in Washington to consider such an idea. Thus, Project Orbiter was born. The Army was to have primary responsibility for the launch vehicle, a modified Redstone to be capped wth small upper stages, and the Navy would provide the satellite. The program was cancelled a year later, barely before it could clear the drawing boards.

The Government at that time chose to make the first orbit attempt on a pencil-thin scientific launch vehicle called Vanguard. On July 29, 1955, an announcement from the White House proclaimed that the U.S. would launch "small, unmanned, earth-circling satellites as part of this nation's participation in the International Geophysical Year, which takes place between July 1957 and December 1958." And so, despite its promising potential as a space rocket, the Army's Jupiter C was, for the time at least, shelved.

When the Vanguard team arrived at Canaveral and set up shop at Launch Complex 18, adjacent to the Air Force Thor pads, it had a threefold purpose: to place an object in an orbit around earth; to prove the object was in orbit; and to conduct at least one scientific experiment with the object. Though the project was a joint Army-Navy-Air-Force affair, the Navy was assigned to manage it and be responsible for meeting its technical objectives.

To propel a satellite into orbit, the launch vehicle must raise it out of reach of the planet's gravity, and it must project it at a high velocity (17,500 mph or better) for it to attain a circular flight path concentric with the earth's surface. This, at the time, required a multistage rocket. The 72-foot-long Vanguard, less than four feet wide, had three stages, the first two liquid fueled, and the third solid fueled.

Fifteen vehicles were scheduled for the program, nine for testing and backup, and the remaining six for live-run satellite launchings. The first test flight, to check electronic gear, rocket instrumentation, launching facilities, and ground support equipment, took place on December 8, 1956. Test purposes were satisfactorily met, as they were in the next two Vanguard flights. In between, numerous developmental problems cropped up and delays were many. The program was dragging.

Before an attempt could be made to launch a satellite, the Russians beat America into space with the spectacular flight of *Sputnik I* on October 4, 1957. To say the launch crews at Canaveral were disappointed would be a gross understatement. There are no adequate terms to describe accurately the depths of their feelings. The Navy was disheartened at being beaten to the punch, and the Army, with its Redstone and Jupiter C vehicles scoring launch successes, was totally frustrated at having been ordered to sit on the sidelines while Vanguard carried the satellite ball.

It was clearly a major scoop scored on a nation that could, and rightfully should have been first in space. The international repercussions were vast. The Russians were hailed as leaders of world space technology, and their triumph in propaganda and prestige alone was incalculable. The initiative had been snatched from America, and for the first time U.S. leaders were shocked to learn the conquest of outer space was not to be a one-country affair. In addition to the obvious technological barriers the Russians had hurdled with that one tremendous shot, there were other, more fearsome implications. Militarily, the nation that dominated space could dominate the earth.

To compound the situation, Russia launched *Sputnik II* a month later, on November 3. Its payload was an awesome 1,100 pounds—

a clear indication that the Soviets were clustering big rockets. The satellite the U.S. was trying to put up, in disappointing contrast, weighed only about 30 pounds.

Nevertheless, work on Vanguard at Cape Canaveral was speeded up. It now became increasingly important for the United States to salvage whatever pride and prestige it could by placing a satellite into orbit as soon as possible. On November 8, 1957, with the first Vanguard orbital launch still almost a month away, Secretary of Defense Neil McElroy directed the Army to take its Jupiter C space vehicle off the shelf and prepare it for a satellite shot. Thus began an historic crash effort by the von Braun-Debus team, under the direction of Major General John B. Medaris.

By December 6, Vanguard vehicle TV-3 was ready for launch. It was a bright, clear, warm day at Canaveral. All across the country work stopped as network commentators followed the countdown to zero. The beaches south of the Cape were lined bumper to bumper with thousands of cars. People had driven from all over the state to witness this flight. Some camped out overnight on the beach.

At ignition, Vanguard's booster engines roared to life, spewing bright orange flame down onto the pad. But cheers suddenly turned to gasps of disbelief as it rose only about three feet and then fell ingloriously back onto its launch stand and erupted into a prodigious ball of fire that completely consumed the rocket, satellite, and with them, U.S. hopes. In a scant few seconds the failure assumed the proportions of a national disaster. Never had the spirit of those in the U.S. space program been so low. It was one of the Spaceport's blackest moments.

Despite the short deadline imposed by the Secretary of Defense, the Army team put on a record-setting crash program to get the first of their two Jupiter C vehicles ready for a shot at orbit. Coordinated teamwork, the combined skills of a group that had worked together for years, and dedicated effort that meant many sleepless nights was expended at Canaveral's pad 26A. There was much work to be done.

As Dr. Debus recalls, "new materials had to be fabricated to protect the contents of the nose cone during reentry, new fuels had to be concocted, a cluster of rockets had to be added to boost the power of the second stage, recovery gear had to be engineered, and electronic equipment had to be miniaturized to fit in the limited space."

Remarkably, on January 27, 1958, the launch vehicle was announced set for flight—a scant 80 days after the order had been given to get ready. But one uncontrollable factor involving the high-

The United States' first attempt to launch a Vanguard satellite, December 6, 1957, failed when the rocket rose only about three feet, fell back and exploded on the launch stand. (U.S. Air Force Photo)

priority mission caused a postponement—the weather. Air currents about 40,000 feet above the earth in what is called the jet stream were approaching the "red line value," the point beyond which it would be dangerous to fire the Jupiter C. The winds were whipping about in a region where the missile's superstructure would be subjected to its severest strain. There was no choice but to wait things out until the wind speeds slowed. It would be a difficult enough flight without bucking Mother Nature.

Through the 28th and 29th, the winds increased to more than 200 knots per hour, far over the danger point. By the end of the third day Debus was sweating out another problem. A new fuel was being used and it was so corrosive that the rocket would have to be either launched or detanked within five days, or every seal in the fuel system would have to be replaced. When the winds continued on January 30th, General Medaris recommended scrubbing the shot, detanking, and waiting for better weather conditions, possibly a week or so later. Debus checked with meteorological officers. They told him there was a chance the winds would subside just enough the next day to allow the launch. He called Medaris and pleaded for another day before defueling. The general agreed, but only for one more day.

At 3 A.M. on the 31st, the winds showed signs of decreasing. An hour later, when the winds had dropped to 157 knots, Medaris told Debus to start the countdown. At 10:48 P.M., seconds after the sharp "firing command" rang out in the blockhouse, the 70-foot rocket thundered to life. It rose vertically for eight seconds, then began to tilt in accordance with the preset instructions fed into its guidance system. With 83,000 pounds of thrust propelling the bird, the powered stage of booster flight lasted just over 150 seconds. At the precise instant when the assembly reached the trajectory apex, 225 miles above the earth, a radio signal flashed from the Cape, triggering the second stage consisting of 11 scaled-down Sergeant

On the evening of January 31, 1958, the Army team's Jupiter C rocket lifted majestically from its pad to place America's first artificial satellite, Explorer I, into orbit around the earth. (U.S. Air Force Photo)

motors. They burned for approximately six and a half seconds, building up the velocity. Then the third stage of three rockets ignited, burning for another six and a half seconds and further increasing the speed. As the third stage burned out and fell away, the fourth stage, another Sergeant, pushed velocity up to orbital speed of 18,000 mph.

The job of the 50-member launch crew in the blockhouse was over. They had done all they could. Everything had looked good as the bird went over the horizon—velocity, pitch, roll, and yaw—but it would be more than an hour before word could be received from West Coast tracking stations confirming orbit. Despite the fact that everyone had gone virtually without sleep for more than 24 hours, no one went home.

When word arrived an hour and a half after liftoff that California had picked up the new satellite's signal in orbit, there was a deep, inner joy felt that defies description. Army Secretary Wilbur Bruckner wired General Medaris that the artificial moonlet would be called Explorer I.

The United States was in space to stay!

"More achievements will be credited as rocketry progresses," Medaris said, "but it is doubtful if the joy and relief experienced in America on the night of January 31, 1958, will ever be equalled by a single technological feat." A member of the launch team put it in more simple wording: "It was a grand feeling, like a homecoming football game where the local team pulls the big upset victory."

In addition to the many precedents it set, and the much-needed renewal of confidence and prestige in the U.S. space program, Explorer I also made a major scientific finding: the discovery of the Van Allen radiation belt above earth.

Another Vanguard was launched five days after Explorer's triumph, but following only a minute of flight, it pitched violently. The sudden strain ruptured the slender airframe, and the broken pieces fell in flames into the sea. It had flown less than four miles.

But on St. Patrick's Day, 1958, the determined Vanguard launch team, many members of whom hold key positions in unmanned space flight programs at the Kennedy Space Center today, tried again. This time they were successful, placing a tiny silver ball into such a perfect orbit that it will likely circle earth for another 200 years. For more than six years, as if to make up for past failures, Vanguard I transmitted useful radio signals from its orbit. Probably the most noteworthy of its many major contributions to science and knowledge was its discovery that the planet we live on is pear-shaped.

Chapter 5

NASA IS BORN

Within a three-month period early in 1957, two new missiles of widely varying characteristics were introduced at Canaveral; one, Bull Goose, faded quickly into obscurity; the other was to become world famous. First flown on March 13, 1957, Bull Goose was a delta-winged missile designed to confuse enemy defenses as a decoy. It was conceived as an aid to the U.S. Air Force Strategic Air Command's missile and aircraft squadrons. The program was cancelled a year after the inaugural flight.

The first test version of the liquid-fueled Atlas Intercontinental Ballistic Missile was launched June 11, 1957. Its structure was a radical departure from conventionally designed rockets such as the Thor and Jupiter. The unique Atlas propellant tank was made of tough, lightweight stainless steel, thinner than a dime! It had no internal framework. It was, instead, kept under pressure to retain its shape. This resulted in a tremendous weight saving at liftoff. It was classified as "a stage and a half vehicle" because after two minutes of flight it jettisons two of its three powerful engines and continues flying on the thrust of a single "sustainer" engine. All three engines were built by the Rocketdyne Division of North American Aviation (now North American Rockwell Corporation).

The Air Force had been interested in the prospect of developing an ICBM since the end of World War II. In 1946, a research and development contract was awarded to Convair, a division of General Dynamics Corporation, to design a missile capable of carrying a warhead 5,000 miles. It was several years later, however, following economy cutbacks and reevaluations, before a production contract was made to Convair. In August, 1955, the California-based company had one man at its new Canaveral field office. He was B. G. McNabb, the colorful, hard-driving launch project manager for Atlas who was to make quite a name for himself and his new missile.

Following its initial launch, Atlas began dominating the Cape skyline. Towering aviation-orange gantries rose at Complexes 11, 12, 13, and 14, starting what came to be known as "ICBM Row." And the 1,000 Convair employees who moved to the Florida east coast kept the pads busy during the late 1950's. As in most test programs, there were growing pains involved. When a 245,000 pound, 82-foot-tall Atlas exploded on the pad, it was a blast of monumental

Atlas, first ICBM to fly 5,000 miles. (U.S. Air Force Photo)

proportions. With a liftoff thrust of more than 360,000 pounds, the vehicle was the largest yet to be tried at Canaveral, and its throaty roar was the loudest. The ground rumbled and dishes rattled on tables and shelves for miles around each time the big bird took off. The Air Force was besieged by irate citizens of communities surrounding the Cape who claimed their house windows were shattered and their walls cracked by the air shock waves created by Atlas during its powered phase of flight.

On the first two launches, exhaust gases from the engines flowed back into the engine compartment and melted critical electrical cabling and plumbing lines. Both vehicles blew up shortly after liftoff. To correct the problem, it was decided to add a heat shield just above the engines to deflect the gas flow away from the base of the bird. After this modification, Atlas straightened out, proving once again the worn but ever-so-true adage that much is learned from failures, and this was one of the reasons Atlas was at the Cape— for engineers to learn how to perfect it in flight.

There were many memorable launches in the 85-flight program that lasted through December 5, 1962. One of the most famous started out under a thick veil of secrecy. Less than 100 people, in fact, knew the mission of Atlas missile 10-B when it was flown into orbit at 6:02 P.M. December 18, 1958. Its 122-pound payload consisted largely of duplicate communications relay equipment, designed to tape record radioed voice or code messages and rebroadcast them upon command from the ground. The first words broadcast from space were those of Dwight D. Eisenhower:

"This is the President of the United States speaking. Through the marvels of scientific advance, my voice is coming to you from a satellite circling in outer space. My message is a simple one. Through this unique means I convey to you and to all mankind America's wish for peace on earth and good will toward men everywhere."

Atlas was also the first ICBM to fly 5,000 miles (November 28, 1958), following Snark's trailblazing path of a year earlier. From another Atlas, flown August 24, 1959, the first films ever taken of the earth from 700 miles up were recovered. And, on May 20, 1960, the thin-skinned bird set new long-distance records by sailing 9,000 miles down an extended tracking range that passed Ascension Island, skipped around the southern tip of South Africa, and ended in the Indian Ocean.

Atlas achieved operational status in 1959, with an accuracy in landing averaging less than two miles from the target in test launches up to ranges of 5,000 miles. It was subsequently positioned at military sites across the United States, but was later replaced by the more advanced Titan ICBM. It also became a space booster wheelhorse both for the Air Force and for NASA.

Atlas also became the booster vehicle for the Air Force's Midas program, designed to develop an early warning system against enemy ballistic missile attacks. It is based on the use of satellites carrying infrared sensors, to detect ICBM's immediately after launching. Project Samos, which also employed the booster, is an advanced satellite reconnaissance system. Use of the basic vehicle in NASA's Atlas-Agena, Centaur, and Mercury programs will be discussed in later chapters.

Exactly two weeks before the flight of Explorer I, another important "first" occurred just south of the Jupiter C pad. An A-1 Polaris Fleet Ballistic Missile was launched. Named for the North Star and built by Lockheed, this was to be the Navy's answer to the Army's Redstone and Jupiter and the Air Force's Thor and Atlas. But Polaris was even more. It was to batter down technological barriers that many thought would never fall. Polaris was to be launched *underwater,* from the bowels of nuclear submarines.

The concept was daring and had tremendous military potential. With almost unlimited cruising range, nuclear subs would be capable of patrolling 70 percent of the earth's surface—the international waters of the world. Mobile, hidden by an oceanic curtain, and ready for instant action, the subs, loaded with accurate Intermediate Range Ballistic Missiles, would provide the U.S. a powerful deterrent to those who might threaten a global war.

But before such unprecedented subaquatic firings could be made, the vehicle first went through its developmental paces on solid land at the south end of Canaveral. There were many who thought it would never make it to water. For a while the early Polaris flights gave Air Force Range Safety Officers in Central Control nightmares.

One launch, in September, 1958, was particularly memorable. The first stage of the 28-foot-long bottle-shaped bird flew straight up, without pitching over eastward as programmed. When it was several hundred feet above the pad, the Range Safety Officer pushed his destruct button. Instead of blowing up, however, the second stage continued flight, arcing *westward,* toward the Florida mainland! It was now roaring completely out of control. A frantic voice boomed over a loudspeaker system: "Attention in the Cape area. All personnel

Spectacular launch of a Polaris missile from the Cape on July 26, 1963.
(U.S. Air Force Photo)

take cover!" No one had to be told. One glimpse at the looping, spinning, flipping second stage was enough to convince anyone to head for shelter.

Sirens screamed as Cape fire trucks sped southward in the general direction of the errant missile. When the trucks reached Port Canaveral, just outside the south gate, firemen spotted a lone carpenter at work. They rushed over and asked him had he seen a missile flying overhead. "She went thataway, bud," the tradesman answered, nonchalantly, pointing south without even looking up. Luckily, the second stage had nosedived into the Banana River, which runs along the western edge of the missile base and the small town of Cape Canaveral, south of the port. It had missed hitting a heavily populated trailer park by 100 yards! It was the closest any missile has ever come to endangering life or property in the area.

It wasn't long afterward that another Polaris went off course. This one went straight up and came straight down. Office workers who had filed out of hangars and buildings to view the launch were suddenly terrified. They scrambled in all directions. But the most bizarre incident was yet to happen. The flaming Polaris landed in the middle of some thick scrub palmettos, setting off a blazing brush fire. Within minutes, dozens of poisonous diamondback rattlesnakes slithered out of the woods, escaping from the fire, and crawled onto paved roads and into work areas. Squads of security policemen were dispatched to the scene and literally shot large numbers of the rattlers with their pistols.

As time went on, Polaris missiles straightened up. Next to the standing launch pad, a ship's motion simulator was built. It rolled during the countdown and launch of the Polaris in a manner closely approximating the movements the bird would encounter in a ship at sea. The next logical step in the progression of the test program was actually to fly Polaris from a vessel. A post-World War II Mariner-class cargo ship, the EAG-154 *Observation Island,* was modified and refitted with launch tubes to fire the Polaris from its decks. The *Observation Island* was equipped with a complete, submarine-type fire control, navigation, and launching system to serve as a floating school for training Polaris submarine crews.

When the first missile thundered off the *Observation Island* on August 27, 1959, the Spaceport had in effect been extended several miles out to sea.

Less than a year later, at 12:39 P.M., July 20, 1960, 30 miles off the Canaveral coastline, the water erupted with a convulsive fury and disgorged a monster metal fish. For a breathtaking instant it hung in midair, then flames spouted from its tail and it roared skyward and quickly sped out of sight. Polaris had been successfully launched from a submerged submarine, the 380-foot, nuclear-powered USS *George Washington.* Three hours later, to prove the point, a second Polaris was launched from beneath the surface. Both were fired by an air eject system which forces the missile from its launching tube and propels it up through the water to a point above the surface. At that point, the rocket motor ignites and sends Polaris on its way.

Flight tests of the second generation Polaris A-2 began in November, 1960, and the first submerged launching of the 1,725-mile-range

A Polaris test vehicle of the Fleet Ballistic Missile Program is fired from the submerged submarine U.S.S. George Washington. *(U.S. Air Force Photo)*

A-2 was from the USS *Ethan Allen* off the Florida coast on October 23, 1961. The third generation A-3 Polaris was first tested August 7, 1962. Its initial submerged launching, aboard the USS *Andrew Jackson,* occurred October 26, 1963. Polaris uses an inertial guidance system that automatically computes a new course using gyroscopes, accelerometers, and electronic computers if the missile should be moved off the planned flight path because of high winds or other effects such as pitch, yaw, or roll planes.

Today, advanced systems of the two-stage, solid propelled Polaris stand guard in nuclear submarines stationed all over the world. Its original range of 1,200 nautical miles has been more than doubled, and its successful on-time development against almost insurmountable problems is a tribute to the technological capability of the United States. Much of that development was carried out, painstakingly and with much sweat and perseverance, at Canaveral and in the waters just off its sandy shores.

Repercussions from *Sputnik I* shook official Washington as hard as they did Canaveral. U.S. military missile programs were under varying degrees of development on several fronts at the time the Russian satellite entered orbit. But the exploration of outer space for peaceful scientific purposes had not been running on all cylinders. One of the first things the Government began to realize, in the sobering months of study following *Sputnik,* was the need for a central organization to direct a fledgling space program.

Both President Eisenhower and the Congress worked steadily toward the creation of such an organization. By July 29, 1958, a National Aeronautics and Space Act was signed by the President. It laid down the basic goals of the United States in the conquest of space. It said that American aeronautical and space objectives should be conducted so as to contribute to one or more of the following national goals:

(1) The expansion of human knowledge of phenomena in the atmosphere and space;

(2) The improvement of the usefulness, performance, speed, safety, and efficiency of aeronautical and space vehicles;

(3) The development and operation of vehicles capable of carrying instruments, equipment, supplies, and living organisms through space;

(4) The establishment of long-range studies of the potential benefits to be gained from, the opportunities for, and the problems in-

volved in the utilization of aeronautical and space activities for peaceful and scientific purposes;

(5) The preservation of the role of the United States as a leader in aeronautical and space science and technology and in the application thereof to the conduct of peaceful activities within and outside the atmosphere;

(6) The making available to agencies directly concerned with national defense of discoveries that have military value or significance, and the furnishing by such agencies, to the civilian agency, established to direct and control nonmilitary aeronautical and space activities, of information as to discoveries which have value or significance to that agency;

(7) Cooperation by the United States with other nations and groups of nations in work done pursuant to this Act and in the peaceful application of the results thereof; and

(8) The most effective utilization of the scientific and engineering resources of the United States, with close cooperation among all interested agencies of the United States in order to avoid unnecessary duplication of effort, facilities, and equipment.

It was also clearly explained that the Department of Defense would remain responsible for potential military application of space technology. The new organization would be charged with the peaceful exploration of outer space and to ensure that the widest possible benefits would be gained from such exploration.

Thus, on October 1, 1958, the National Aeronautics and Space Administration was born. Its creation had far-reaching effects on the Spaceport.

Specifically, Vanguard, two lunar probe vehicles, and three satellite projects were transferred to the new organization by other agencies. Conspiciously missing, however, was a competent launch team. NASA made a pitch for the Army Ballistic Missile Agency group, for its record of accomplishments, led by Explorer I, was impressive indeed. The Army violently opposed such a move, stating that if they lost ABMA their own missile programs would collapse. As a partial compromise, veteran launch team members of the Jet Propulsion Laboratory, a part of California Institute of Technology, were transferred to NASA. Many of JPL's engineers and technicians, led by Dr. William Pickering, had worked closely with von Braun, Debus, and others in ABMA on Explorer I and several additional programs.

America's new space agency was in business only 11 days when it directed its first launch. It was an ambitious one, a moon probing spacecraft named Pioneer I. Launched atop an Air Force Thor-Able, it traveled 70,700 miles before falling short of its target. Still, it had set new long-distance records as the country's first true space-probing vehicle. For the scientists, Pioneer I made the first observations of earth's and interplanetary magnetic fields, and recorded the first measurements of micrometeorite density in interplanetary space.

Pioneer IV, flown on a different rocket five months later, went much further. This time a Juno II vehicle, developed by the ABMA-JPL team, was used. Juno II had a modified Jupiter as first stage, and a three-stage cluster of solid-propellant rockets placed in a spinning "tub" mounted on the nose of the first stage. Standing 76 feet tall and weighing 60 tons at liftoff, it had first been launched at Canaveral on December 6, 1958—a year to the day from the Vanguard failure on the pad.

Pioneer IV, a 13-pound satellite package, began what has become an epic journey at 12:11 A.M. March 3, 1959. It passed within 37,-000 miles of the moon and then went into permanent orbit around the sun, becoming the first man-made solar satellite. Signals were received from Pioneer IV until it reached a distance of 407,000 miles, and the probe recorded radiation at an altitude of more than 52,000 miles, much higher than that found by Pioneer II earlier.

There were two other ABMA-directed launches during this period that are well remembered, and for two very diverse reasons. On May 28, 1959, a Jupiter missile, with a secret cargo in its sealed nose cone, roared into the predawn Canaveral blackness and streaked down range, trailing a long pencil of flame. The flight reached up 300 miles and rocketed southeastward for 1,500 miles. When the nose cone hit the ocean's surface after a fiery reentry through the earth's atmosphere, special teams of divers were quickly dispatched to recover it.

Inside the cone, in specially built compartments, were two live monkeys. Able was a seven-pound American-born rhesus monkey, and Baker was a tiny, one-pound Peruvian squirrel monkey. Medical portions of this unique experiment were carried out by the Army Medical Service and ABMA, with the cooperation of the Navy School of Aviation Medicine and the Air Force School of Aviation Medicine.

It was, at this point in time, clearly evident that man would one day soon go into space, and there was little usable information available on the effects of rocket travel on living creatures. Unfortunately, Able died a few days later from effects of anesthesia given while

A Juno II lifts off. (U.S. Air Force Photo)

technicians removed the critical sensors and electrodes that had been strapped to him to gather in flight data. An autopsy revealed, however, that he had suffered no adverse effects from the ride on Jupiter. Miss Baker survived in fine fashion, and today is still frisky as ever at the Pensacola Naval Air Station's Institute of Aerospace Medicine in Florida.

The second launch that will never be forgotten at the Spaceport took place July 16, 1959. For weeks leading up to the flight of a Juno II, carrying an all-purpose satellite, every step in the checkout procedure, every major test had been recorded on film. The late CBS newsman Edward R. Murrow and hosts of his crewmen literally lived with the launch team. They were filming a television documentary special to be called "Biography of a Missile."

At 12:38 P.M., the countdown reached zero, and the bird mounted a brilliant ribbon of fire-orange flame. It had barely cleared the pad when there was a complete loss of the guidance and control system, and the rocket suddenly lurched into a sickening horizontal arc, heading due *west!* Murrow, who had fallen back to the press site at a safety perimeter several thousand feet away, looked on incredulously as the runaway Juno bored directly toward him. Dozens of newsmen scattered like buckshot, diving into sand dunes, among the scrub growth, and under vehicles. One reporter, ironically, crawled under an explosives truck.

Two miles north of the launch pad, inside the Central Control Building, Range Safety Officer Major Al Fitzpatrick instinctively threw a switch that transmitted a lethal electronic signal to a destruct package installed in the maverick missile's innards. The signal triggered a prodigious blast that ripped the Juno and its precious satellite payload into metallic shreds which rained down on the Cape a scant few hundred feet from the blockhouse full of launch personnel. Fitzpatrick had killed the bird in five and a half seconds, a record for swift action that still stands. Had he not acted so fast under such immense pressure, there is no telling where the Juno would have landed, how many lives it might have taken, or how much damage it might have caused.

With ever-increasing emphasis being placed on NASA activities at Canaveral, and with the Army's large missile programs being overshadowed and outfunded by Air Force IRBM's and ICBM's, the transfer of the ABMA team—the rocket designers and planners under von Braun, and the launch crews under Debus—became inevitable. By October 20, 1959, an agreement was worked out for the change-over, and it was announced to the press the next day. It was another eight months, however, before the physical move could be completed. On July 1, 1960, NASA's George C. Marshall Space Flight Center was established at Huntsville, Alabama. Personnel included most of ABMA's development operations division. Dr. Wernher von Braun was named director.

At the Cape, ABMA's Missile Firing Laboratory now became the Launch Operations Directorate, the firing arm of the new Marshall Center. Dr. Kurt H. Debus was named to head LOD. Though the overall transition involved a number of highly complex intergovernmental agreements, it was carried out efficiently and with a minimum of disruption to the nation's space effort.

During this transitional period, two more important launch vehicles were under testing at Canaveral—one by the Air Force and one by the Army. The first Titan I ICBM was flown February 6, 1959, For it, new Complexes 15, 16, 19, and 20 were built just north of the Atlas pads on ICBM row. It was a two-stage, 98-foot-tall, Martin Company-built bird that weighed 220,000 pounds. It was initially planned to be a second, or backup ICBM, which, with the Atlas, would give the Air Force a solid one-two long-range punch. As it worked out, Titan was to play a much more dominant role in the nation's space efforts, for both military and peaceful ends.

Unlike most of its liquid-fueled predecessors at the Cape, Titan did not use the conventional propellants of RP-1 for fuel and liquid oxygen for oxidizer. Instead, it employed a blend of unsymmetrical dimethyl hydrazine and hydrazine, and nitrogen tetroxide, more dangerous liquids to handle, but ones that were more easily storable, and they could add more power per gallon. They are stored at ambient temperatures and ignite spontaneously upon contact.

Titan's first-stage engine has two thrust chambers which generate 300,000 pounds thrust, equal to the combined horsepower of 15,300 average-sized American automobiles. The second-stage engine has a thrust of 80,000 pounds at altitude. At launch, after being held on the pad for about four seconds, Titan rises vertically and then arcs over into a curving trajectory toward its target. When it has attained a speed of 5,300 mph, the first-stage engine cuts off and separation of the second stage from the booster occurs. Shortly thereafter, following second-stage ignition, powered flight continues up to speeds of 17,000 mph. Its nose cone separates from this stage and continues in a free-fall path on course, after reaching a peak altitude of about 500 miles.

Massive fireworks as a Titan explodes on the stand during an attempted launch. (U.S. Air Force Photo)

Titan I had its share of early developmental problems at Canaveral. More than one bird, in fact, did not get off the pad at all, blowing up on the launch stand and causing considerable damage to support facilities. But, by the end of its 47-vehicle test program, it had achieved one of the better flight success records.

A little more than a year after the first Titan launch, the Air Force announced plans to develop a successor: Titan II. It was to be a totally different missile system. This vehicle, 102 feet tall, was 80,000 pounds heavier, with a thrust total of 530,000 pounds. Only 23 experimental test launches were needed at the Cape to declare it ready as an awesome operational weapon. Titan II was then manufactured on a production line basis at Martin's Denver, Colorado, plant and installed at Air Force underground silo sites throughout the western United States as one more intercontinental range deterrent to nuclear aggression.

To bird watchers who followed the flights at Canaveral, Titan was a peculiar vehicle; because of the nature of its propellants, hardly any flame was visible at liftoff, unlike most other missiles. Instead, Titan appeared to be rising on nothing. Actually, there were transparent exhaust gases.

The other new weapons system undergoing testing during this time period was the Army's Pershing ballistic missile, first launched at Canaveral February 25, 1960. Again, the Debus-led team of veterans were instrumental in the successful beginnings of the test flight program. Pershing was smaller (34 feet), lighter (10,000 pounds), and more mobile than the bulkier Redstone it was to replace in the field.

Also built by Martin, Pershing was capable of being transported by helicopter or could roll along the ground on a tracked vehicle. Indeed, many of the 53 test launches at the Cape over a three-year period were fired from such vehicles, which served as portable transporter-erector-launchers. Additional goals achieved by Pershing were its greater reliability, the shorter time required to prepare it for launching, its utilization of more simplified support equipment, and its versatility in all kinds of terrain and climate. At Canaveral, it was nicknamed the "Shoot and Scoot" missile, because a caravan of vehicles could theoretically roll to a stop, fire it in a matter of minutes, then pack up and move on almost before its devastating warhead hit target. Pershing is a two-stage, solid-propellant bird with a range of 400 miles. It is named for General of the Armies John J. Pershing of World War I fame.

Chapter 6

ANATOMY OF A ROCKET FLIGHT

There is much more to launching a missile than just "sticking a match under it."

Preparations begin months, in some instances years, before the actual flight date is reached. Hundreds of thousands of people, at plants scattered across America, are today involved in the aerospace program. Since the early days of Cape Canaveral, most of the finished hardware, launch vehicles, and spacecraft have been manufactured on the western coast of the United States, at the giant industrial corporations in California and Washington.

On some missiles there are literally hundreds of thousands of separate parts. Each component, no matter how small, is tested and approved before being assembled into a subsystem. Once this is done, the subsystems are checked and they become systems. Finally, an entire rocket stage becomes a reality in the plant, complete with engines. Dozens of subcontractors may have contributed individual sections to the final product. Some of the stages are then static tested; that is, their engines are fired under flight conditions while the stage itself remains bolted to the test stand.

Once the stage has met all factory specifications, it is shipped to the Spaceport. Most are flown to the Cape's "skid strip," an asphalt runway carved out of the underbrush that can handle anything from small planes to commercial jets, and, more appropriately, the huge cargo planes that ferry large missile boosters and upper stages from coast to coast. The skid strip is so named because early-day Snark missiles were sometimes returned here and landed on skids rather than wheels.

Each major missile contractor maintains a field force at the Cape. They go to work the minute parts of their vehicle arrive. Stages are first taken to an assembly area, where they are thoroughly inspected. Next come weeks of checkout work, including more tests and retests of subsystems and systems. When this work is completed satisfactorily, the stage is ready to be taken to the pad at the launch complex. It is usually trucked the four or five miles separating the pad from the assembly area.

The typical launch complex is a large, fenced-in area, covering several acres. Usually, it is either circular or octagonal. The dominant structure of most Cape complexes is the service structure, or gantry. Some are more than 300 feet high, and can be moved 100 yards or more to and from the pad on railroad tracks. The gantry is positioned on the pad when the missile stages arrive. These stages are then erected by giant cranes which extend from the top of the service structure. The pad itself is usually a concrete-hard stand that has a slender tower standing opposite the gantry. This is the umbilical tower. Through its lines, power and propellants, among other things, are fed to the missile.

At outlying sites from the pad, which is located in the center of the complex, stand huge hollow spheres. These are propellant storage

Fuel mechanics load a truck for delivery to the pad. (U.S. Air Force Photo)

tanks. Most birds at the Cape are liquid fueled, using a combination of RP-1, a high grade kerosene, as fuel, and liquid oxygen (lox) as oxidizer. Propellants used also include UDMH (unsymmetrical dimethyl hydrazine), red fuming nitric acid, and liquid hydrogen, among others. Some military missiles tested at the Spaceport use solid propellants; the fuel and oxidizer are packed together in a rubbery mass inside the bird's firing chamber. They are burned together, from the center outward. When liquid fuels are used, they are put inside the rocket in separate tanks and are only brought together when they are to be burned.

Most complexes using liquids have storage tanks nearby, with lines running directly to the pad so propellants can be pumped into the rocket on site. These lines have to be spotless, for even a tiny foreign object could contaminate the fuel. Solid propellants are stored at the Cape in ordnance bunker areas, covered with grass, giving portions of the land a hilly appearance. One oversized bunker houses a large Betatron X-ray machine which photographs the insides of solid stages to detect any cracks or flaws in the grain of the propellant.

Both types of fuel have their advantages and disadvantages. In general, liquids are more suitable for space vehicles, because the thrust developed can be very precisely controlled and the fuel can be shut off in the tank chambers at any point in the flight. A solid propellant's burning rate is not so easily controlled, but it is more suitable for military missiles, because it is easier to handle and may be stored for indefinite periods, like an artillery shell or a bomb.

Different rockets consume varying amounts of fuel during launch, but all have enormous appetites. A typical Air Force ICBM, for instance, may gulp 100 tons of propellant in a normal flight. At liftoff, it burns as much fuel in one second as the average family car uses in six months.

Eight hundred feet from the pad there is an immense, igloo-shaped concrete structure. This is the blockhouse. The firing crews man positions in it during the countdown and launch. Because it is located so close to the pad, blockhouse walls are fortified with steel and reinforced concrete several feet thick. It is capable of withstanding a direct hit from an off-course rocket. For obvious safety reasons, there are no windows in the blockhouse. Launch crews can see their bird either by closed-circuit television monitors, fed by dozens of remote cameras on the pad, or through the periscopes that poke through the blockhouse roof. At a certain point in the countdown, usually about 90 minutes to two hours before scheduled liftoff, the massive, bank vault-type door to the blockhouse is swung shut. Some are two feet thick and weigh 44 tons. The launch crew is then sealed in for the duration of the count and through the powered phase of the missile's flight, until it has safely cleared the Cape.

But the blockhouse is not merely an elaborate bunker provided for the safety of the men inside. It is the electronic brain center from which the final preflight preparations, the countdown, are controlled. The circular main floor of a blockhouse is lined with racks of complex equipment that measures the missile's "heartbeat and blood pressure" in the final hours before it is allowed to fly. Cutting across the room are several rows of consoles. On each is a literal maze of lights, switches, dials, buttons, and knobs that would completely bewilder a layman. It has been calculated that there is enough wire installed in one Cape blockhouse to completely encircle the earth. Behind each console is a man, a specialist, who by checking his particular phase of the operations, contributes a small individual, but vital part to the overall countdown. Below the main room is another floor containing offices, ready rooms, and more equipment, including computers.

The countdown itself is often misunderstood. To most people unfamiliar with actual operations, it seems to begin only a few minutes or at the most an hour or two before liftoff, and culminates with the dramatic "T minus 10 seconds and counting," down to zero. In reality, the countdown usually starts a day or two before launch and is divided into different parts or segments. What is more familiar is the terminal phase of the countdown. This usually is picked up several hours before scheduled liftoff. An hour or two prior to T minus zero, the gantry is rolled back to a safe, parked position, leaving the naked bird on the pad. One definition of the countdown is that it is a numbered and timed sequence of events that must take place in progressive order.

In some respects, the launch team functions as a symphony orchestra. They are led by a test conductor, or if it is a flight involving a large, multistage vehicle, by a test supervisor. The libretto is a thick volume containing thousands of separate entries—the countdown manual. It is, in simplest terms, a master checkoff list. After each function in readying the rocket is performed, it is checked off in the manual. Because of the number of items involved and the complexity of operations, these functions are usually performed and checked off simultaneously. Although each listing is critically timed to the second, no job can be rushed. If more time is needed to double check something, a "hold" or stoppage in the count is declared until the item can be okayed.

After fueling of the stages has been completed, the test supervisor asks for a final check. When everything on the vehicle, and the spacecraft if there is one, has been verified by the specialist in charge as "go," permission is asked of the range for clearance to launch. All tracking stations must be ready too. By this time the countdown has usually been taken out of the hands of humans. At a certain point, usually two or three minutes before liftoff, everything is switched to an automatic sequencing system. Final items, the last readings, are done by automation. There is no one man responsible for pushing a button that fires the vehicle, contrary to what B-type space movies have often depicted. If trouble develops in the final seconds, even at the instant of ignition, it is automatically sensed and the engines are shut down.

At launch, the rocket beats flames back onto the pad in temperatures ranging up to 3,500 degrees Fahrenheit. To protect equipment as much as possible, a steel flame deflector, coated with special, heat-resistant, ablative material, is placed directly under the pad. It is in an inverted V-shape, and the flames funnel out and away on each side of it. At the same time, thousands of gallons of water are poured onto the pad from the moment of liftoff to help cool it down.

While the job of the launch crew in the blockhouse is essentially complete once the bird clears its stand, the work is just beginning for hundreds of others. All during the final preparations, in fact, a similar countdown has been in progress, conducted by the superintendent of range operations in Central Control (now called the Range Control Center). Checks are made on tracking systems, telemetry and communications equipment down the entire Air Force tracking range. Cameras are set up, film packs and magazines loaded, and lights, power, air conditioning, safety measures, and security roadblocks are made ready.

At liftoff, the rocket, weighted down by its mass of propellants, rises slowly off the pad. For a while it goes straight up. It passes through the densest part of the atmosphere. At about 40,000 feet it reaches the region called "Max Q": the area of upper air turbulence which places the greatest stress upon the bird's superstructure. Gradually, it pitches toward the southeast. Powered flight takes only about five minutes.

With the expenditure of fuel, the rocket becomes lighter and accelerates at a greater rate, reaching a speed of several thousand miles an hour. Inside the average missile fired from the Cape, tiny transistors send back hundreds of "pieces of information" to ground receiving stations, including such items as acceleration, temperature, rate of climb, fuel consumption, and others. All this is recorded on tape.

About 90 cameras are close to the vehicle at launch; some are actually on the pad only six feet from the flaming engines. Most of these remotely run cameras operate at very high speeds (1,000 frames per second) for only a few seconds. They provide information about the bird's exterior behavior, the flight path it follows, and certain facts about the exhaust. As indicated earlier, for example, the color of the exhaust reveals how hot it is.

Cameras are also used to provide position information on flights. Tracking cameras called theodolites—photographic versions of the surveyor's transit—record on film the vehicle's picture and the way the camera had to point to get the picture. Each camera then determines a straight line in space for every instant of the flight; the imaginary lines from different cameras cross at a point in space, indicating the rocket's position.

The most accurate position information comes from a camera that works only at night. Ballistic plate cameras, which operate with their shutters wide open, take time exposures of a blinking light on a bird

Eerie-looking Rantec antenna at Cape is used to track missiles in flight. This one also follows space vehicles to the moon and farther. (U.S. Air Force Photo)

The ROTI telescopic camera, used to record rocket performance, can photograph a baseball at a distance of eight miles. This one is at Melbourne, on the Florida coast south of the Spaceport. (U.S. Air Force Photo)

against the background of the night stars. Just as stereoscopic photography uses two views of the same thing to give a three-dimensional illusion, the pictures from several of these cameras can be used to determine the position of a vehicle in three-dimensional space within a few feet.

ROTI (Recording Optical Tracking Instrument) is a telescopic camera used to get pictures of rocket performance up to 100 miles away. It is capable of taking a picture of a baseball at a distance of eight miles. Cameras are also mounted on some launch vehicles. They are placed in cassettes which are jettisoned into the Atlantic, usually after stage separation. Pararescue specialists are dispatched to recover the film, which records such critical events as first-stage dropoff and ignition of second-stage engines.

While the various cameras are whirring as the bird rises, the center of activity shifts from the blockhouse, where the prelaunch preparations were directed, to the Cape's Range Control Center, where the flight is followed and tracking down range is coordinated. As the countdown progresses, the SRO (superintendent of range operations) insures that all range stations needed to support the mission are operational and ready.

One of the toughest and most important jobs during the early moments of a rocket's flight belongs to the Air Force Range Safety Officer (RSO). He sits in Range Control completely surrounded by banks of imposing electronic instruments. It is his responsibility to disarm and sometimes destroy the rocket if at any point during its flight it threatens destruction of life or property. As was evidenced in the flight of a Juno II in July, 1959, when the RSO destroyed it five and a half seconds after liftoff, his is an exacting, pressure-filled duty that only a small percentage of applicants can qualify for.

How well this job has been performed is reflected in the overall Spaceport safety record. Never has there been a fatal accident resulting from a live missile launch. Extensive preflight precautions are taken before each mission. The entire range corridor over which the bird is programmed to fly is cleared of boats and ships, and airliners are rerouted to fly around the danger zone.

Once liftoff has occurred, an outside observer is the first to feed information back to the prime RSO; usually just a quick word—"normal," or "erratic." At about T plus four seconds in the flight, the television monitors in Range Control pick up the rising vehicle and visually record any pitch, roll or yaw. Radars take over at about seven or eight seconds, and once the rocket has cleared the Cape and is over water, an impact predicting computer then follows it for the duration of the flight.

Of all individual pieces of machinery at the Cape, this electronic impact predictor is most vital to overall safety. The backbone of this system is a brainy computer, one of the most advanced data processing machines in production. The missile's position in space is relayed automatically by an advanced tracking system into this high-speed

When this errant Juno II threatened, in July, 1959, to destroy lives and property near the Cape, the Range Safety Officer pushed the destruct button to explode the rocket only 5½ seconds after liftoff. (U.S. Air Force Photo)

predictor, and it immediately tells precisely where the bird would impact at any given point on its trajectory. This position report is updated 10 times a second. This is done through the instantaneous solution of complex ballistic equations describing the motion of a missile in free flight after considering the rotation of the earth and the appropriate laws of gravity and motion. The output of the computer is progressively marked on a large plotting board and the RSO watches this closely and terminates the flight if it appears the rocket might approach a land mass.

Since the most critical phase of every launching is during the first 60 seconds, the bulk of the RSO's gear is adapted to cover this part of the test. Vertical wire and electronic skyscreens, radar, and Azusa (a special continuous-wave radar) are all used, as well as the TV monitors. The skyscreens accurately reveal any angular deviation of the missile and define an acute vertical plane with two parallel lines.

To execute a wandering bird, the RSO has two toggle switches on his console, labeled "arm" and "destruct." By flipping the arm switch, he cuts the missile's fuel supply and terminates thrust. The destruct switch is thrown only when a bird is uncontrollably off course and a land area is threatened. By rupturing the fuel tank, RSO's cause fuel dispersion prior to impact; consequently, dangerous, highly flammable propellants can be burned or harmlessly strewn in the air. This cuts down the possibility of an explosive detonation upon a high-speed missile impact. In the case of solid-fueled missiles, like the Polaris, both arm and destruct switches are thrown at the same time, because there is no way to cut off solid fuel completely once it has ignited.

Assuming the launch is on course, however, the RSO takes no action, and within minutes the bird is out of range of the Florida coast. In addition to the cameras, giant radars have followed it from the instant of liftoff. Some are powerful enough to tell, at a distance of 88 miles, whether a baseball hit in a ball park has gone foul or fair! Intricate electronic radar devices pick up a radio tracking beacon on the rocket, feed this signal to computers, and get position reports on the flight path every second. When the missile has passed over the horizon of Canaveral and radar signals are lost at the Cape, the down-range stations come into play. At no point in the flight path, whether it's 500 or 10,000 miles, is there a time when the vehicle is not tracked. Soon, Grand Bahama equipment locks onto the fleeting projectile. Coverage is overlapping at all stations.

Continuous-wave tracking stations all use some variation of one basic principle: they send a signal to a flying rocket and it sends the signal back changed in some way. From the change, the tracking systems can tell how far away the rocket is and how fast it is traveling. Some of the systems that have been employed on the range include UDOP (Ultra High Frequency Doppler Position), Azusa, MISTRAM (Missile Trajectory Measurement System), and GLO-TRAC (GLObal TRACking).

A large percentage of all information obtained from flights down the range is gathered by telemetry. Originating from a Greek word meaning to measure from a distance, telemetry was originally developed so weathermen could get remote broadcasts on atmospheric conditions from balloons at high altitudes.

Huge telemetry antennas are positioned on several island stations of the range, but if someone were to tune in on a telemetry broadcast from a rocket, he would hear simply a high-pitched squeal, the kind of sound that comes from an improperly tuned radio set. The difference is that the telemetry squeals are intelligent; they can be decoded into useful information. It is common to have data on as many as 5,000 different functions telemetered back to the ground stations along the route of the speeding missile.

Telemetry answers some vital questions involving the flight, including:

—How fast did the rocket burn fuel?
—How quickly did the flight controls respond to commands?
—How much stress and strain were put on the rocket's airframe?
—What was the pressure inside the fuel tanks? Was it too high?
—How much did the rocket vibrate during flight?

Range communications may seem simple at first, until one considers the vast area to be covered, and the fact that up to 4,000 people may need to be told the same thing at the same time, from Cape Kennedy to South Africa, in the air, at sea, and at all points in between. The range uses virtually every type of communications system. The heart of all the communications on the range, however, is a cable running along the ocean floor from the Cape to Antigua, with stops at the active stations along the way. Sixty channels of information can be sent along this cable, including timing and telemetry information in the form of "beeps," as well as teletype and voice. Radio, of course, is used to reach the stations not connected by the cable.

Over 1,000 engineers and technicians along the island tracking stations are employed to gather such critical data of a flight from such sources as cameras, radar and telemetry. More than 150,000 vacuum tubes may be expended on one mission alone.

As Major General Donald N. Yates, former Commander of the range, once explained: "To keep the numbers of missiles low—and this is important from a cost standpoint—we try to obtain as much information as possible from each flight. On a ballistic flight of only 15 minutes we may get a quarter of a million discrete data points [individual readings]—instantaneous temperatures, switch positions, pressures, velocities and so forth."

Once a flight has terminated, all raw data gathered on it, which may include up to three miles of magnetic tape and two miles of photographic film, plus punched cards and pen-recording rolls, is carefully packaged at the down-range stations that were involved in tracking, and is then flown back to Patrick Air Force Base. There, in one wing of the sprawling, three-story Air Force Technical Laboratory, several hundred skilled technicians are ready to reduce the raw data to usable information.

The heart of the data processing system is computers. Most of the computer work consists of adjusting for known errors in tracking systems, and converting tracking information into actual position. Information from a radar, for example, gives the rocket's position with respect to the radar's location; the computer translates this into the vehicle's actual position in space.

Most of the information emerges from the computers in the form of magnetic tape containing the corrected, refined data. These tapes are then played into a printer which types out the information, complete with column headings and notes. When these pages are run off, copies of certain graphs are put in, and all the pages are collected into a book known as the Flight Test Report.

This document, which may be thought of as a laboratory report on the rocket flight experiment, is sent to the military services, NASA, and contractors involved in the particular mission covered. The report is a detailed resume of the events that took place. Engineers can then figuratively "fly" the bird over and over again in their development programs—on paper. The Flight Test Report represents the range's end product—the priceless bulk of test information sent back from a missile in flight across the ocean.

This, then, is the colorful story of a vehicle's life at the Spaceport, from the day of its arrival at the Cape to the end of its life thousands of miles away. In between these periods of time, to the thousands of workers involved, their is rarely a dull moment.

Chapter 7

MANNED MISSION: MERCURY

From the earliest days of missile testing at Canaveral, an overriding factor in all launches has been safety. Every imaginable precaution had been taken, despite the crude facilities of the Cape's first days, to protect personnel. No matter now important the flight, regardless of how far the countdown had progressed, everything stopped if any life was endangered. Only when safety officials were completely satisfied could any operation continue.

Likewise, reliability of missile components has always received top emphasis. Engineers know one faulty part, one sloppy inspection could, if left undetected, destroy an entire mission. No job, no matter how indirectly involved in launch preparations, is ever taken light-heartedly. The work at Canaveral is serious, expensive, and always potentially dangerous. The men understood this, accepted it as part of the job, and went about their business as the young professionals they were.

Yet with one single announcement on December 17, 1958, appropriately enough the 55th anniversary of the Wright Brothers first aircraft flight at Kitty Hawk, North Carolina, everyone at the Spaceport knew that despite how good their safety and reliability programs had been in the past, completely new standards would have to be set in the future; standards of the highest degree.

The announcement, released by NASA's first Administrator, Dr. T. Keith Glennan, introduced Project Mercury to the world. No longer was space to be the private domain of artificial satellites, of mice and monkeys.

Now, man was to ride Canaveral-launched rockets into the skies! Of course, the announcement was not totally unexpected. Actually, Mercury had been born as a major space program two months earlier, on October 5. It had been obvious, too, from the earliest days of missile launchings at the Cape, that someday men would man these fire-breathing monsters. It was the fact that now it had become official that created the excitement.

Mercury's main objective was to orbit a manned spacecraft around earth and safely recover the man and machine. In outlining the scope of the program, NASA specifically wanted to learn how man would adapt to the new ocean of space. How would he fare in this unknown and possibly hostile environment? Could the space-craft be flown by an astronaut, or would everything have to be con-trolled from the ground? None of these and scores of other searching questions could be answered until man investigated for himself. Pro-ject Mercury was designed to begin unlocking such mysteries, ones that had intrigued earthbound man for centuries.

By mid-April, 1959, America's first seven astronauts had been selected. Their names would soon have as entrenched a household familiarity as those of the nation's top dozen movie stars or sports heroes. The seven were Scott Carpenter, Gordon Cooper, John Glenn, Virgil Grissom, Walter Schirra, Alan Shepard, and Donald Slayton. They had been selected from three branches of the military service after months of painstaking screening of hundreds of volunteer appli-cants. There were seven prime prerequisites for the job:

1. Age—less than 40.
2. Height—less than five feet 11 inches (later increased to six feet).
3. Excellent physical condition.
4. Bachelor's degree or equivalent.
5. Graduate of test pilot school.
6. 1,500 hours total flying time.
7. Qualified jet pilot.

Also considered by the selection committee were these three points: (1) willingness to accept hazards comparable to those encountered in modern research airplane flight; (2) capacity to tolerate rigorous and severe environmental conditions; and (3) ability to react ade-quately under conditions of stress or emergency. The original seven astronauts more than met these qualifications.

In addition to the program name, "Mercury" was also what the spacecraft would be called. It was to be a one-man capsule, bell-shaped, nine and a half feet high, six feet across, with a liftoff weight of about two tons. NASA went to American industry with its space machine specifications. After competitive bidding among many of the country's industrial aerospace giants, the McDonnell Aircraft Company of St. Louis was selected as the prime contractor for the building and delivery of the Mercury spacecraft. Though the total original contract was under $20 million, not a monumental figure when compared to some defense contracts, the selection of McDonnell officially set into motion what was to become one of the largest technical mobilizations in American peacetime history. Some 4,000 suppliers, including 596 direct subcontractors from half the 50 states, and over 1,500 other subcontractors were used in the supplying of parts for Mercury alone.

Heart of the spacecraft was the environmental control system (ECS). It provided the cabin and the astronaut's pressure suit with a 100 percent oxygen environment and pressurization for safety and comfort. The cabin of Mercury was not designed for luxurious comfort. One reason for the height limit on astronaut candidates was the plain fact there wasn't any more room inside the cockpit. As it was, there was just enough inner space for the pilot to sit or lie in a contour-shaped couch. It was comparable to riding in a small foreign sports car. Facing the astronaut inside the cabin was a panel of instruments that would bedazzle a commercial jet flyer. At the bottom of the spacecraft there was a thick heat shield, made of special ablative (heat-resistant) material. This would protect the occupant during Mercury's fiery reentry through the earth's atmosphere at the end of the flight. Retrorockets strapped onto the rear of the capsule would slow it down enough to allow the gravity drag of the earth to do the rest when it was time to come down. Once in the atmosphere, specially packed parachutes would slow the fall before the spacecraft hit the ocean.

After an equally careful consideration of existing hardware to serve as the booster rocket for Mercury, NASA settled on two vehicles of proven reliability. The Army's Redstone was chosen for suborbital launches, and the Air Force's Atlas was named as the missile to project the new craft into earth orbit.

At the Cape, Mercury activity centered in Hangar S, located at the southern end of the industrial area. Astronaut quarters were set up on the second floor of the south wing. It was their home away from home while in training for flights. The living area was small but smartly furnished, and included individual bedrooms, living rooms, and baths. Separate kitchen quarters were also set up, as were medical facilities. There were offices, too, and a briefing room. To allow the crew members some semblance of privacy, their quarters were placed off limits to the average employee.

A large contingent of spacecraft specialists set up shop downstairs in Hangar S. These were members of the NASA Manned Spacecraft Center's Florida Operations team. They were directed by longtime aerospace veteran G. Merritt Preston. Office and laboratory space was shared with McDonnell employees, led by John Yardley, and with other subcontractors. Preston's job at Canaveral was to receive the Mercury spacecraft from the McDonnell plant in St. Louis and put the final checkout touches on them before flight.

With the selection of the boosters for Mercury, the next step was to "man rate" them. Both Redstone and Atlas had been developed as operational weapons systems. Now, the ballistic missiles would have to be modified before they would be suitable to carry man into space. Adaptations would have to be made, obviously, to fit the capsule on top the launch vehicle. But one of the essential additions would have to be some sort of sensing device that could detect trouble in the rocket in time to eject the astronaut before the bird could explode. This was designed, along with a launch escape tower that fit above Mercury. Should serious problems develop in flight, an automatic system would sense this and trigger the tower's small rockets, which would yank the spacecraft and astronaut completely free of the booster.

Every precaution had to be taken. It had to be assumed that the bird could blow up on the pad or at any point on the projected flight path. Thus, teams of Pan American specialists drove four-wheel-drive vehicles over every acre of the Cape, no matter how thick the underbrush or how deep the swamp. This was done so each square foot could accurately be charted. If an astronaut had to bail out, rescuers would have to know exactly where he landed and what type of terrain they would have to cover to get to him.

Special vehicles were ordered. One was a heavily armored modified Army personnel carrier. It was thickly coated with asbestos-type material and fitted with a large scoop in front. Should a fire on the pad engulf the spacecraft, this vehicle would plow through the flames and push it free with the scoop.

Amphibious Larcs, vehicles capable of traveling on land or sea, were procured and assigned positions around the launch pad. If the escape tower carried the capsule into the brush or deposited it in shallow offshore waters, these vehicles would be capable of reaching virtually any point within minutes. Helicopters were also planned in the launch site recovery force. Emergency crews would include firemen and medical technicians or doctors.

Never before at the Cape had so many concentrated their efforts for a single project. Spacecraft specialists were working several shifts, the launch crew was checking and double-checking its vehicle, and hundreds of support personnel were taking care of everything between the pad and Hangar S.

The capsule for the first Mercury flight arrived at the Cape on July 23, 1960. Though this wasn't to be manned, it would be a thorough test of the spacecraft and its systems; a dress rehearsal for the manned launches to follow. Since it was the first complete capsule

Cutaway view of Mercury spacecraft, with escape tower and retrorockets. (Courtesy of NASA)

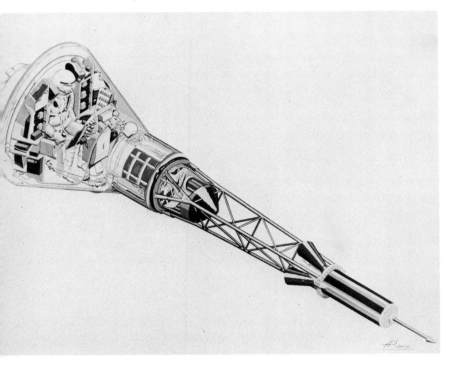

to be subjected to extensive preflight tests by the Florida Operations group, it was impossible to predict with precision how long the checkout would take. The Redstone booster arrived August 3.

By November 21, 1960, the spacecraft and launch vehicle were ready. There had been problems. A helium leak in Mercury and some necessary rewiring work caused delays. The initial launch date of November 7 was slipped when pressures dropped in the capsule's control system. But now, on the 21st, everything seemed to be set.

In the Redstone blockhouse, the experienced Debus team carried through the countdown smoothly, with only a one hour hold to patch another leak in Mercury's hydrogen peroxide system. At 9 A.M., ignition occurred exactly as scheduled. Thousands of Cape workers, newsmen, and several astronauts watched and waited. There was a momentary blast of air around the pad and an instant of roaring from Redstone's engine, but to the shock of everyone, *there was no liftoff!*

Actually, the vehicle had risen about four or five inches, but then the booster wobbled slightly on its pedestal and settled back on its fins. The engine shut down, and then a bizarre sequence of events happened. The launch escape tower soared up 4,000 feet and landed about 400 yards away—without doing its job of hauling the spacecraft free of the danger area! Actually, it had gotten a normal shutdown signal. Three seconds after the escape rocket blew, the drogue package shot up out of the capsule and then the main chute came out, and with the reserve chute, fluttered embarrassingly down alongside the Redstone. Had a man been in MR-1, his life would have been in extreme danger.

The debacle couldn't have come at a more inopportune time, for the eyes of the world were on Launch Complex 5-6 that day. It was the worst blow to the space program since the explosion of the Vanguard three years earlier. But there was little time to think of damaged prestige that morning. Blockhouse personnel quickly assessed the situation and came up with a frightening conclusion: the fully fueled, fully armed Redstone teetering on the pad was a live bomb! It could go off at any moment. The booster destruct system was armed, and to complicate matters, it could not be disarmed until on-board batteries ran down. This would take a day. Capsule pyrotechnics were also alive. But the most pressing problem was the main parachute, still dangling from the spacecraft. Engineers feared a gust of wind could fill it and pull the entire missile over. Despite the grave hazards, there was nothing to do but wait it out until the batteries ran down and hope MR-1 would maintain its precarious balance.

Early the next morning Pan American mechanical operators J. E. Cromer and Jay Hunt carefully inched the Redstone gantry up to the pad. Then a McDonnell team led by volunteer Walter Burke began the ticklishly dangerous job of disarming the vehicle, as squads of firemen and medical personnel stood by. It was later determined that a booster tail plug had malfunctioned, triggering a premature engine cutoff signal.

From the near catastrophe, success was achieved less than a month later, on December 19, 1960. A new booster was brought in for the rescheduled launch, but the same capsule was used. This time it lifted off the pad perfectly, pushing Mercury 235 miles down range, just 18 miles past its target area. The spacecraft was retrieved from the ocean's surface by a helicopter, and was safely bolted to the deck of the aircraft carrier *Valley Forge* just 48 minutes after launch. All systems worked as planned and the flight was declared an unqualified success. To the men at the Spaceport, it was a cheering Christmas present.

The holidays were short, for there was much work to catch up on. MR-2 was next on the launching pad. It, too, was unmanned, but there was a difference. It would carry a live cargo: a trained chimpanzee named Ham. His job was to prove the environmental control system in the Mercury spacecraft worked. This was a milestone that had to be accomplished before man could be committed to space flight.

Ham was accorded all the attention of a VIP, and was thoroughly examined and placed on a special diet before his flight. On January 31, 1961, the third anniversary of Explorer I from adjacent Pad 26A, the frisky chimp was suited up and placed in the capsule. Five minutes before noon he was launched. His was not a perfect flight. The spacecraft sped down range at better than 5,800 miles per hour, more than 1,400 mph above what had been planned. Consequently, Ham overshot his landing area by 132 miles. Again, had man been inside, he could have been in trouble. There was no recovery ship within 60 miles of the impact point and it was a half hour before the first aircraft arrived on the scene. By the time helicopters came, later, the capsule was on its side and fast taking on water. A few minutes more and it would have sunk.

Though it had been a rough ride, which included more than six minutes of weightlessness, Ham survived it well. Still, to straighten out the problem of overshooting the target area, an additional unmanned flight, using a boilerplate, or stripped down Mercury spacecraft, was launched on March 24. It landed only five miles off course.

With its success, officials had the confidence and experience needed to declare that the next shot—MR-3—would be manned.

The big question at Canaveral was who would be first? Three of the seven astronauts, John Glenn, Virgil Grissom, and Alan Shepard, were selected for special training for the flight. Even pad personnel didn't know the ultimate choice until a few days before launch. Finally, the decision was announced: Alan Bartlett Shepard, 37 years old, a commander in the Navy, would be America's first man into space. He named his Mercury capsule *Freedom 7.*

Shepard's training at the Cape was as intensive as the overtime work schedules of the launch crew and spacecraft team. Still, as had been true with earlier MR vehicles, there were slips in the timetable. Before Shepard could get off the pad, the Russians beat America to the punch again, scoring a dramatic world first with the successful launch of Soviet cosmonaut Yuri Gagarin on April 12, 1961, in *Vostok I.* Not only did he beat Shepard into space, but he flew a more complex and difficult mission. Gagarin *orbited* earth. MR-3 was to be only a suborbital shot of but a few minutes duration. The U.S. was still months away from manned orbital missions.

For the low spirits at Canaveral, however, the best antidote was hard work, and there was plenty of that in the last-minute preparations for Shepard's launch. America's Spaceport had a lot of catching up to do. The astronaut was kept busy in altitude chamber runs in Hangar S, where near-space conditions were achieved through pressurization of a tanklike container in which the spacecraft was placed. He also "flew" the mission in a mockup Mercury so many times on the ground that he knew the flight plan inside out. More tests were run at the pad, including full-scale dress rehearsals with practice countdowns, where everything was done except ignite the Redstone.

For the manned flight, a complete new team was added to the line-up, in addition to the launch crews and flight controllers. A massive recovery force of Department of Defense personnel took up stations in an elongated pattern along a 500-mile stretch of the Atlantic Missile Range. Actually, this vast array of personnel, ships, and planes had been on the job for Ham's launch, but now it was to be the real thing. Practice was over. The main recovery force included an aircraft carrier, eight destroyers, and one range radar tracking ship. Two amphibian SA-16 airplanes, complete with pararescue teams, also joined the fleet. No chances were to be taken if Shepard, like Ham, overshot his mark.

Launch day was May 5, 1961. For the astronaut, it began early.

He was awakened at 1:10 A.M., examined, and suited up. At 5:20 A.M., he was in the capsule, high atop the Redstone. Fifteen minutes before zero, a bank of clouds rolled in, threatening to scrub the launch. A hold was declared and they cleared. There were other minor difficulties. Inside the blockhouse tensions were high and cigarette smoke was thick, but experienced professionals were manning the consoles, and they carried through the countdown with a methodical thoroughness that left nothing to chance. At 9:34 A.M., engineer Jack Humphrey pushed a button setting off the Redstone's automatic sequencing system, and seconds later the tail of the booster caught fire. America's first manned launch was under way. Thousands

Launch of the Redstone carrying Alan Shepard, America's first man in space, on his historic suborbital flight, May 5, 1961. (U.S. Air Force Photo)

of people stood breathless at Canaveral and along the beaches that run north and south of the Spaceport. An estimated 45 million more watched on live network television. Astronaut nurse Dee O'Hara squeezed her rosary and prayed. There were tears in the eyes of many others. This was a moment of epic proportions in the history of the United States of America, a nation famous for its fearless explorations. Shepard was following the traditions of men like Daniel Boone, Lewis and Clark, Orville and Wilbur Wright. MR-3 was probing a new dimension, a vast unknown frontier. The time 9:34 A.M., May 5, 1961, certainly would be a moment frozen forever in the annals of man's progress.

Two and three tenths seconds after liftoff, as the Redstone generated its full 83,000 pounds' thrust, Shepard spoke: "Ahh, Roger; liftoff and the clock is started. Yes sir, reading you loud and clear. This is *Freedom 7*. The fuel is go; 1.2 g; cabin at 14 psi; oxygen is go. Freedom 7 is still go."

For 45 seconds the flight was smooth, then, as the launch vehicle passed through the point of maximum aerodynamic pressure, it vibrated badly, buffeting Shepard about so much he couldn't read his panel dials. Seconds later he passed through the turbulence and was on his way. When he switched the control panel to manual and maneuvered his pitch rate, he became the first man ever to fly a craft in space. Gagarin's entire orbital mission had been controlled from the ground.

Redstone's engine burned only 142 seconds, but by that time the spacecraft was hurtling down range at a velocity of better than 5,000 mph. The astronaut could see both coasts of Florida and some of the Bahama Islands, but, all too quickly, the flight was over. The retrorockets fired on schedule, and the parachutes popped out, slowing the spacecraft's rate of descent. Shepard's ride lasted only 15 minutes. He landed 302 miles southeast of Canaveral, and, as all the world listened, he reported to pilots aboard recovery aircraft that he was all right. Minutes later he was hoisted aboard a helicopter and flown to the carrier *Lake Champlain* for a medical checkup. Later, he was taken to Grand Bahama Island for more physicals, and for all-important flight debriefings.

Alan Shepard had proven a number of vital points with his short but impressive ride. Perhaps the most important was the fact man could not only survive, but could perform well in space.

It wasn't long before the first congratulatory messages came in. One of the first, 11 minutes after splashdown, came from President

Alan Shepard, first American to be lofted into space, traveled 115 miles high and landed about 300 miles from Cape Canaveral. Here he is recovered by helicopter. Capsule is at lower left. (NASA Photo)

John F. Kennedy, who called Shepard aboard the carrier. JFK later issued a more formal proclamation: "All America rejoices in this successful flight of astronaut Shepard. This is an historic milestone in our own exploration of space. But America still needs to work with the utmost speed and vigor in the future development of our space program. Today's flight should provide incentive to everyone in our nation concerned with this program to redouble our efforts in this vital field. Important scientific material has been obtained during this flight and this will be made available to the world's scientific community."

Telegrams poured in to the Cape with heartwarming messages to launch personnel who had experienced their share of defeatism in days past.

—"Congratulations on one of the world's greatest achievements. This will restore much of our great republic's prestige."

—"Well done. The brilliant success today has much satisfaction in it for the launch crew. Congratulations to each one of you."

—"Congratulations on today's wonderful accomplishment. We have the American flag flying at our house."

In all the colorful history of the Spaceport, this was one of its proudest moments.

Alan Shepard was the hero of the day, his name emblazoned on a thousand banner headlines around the world, but he was the first to say that his success was made possible only through the dedicated efforts of thousands of his coworkers.

Three weeks after Shepard's flight, President John F. Kennedy, who had greeted the astronaut at the White House earlier, spoke to Congress. His message contained four paragraphs on space exploration that were to have sweeping repercussions at Canaveral.

"Now is the time to take longer strides—time for a great new American enterprise—time for this nation to take a clearly leading role in space achievement, which in many ways may hold the key to our future on earth.

"I believe we possess all the resources and talents necessary. But the facts of the matter are that we have never made the national decision or marshalled the national resources required for such leadership. We have never specified long-range goals on an urgent time schedule, or managed our resources and our time to insure their fulfillment.

"Recognizing the head start obtained by the Soviets with their large rocket engines . . . and recognizing the likelihood that they will exploit this lead for some time to come in still more impressive successes, we nevertheless are required to make new efforts on our own. For while we cannot guarantee that we shall one day be first, we can guarantee that any failure to make this effort will make us last. We take an additional risk by making it in full view of the world, but as shown by the feat of astronaut Shepard, this very risk enhances our stature when we are successful."

Then JFK spelled out the 30 words that would change history and present the United States its greatest single challenge.

"I believe this nation should commit itself to achieving the goal, before this decade is out, of landing a man on the moon and returning him safely to the earth." He completed his remarks on space by adding, "No single space project in this period will be more impressive to mankind, or more important for the long-range exploration of space; and none will be so difficult or expensive to accomplish."

As has been borne out in the years since 1961, he did not understate the case. Characteristically, the Spaceport set to work with renewed spirits.

Two and a half months later another Redstone booster was ready for launch at Complex 5-6. Atop it was *Liberty Bell 7:* the Mercury spacecraft of astronaut Virgil I. (Gus) Grissom. Jaunty and crew cut, the 35-year-old Air Force captain was, at five feet seven, the shortest of the original space pilots.

The flight began, routinely enough, at 7:20 A.M., July 21, 1961. It was to be, essentially, a repeat of Shepard's shot, and a final tune-up before the first orbital mission attempt would be made. For a while, Grissom followed closely in his predecessor's flight steps, landing 299 miles down range. When *Liberty Bell 7* splashed down, however, things got hectic.

Grissom was awaiting recovery, as his capsule rolled in the Atlantic swells, when, in his own words, "I was lying there minding my own business when I heard a dull thud." Unexplainedly, his hatch cover blew away and salt water began pouring into the cabin. The shocked astronaut quickly abandoned ship. By the time a recovery helicopter could hook onto the badly listing craft, it had filled with water and was fast sinking. The added weight was too much for the chopper engine and the line had to be released, sending the MR-4 spacecraft to the bottom of the sea, 17,000 feet down.

Grissom very nearly followed it. As he patiently treaded water while the recovery crews concentrated on the sinking Mercury, he suddenly noticed that his spacesuit, too, was filling with water. Air escaped through the suit's collar, and the more that escaped, the more buoyancy he lost. By the time a hoist was dropped for him, the astronaut was literally swimming for his life. Examining physicians aboard the recovery carrier *Randolph* found Grissom "extremely tired" but there was no way to measure his gratefulness at having been plucked from the ocean before going under. Program planners learned a hard-earned lesson: on manned flights, not all problems were to be encountered in space. It was a point that would be re-emphasized in tragic underlining five and a half years later.

Work on converting the Atlas from an ICBM to a vehicle capable of safely inserting a manned spacecraft into earth orbit was being done at the same time Mercury-Redstone flights were under way. While Redstone was fine for the short, suborbital shots, more booster punch was needed to free astronauts of earth's gravitational pull.

The first unmanned Mercury-Atlas launch, MA-1, in fact, beat the initial Redstone to the pad by nearly five months. It is just as well no astronaut was aboard, however, for it exploded a minute after liftoff. MA-2, launched February 21, 1961, fared better, and contributed important data that was needed before man could fly it. Specifically, it flew in a trajectory that subjected the Mercury spacecraft atop it to fiery reentry temperatures. The test was a total success.

MA-3 was launched just 10 days before Alan Shepard's flight, on April 25, 1961. It was to be an orbital dry run, a final tune-up of the Mercury-Atlas configuration. It soared straight up over pad 14, several miles north of the Redstone complex. When it didn't pitch over because of an inertial guidance system failure, a Range Safety Officer blew it up. It had been airborne 40 seconds.

There seemed to be no middle ground for the Mercury program; it was either feast or famine, total success or complete failure. The next two unmanned Mercury-Atlas missions, MA-4 on September 13, 1961, and MA-5 the following November 29th, both put the spacecraft into orbit, and they were successfully recovered. MA-5 had a passenger, a chimpanzee named Enos. With these twin triumphs, the project was back on the track. The next step would be to orbit man.

For astronaut flights, an impressive new facility had been added in the heart of Canaveral's undeveloped acreage. Its name would soon be world famous: Mercury Control Center. Inside, in a modernistic mélange of electronic wonder, manned missions would be controlled. There were rooms for operations, telemetry, command systems, air-to-ground equipment, data selection, network support, data analysis and flight control, recovery control and communications.

On the entire west wall of the main operations room was an immense world map, punctuated with lighted circles and long wavy lines. On this, each orbiting spacecraft would be tracked every moment of its journey. From behind sweeping banks of electronic consoles, specialists in every conceivable phase of such a mission would man their posts for the duration of each manned flight in the Mercury-Atlas series.

Here would sit the men who held the strings on the spacecraft, no matter how far up or over what portion of earth it was flying. Their decisions would be final. They could order the astronaut to fire his retrorockets and return to his home planet at any point in the mission. This was a responsibility of staggering proportions. At other consoles were more members of the flight control team. Aerospace medical experts would monitor every heartbeat of the astronaut. They would be able to tell, from the marvels of instrumentation before them, not only how the pilot was feeling and performing, but they would also be able to accurately forecast how well he would continue to do under any given set of circumstances.

Of course, the men in Mercury Control would not be in direct contact with the man in flight at all times. In fact, they would be able to talk to him only a few minutes during each orbital passover when the spacecraft was within range. When the capsule was on the other side of the world, reports would be transmitted via one of the most elaborate and efficient communications systems ever devised: the Manned Space Flight Tracking Network.

Stations were set up around the world, so at no point would the circling astronaut be more than a few minutes from direct contact with the ground. Primary stations, in addition to MCC at the Cape, included: Bermuda, Grand Canary Islands, Muchea, Australia (later switched to Carnarvon), Hawaii, Guaymas, Mexico, Corpus Christi, Texas, and two ocean range vessels. Additional stations were located at Kano, Nigeria, Madagascar (Tananarive), Canton Island, Point Arguello, California, White Sands, New Mexico, and Eglin AFB, Florida. In addition, a major portion of the Communications Division of NASA's Goddard Space Flight Center in Maryland (NASCOM) would be used to support orbital missions. This net linked almost 90 stations, 34 overseas, with message voice and data communications.

Its circuits and terminals spanned 100,000 route miles and almost half a million circuit miles.

Now, all that was needed was a man in orbit to be tracked. That man was to be John Herschel Glenn, Jr.

It is doubtful if any astronaut trained harder, practiced more, or had so long to wait as did this genuinely warm, personable Marine Lieutenant Colonel. Technical troubles and stubborn weather conditions forced postponement after postponement, and the entire nation began to sympathize with the anxious Glenn. Finally, on February 19, 1962, officials were told the weather would likely break the next morning. The countdown began.

Launch Complex 14 at 4 A.M. February 20th was a spectacularly beautiful sight. The shiny silver Atlas shell gleamed brilliantly in the glare of dozens of high-powered searchlights which rimmed the pad. The bright red gantry added to a splash of colors that dazzled onlookers for miles around. At the press site, two miles away, hundreds of newsmen, representing media across the United States and abroad, sipped coffee and waited. On the beaches, more than 50,000 "bird watchers" were lined in their cars, bumper to bumper. Many had driven far and camped overnight. The Spaceport had an electric atmosphere that saturated everything. When Glenn stepped from Hangar S and walked toward the van that would carry him to the pad, there was a spontaneous burst of applause from the crowd of workers who had assembled there. Characteristically, the popular astronaut smiled and waved.

It is estimated that 100 million people watched on television as *Friendship 7* was launched at 9:47 A.M. It ranks as one of the most exciting moments in American history. Five minutes later, John Glenn was in orbit. For the next four or five hours, this great industrial nation went through only the motions of production. Everywhere, people followed the flight, on TV, radio, by word of mouth. Hour after hour the reports crackled in from Mercury network stations around the globe. The flight was going like clockwork. Through the tiny window in his spacecraft, the astronaut saw earth spinning far beneath him. He watched sunrises and sunsets, and saw the lights of Perth, Australia, as he passed overhead.

The mission plan called for three orbits, and as the flight was nearing completion, an engineer in Mercury Control spotted an ominous signal. The capsule's heat shield apparently was no longer locked in position. If this were true, this life-protecting shield, which

The Atlas bearing John Glenn, in Friendship 7, *on America's first orbital flight, rises from the Cape on February 20, 1962.* (NASA Photo)

would fend off the searing heat of reentry, was being held in place only by the straps of the retrorocket package. Flight controllers quickly huddled, and decided that after Glenn fired his retrorockets, he should not jettison the package, as was normal procedure. This would possibly keep the shield in position. The concern among officials was shared around the world. If the retropack failed and the heat shield came loose, America's first orbital astronaut would be incinerated, and the entire manned flight program would be on trial.

As Glenn reentered the earth's atmosphere over the United States, he heard noises brushing against the spacecraft. "There's a real fireball outside," he reported. Chunks of debris passed by his window and were instantly consumed in flames. For a fearful second he thought the shield was disintegrating. But moments later he had passed through the danger zone, and when, at 28,000 feet, his drogue parachute deployed, there was an audible, collective sigh of relief in Mercury Control and everywhere else. His splashdown, 40 miles short of the bull's-eye, and recovery 17 minutes later aboard the destroyer *Noa* were anticlimactic.

President Kennedy summed up the sentiments of the nation when he said: "I know I express the great happiness and thanksgiving of all of us that Colonel Glenn has completed his trip. Those who worked with him at Canaveral faced many disappointments and delays—the burdens upon them were great—but they kept their heads. We have a long way to go in this space race. But this is the new ocean, and I believe the United States must sail on it and be in a position second to none."

Following exhaustive examinations and debriefings down range, John Glenn flew back to Patrick AFB to a roaring reception. More than 100,000 people crammed into the small seaside city of Cocoa Beach to view him in a motorcade with Vice President Lyndon Johnson as they drove back to Canaveral to meet the President.

Never had the spirits of those who worked at the Spaceport been so high. Not since Charles Lindbergh, 35 years earlier, had America cheered such a popular hero.

Three months later, Malcolm Scott Carpenter, a Navy Lieutenant Commander, followed Glenn's triumph in *Aurora 7,* the Mercury-Atlas 7 spacecraft. He, too, circled the earth three times, and though his reentry didn't cause the nail-biting anxiety that Glenn's had, Carpenter's recovery was anything but routine. He overshot his landing mark in the Atlantic by nearly 200 miles.

To the public it was to be another cliff-hanger. They did not know where the astronaut had landed or how he was. Carpenter, meanwhile, checked his gear, then crawled out the top of the capsule, inflated his small life raft, and calmly waited for recovery forces to find him. It took them nearly an hour. Carpenter was watching a circling aircraft when a voice from the water yelled "hey." He turned in surprise to see a frogman swimming toward the raft. From Mercury Control came the comforting announcement: "We have just sighted a life raft with a gentleman by the name of Carpenter in it."

Next to be launched was Walter M. Schirra, another Navy man, and his *Sigma 7* spacecraft. The flight began at 7:15 A.M., October 3, 1962. To outside observers, all appeared fine, but inside the

Cape's Central Control Building another drama was beginning. Air Force Range Safety Officer Winton G. Hammond, the man who would have to blow the Atlas up if it strayed off course, remembers it well as his "10 seconds of hell at Canaveral." The action is best described in his words:

"For the first 130 seconds after liftoff, the booster flew beautifully, but in a minute I began to worry. Schirra's capsule wasn't accelerating as fast as it should. To go into orbit it would have to reach a speed of 17,500 mph. I began to sweat when, after two and a half minutes, the flight was 20 seconds behind schedule.

An entire nation shared one of the greatest moments in our history when Astronaut John Glenn became the first American to orbit earth, February 20, 1962. (NASA Photo)

"Suddenly, I was faced with a tough decision. Schirra still could make orbit before his fuel ran out, but then again, there now was a strong chance he wouldn't. If he didn't, he would float down in a preplanned recovery zone near the Canary Islands, and the Atlas booster, weighing 10,000 pounds, would also impact, more abruptly, somewhere on the African continent. Although the odds of it hitting anyone were considerably remote, there was always that possibility, and with it the probability of a major international situation arising from the repercussions.

"If I acted now by destroying his rocket, I could bring him down safely. I knew such action could not really endanger Schirra's life, because before the bird flew, the capsule would separate and be parachuted back to earth much like a normal reentry. I finally decided, in the last few seconds, to ride the flight out and give Schirra every reasonable chance to succeed. Then, all of a sudden, it was over. His orbit was assured and I could breathe easy again. I learned later from flight data that very little fuel remained when *Sigma 7* went into space. It was a close one."

For the next six hours, however, while Schirra zipped around the earth six times, it was what Mercury historians have since described as a textbook flight. The cool astronaut maneuvered his spacecraft down less than five miles from the planned recovery point. His mission went without a hitch, giving planners the confidence to map out the next step in manned space flight—a long-duration shot of 18 or more orbits lasting a full day or longer. Air Force Major Leroy Gordon Cooper was named pilot.

His *Faith 7* capsule lifted off Pad 14 at 8:04 A.M., May 15, 1963. It was the last launch of a manned Mercury spacecraft. Cooper surpassed all American space flight duration records with his 22-orbit, 34 hour and 20 minute performance. There were a few problems, particularly during the final portion of the mission, but everything worked out nicely, and the astronaut guided his craft to within four miles of the prime recovery ship, this time in the Pacific Ocean.

For a while there was talk of a Mercury-Atlas 10 flight, an openend one that would stay up as long as possible, until trouble developed or all objectives were met. But officials ruled against such an extension, feeling the advantages to be gained would not be worth the efforts involved. The job of the launch crews at Complex 14 was over. They had performed magnificently. To commemorate the four completely successful manned launches at the pad, a handsome stainless steel monument was erected at its entrance and a time capsule was buried beneath it, containing important documents and artifacts of the day. It is to be opened in 500 years.

Much was learned from Project Mercury. They had been expensive lessons, for the total program costs were over $400 million, but the benefits gained were invaluable at any price. Principally, scientists verified their beliefs that man could function well in the unknowns of space if he were well protected. And, in Mercury, the astronaut became more than just a passenger. He flew the spacecraft, adapting to differing flight situations on the spot, and in so doing proved conclusively the importance of manning the machine. Cooper punctuated this point when *Faith 7* short circuited late in the flight. He worked around the problem and manually flew the capsule through the critical reentry part of the mission. Had the spacecraft been unmanned, it might have been lost.

There is much to be said about the economics of sending robots into space, not to mention the safety factors, but as Mercury Flight Director Christopher C. Kraft explained: "Man is the deciding element. As long as man is able to alter the decision of the machine, we will have a spacecraft that can perform under any known conditions, and that can probe into the unknown for new knowledge."

The Spaceport matured during Mercury. Never before had it been issued such a severe challenge, and never before did its people respond so well. Cooper's successful 22-orbit trip was a long way down the road from the futile launch attempt of Mercury Redstone I, yet only two and a half years spanned the difference.

Mercury was a masterful triumph of American skills and technology, perhaps unmatched in the long, proud history of the nation. The problems involved, at times, were monumental; the delays and frustrations were taxing; the work load was staggering, and the pressures immense. The whole world watched every step.

Reliability became the keynote of launch and spacecraft personnel. All the men and women at Canaveral performed their jobs as if they would be the ones to climb into the capsule and be blasted off into orbit. It was this attitude that contributed greatly to the achievements of the program. A new capability had been developed, a new confidence won. It became evident now, with the success of Mercury, that no goal in the exploration of space, no matter how difficult, would remain unattained. It would just be a question of time before new horizons would be reached.

It would be 22 months before the next manned space flight.

Chapter 8

SATURN SCORES

There was no dearth of activity at the Cape during the 22-month void, however.

The Air Force was busy test firing and bringing to operational status a number of missiles, and NASA was engaged in several accelerated projects at both ends of Canaveral.

On October 29, 1959, the Air Force launched its first Mace, a streamlined successor to the earlier Matador. It was the last of the cruise-type birds to be processed at the Cape. Built by Martin, it weighed 18,000 pounds, was 44 feet long, and flew at near supersonic speeds. It was tested through July, 1963, and was deployed as a tactical weapon in Europe and the Pacific.

On May 31, 1960, Major General Leighton I. Davis took over command of the Air Force Atlantic Missile Range from Major General Donald N. Yates. Like Yates, Davis was a West Pointer and a command pilot. And he had a strong technical engineering background, a necessity for running such a vastly complex and rapidly developing installation as the range was becoming.

A few months later, General Davis witnessed the first Cape launching of a Blue Scout, the "poor man's missile." Scout is a needle-shaped, solid-fueled, multipurpose vehicle that is used to boost a variety of small payloads aloft. One version of the rocket can place a 150-pound object into a 400-mile polar orbit. Although several four-stage Scouts were test fired at Canaveral, the majority of them today are launched either at Wallops Island, Virginia, or at the Western Test Range, Vandenberg AFB, California.

Launching of a Mace missile, streamlined successor to the Matador.
(U.S. Air Force Photo)

The first Minuteman Intercontinental Ballistic Missile was fired February 1, 1961. Unlike Atlas and Titan, Minuteman uses solid propellants, thus giving it the nickname "Instant ICBM." It can be easily stored and needs only a brief period of time to be combat ready.

Its maiden flight from Canaveral ushered in a new type launch concept. In the past, multistage birds had been tested one stage at a time. The first few launches would be of the booster, usually with dummy upper stages. As the program progressed, these dummies would be replaced, one by one, with the real thing. With Minuteman, however, all three stages were live on the first crack out of the box, and when the sleek, swift missile charged all the way down the range, it was a major step ahead in its development program.

Built by Boeing, and named for the American Revolution heroes who were ready to fight on a moment's notice, Minuteman is 53 feet long and covers a range of better than 6,300 miles, at speeds exceeding 15,000 mph. For veterans of the Spaceport, it was a delight to watch at liftoff. Instead of lumbering off the pad, as did most of its predecessors, the bullet-shaped missile sprang off like a shot and was out of sight in seconds, leaving behind a long trail of white smoke.

Since Minuteman was to be deployed at underground sites once it became operational, two "cement silos," one 79 feet deep, the other 86 feet, were dug at the Cape to simulate these conditions. Reinforced concrete caissons outfitted with steel liners were sunk in sections as the pits were dug. On the silo launches, the ICBM swooshed through a huge cloud of smoke which boiled up from the subterranean hole. This caused Range Safety Officers their greatest headaches. On the slow liquid-fueled birds, there was plenty of time to take action if they rambled off course. Minuteman, however, couldn't even be seen until it had passed through the billowing cloud of smoke, and by that time it was climbing fast at a high rate of speed. If it were off course, instantaneous action would have to be taken or it could get out of control.

Minuteman had one of the fastest research and development programs of any arrival at the Cape, and only a year and a half after its first flight, it was declared operational. Missiles were stored in underground silos at six Strategic Air Command bases throughout the far western United States.

A beefed up version of the super-sleek ICBM, Minuteman II, was next tested at the Cape. It has an increased range of 7,000 miles, and is designed to fit the silo launch facilities already built. With Minuteman, the Air Force found a smaller, less complicated ICBM at a bargain price. Should this country need a quick nuclear punch at across-ocean distances, this missile would provide it. The knowledge of its speed and power, standing at the ready, capable of being unleashed against an aggressor enemy within minutes of attack on America, makes it one of our strongest deterrents to such a war.

By mid-1968, full-scale preparations were underway at Launch Complexes 31 and 32 to revamp facilities for the new Minuteman III test program. The latest member of this ICBM family has a major improvement in range capability, plus a warhead capable of carrying several nuclear weapons. There are additional advances in propulsion and guidance.

Even before tiny Explorer I, which weighed only 31 pounds, was launched January 31, 1958, plans were under way in this nation to build massive launch vehicles capable of orbiting payloads of 20,000 to 40,000 pounds. In April, 1957, half a year before *Sputnik,* Dr. Wernher von Braun's teams at Huntsville, Alabama, began such studies.

By December, 1957, a "proposal for a national integrated missile and space vehicle development program" had been drafted. It cited the need for a booster of 1.5 million pounds' thrust. At that time, the largest rocket on the pads at Canaveral was Atlas, which generated about one fourth that amount of power. The quickest way to produce such a large booster at the least expense, von Braun's planners

A swiftly climbing Minuteman ICBM is launched from an underground silo at Cape Kennedy. (U.S. Air Force Photo)

indicated, would be to cluster together a brace of rocket engines already developed.

On August 15, 1958, order number 14-59 was issued to the Army Ballistic Missile Agency by the Department of Defense's Advanced Research Project Agency (ARPA). It directed that ABMA begin development of a large clustered-engine booster. The Saturn program was born, although it was not so named until nearly five months later. In the interim the vehicle was called Juno V.

Previous studies had shown that the liquid oxygen (lox) and fuel tanks for Redstone and Jupiter missiles could, with some modification, be used for the new booster. It was further determined that an existing engine, the S-3D used on both the Thor and Jupiter missiles, could be adapted to produce an increased thrust of 188,000 pounds. By clustering several of these engines together, the proposed 1.5-million-pound thrust requirement could be met. In addition to the money and time saved through such a concept, a greater degree of reliability would be achieved via employment of already tested systems and hardware.

On November 18, 1959, technical direction of the Saturn program was transferred from ARPA to NASA. The basic vehicle configuration for the first of the family series of rockets, Saturn I, was soon after set. Atop the clustered-engine booster would be a second stage using high energy propellants, liquid oxygen, and liquid hydrogen. Saturn I's proportions dwarfed anything else either on the drawing boards or on Canaveral's pads. It would stand 162 feet high, as tall as a 16-story building.

The first S-I booster stages were built at the Marshall Space Flight Center in Huntsville. Later in the program this job was turned over to the Chrysler Corporation at NASA's new Michoud Operations plant near New Orleans, Louisiana. It was powered by a cluster of eight Rocketdyne H-1 engines, each capable of producing 188,000 pounds' thrust at liftoff. Like many missiles of the past, the first stage used conventional propellants—RP-1 fuel and liquid oxygen as oxidizer.

Though Saturn I was to be a two-stage vehicle, there would be no live second stage on the first four flights at Canaveral. Built by Douglas Aircraft, now McDonnell-Douglas, this stage, 40 feet long by 18 feet in diameter, was powered by six 15,000-pound-thrust Pratt and Whitney RL-10 engines.

To accommodate such a giant, a completely new complex of facilities had to be fashioned, one that would change the entire skyline of Cape Canaveral. The site chosen was just under a mile north of Titan Launch Complex 20. Construction of the new facility began July 5, 1959, when ground was broken for the blockhouse. Because of design configuration changes in the launch vehicle itself, the service structure was not begun until a year later.

All elements of the new site were impressive. The gantry alone was built to a height of 310 feet and weighed over seven million pounds. It was designed like an inverted "U," and with work platforms, could literally wrap around the rocket at the pad. Hurricane-proof guard gates were later added. Railroad tracks ran 600 feet away from the pad, and during launches, the service structure is moved back to a parking position. A 500-KVA diesel-electric generator, enclosed in the base of the gantry, supplies power to drive the 100-horsepower traction motors in each truck.

The launch pad is 430 feet in diameter and is covered with refractory brick, which minimizes damage caused by exhaust flames which beat down at liftoff. The umbilical tower is a 240-foot-high, steel-trussed structure which rises alongside the launch pedestal. Four tower swing arms feed ground-based power, air conditioning, hydraulic, pneumatic, fuel, measuring, and command systems to the bird during final launch preparations. Other pad equipment includes two 150-ton flame deflectors. Each has a one-inch steel skin, coated with a four-inch layer of special, heat-resistant ceramic. A deflector is placed beneath the launch pedestal to funnel the main stream of flames away from the pad as the rocket rises.

On the eastern half of the complex, only a few hundred feet from the Atlantic Ocean, are the propellant storage facilities. There are two RP-1 tanks, each with a capacity of 60,000 gallons, and a transfer capability of 2,000 gallons per minute. Liquid oxygen, or lox, is stored in a 125,000 gallon main tank. It is maintained and transferred at minus 297 degrees Fahrenheit. A lox-replenishing tank houses an additional 13,000 gallons. This is used during the final minutes before liftoff when lox vents and has to be continually "topped off," or replenished, until final rocket stage pressurizations occur and the vents are closed in the last couple of minutes before ignition. Liquid hydrogen is stored at minus 423 degrees Fahrenheit in a double-walled, vacuum-insulated 125,000-gallon tank. There is also a 125,000-gallon tank and a 35,000-gallon one for storage of liquid nitrogen. Additional facilities are used for helium and nitrogen batteries and a high pressure gaseous hydrogen battery.

Complex 34's launch control center is a two-story building shaped much like other blockhouses at the Cape, i.e., an igloo. Located just 1,000 feet from the pad, it is constructed of reinforced concrete and varies in thickness from seven feet at the top of the dome to 30 feet at base, enough to withstand blast pressures of 2,188 pounds per square inch—equivalent to the explosion of 50 kilotons of TNT at a distance of 50 feet.

Launches are controlled from the LCC's second deck. This nerve center houses a vast array of instrument panels, control consoles, and recorders, which record or transmit the commands and responses involved in the launch countdown. About 50 consoles are operating stations, such as booster component test panel, networks panel, launch vehicle test conductor, etc. There are another 36 blockhouse racks, including hydraulic control and monitor panels, combustion stability monitors and liquid oxygen computers, each with its own communications code.

Beneath this second deck, on the ground floor, personnel are involved in tracking, telemetry, closed circuit television, and communications. A large computer complex is also operated on the first floor. It is used in hundreds of tests involved in readying Saturn for liftoff. In addition to the remote control operation of dozens of television cameras, focused on critical areas of the vehicle, the communications room also provides for all operational communications during major tests and countdowns, using 42 channels to connect the hundreds of work and monitoring stations throughout the complex.

Main entrance door of the blockhouse is 23 tons of steel, and is slid into place by its own electric motor power. Adjacent to this massive blockhouse is the operations support building, used for measuring and calibrating telemetry and ground support equipment, for electrical networks, and for checkout and evaluation of components.

As 34's imposing structures began to rise from the north sands of Canaveral, parallel development of the Saturn I launch vehicle was well under way. By March 28, 1960, the first static firing of the booster, with the engines strapped to the ground, took place at Huntsville. It was a success. Two months later, assembly of the first flight vehicle was begun. On August 5, 1961, after painstaking fabrication and the most exhaustive testing, the big booster was ready to be delivered to the Cape. Ironically, man's most advanced machine had to be transported to its launch site by one of man's most ancient means of conveyance—barge. The Saturn booster was simply so huge there was no other way to move it. It could not be flown or trucked. Thus began an historic 2,200-mile trip from Huntsville, the first of many, that wound through the Tennessee and Ohio Rivers and then down the Mississippi into and across the Gulf of Mexico, down around the tip of Florida and up the intercoastal waterway on the eastern side of the state to Canaveral. The S-IV second stage came even further. It was shipped by water from its plant in California to the Cape via the Panama Canal.

Ten days later, the converted Navy barge *Compromise* (its name was later changed to *Promise*) arrived at Canaveral and the Saturn booster was offloaded and taken to the pad at 34. The launch complex had been completed and dedicated two months earlier. Within another month, the entire vehicle, live booster, and dummy second stage and capsule payload had been completely assembled.

Spaceport activity was centered in the blockhouse at 34 during the final weeks of preflight preparations. Nearly all original members of the ABMA team that had worked through the Redstone, Jupiter, Juno, and Pershing programs held key supervisory positions during assembly and checkout operations at the pad. But the team had grown tremendously. Stage contractor personnel manned console positions side by side with the NASA veterans. There were more people and there was more rocket. Procedures, plans, and schedules were more complicated, but, overall, final preparations went surprisingly well for the first flight of a new bird.

Still, there was a distinct air of anxiety at the Cape as launch day neared. There were many who feared the monstrous vehicle, all 460 tons of it, would never clear the pad. Pessimists said its explosion would destroy complex facilities and probably the Saturn program with them. Safety engineers were concerned that the noise from the rocket's powerful engines might burst eardrums, and, in fact, ear plugs were issued to newsmen at the press site on flight day.

But through the apprehensions, the launch crews worked with a methodical coolness and attention to detail. Theirs was an inborn confidence in the design and structure of the vehicle, and they labored extra hard and long to give Saturn every chance. The flight was set for the morning of October 27, 1961. Late the night before, 300 men, including Debus and von Braun, filed into the blockhouse and picked up the countdown. The manual they followed contained more than 233 pages of instructions and commands. Launch vehicle test conductor Bob Moser, an old pro with dozens of previous missions behind him, recalls the terminal portion of the count went well, without any major problems.

There was one highly unusual occurrence on the morning of the

27th, however, but it was far from a technical problem. The Canaveral area, for decades, has been a haven for wildlife, particularly birds. Each year the National Audubon Society conducts a nationwide bird count over a one-day period, usually around Christmas. More different species are sighted in the general Cape region, often over 200, during this count than at any other place in America. A few days before the Saturn was to be fired, local Audubon officials had spotted a number of roseate spoonbills, which resemble flamingoes, in the immediate launch area. They were afraid the birds might be cremated in the rocket's exhaust, and wrote NASA. Thus, 90 minutes before liftoff, two security police sergeants drove northeast of the pad and turned their car's siren on full blast. The resulting racket not only drove the spoonbills away, but practically blackened the skies with hundreds of ducks, herons, and various other winged specimens.

With this out of the way, Saturn SA-1 was launched at 9:06 A.M. Because of its great bulk, it appeared for an instant to be stuck on the pad, but ever so slowly the rocket began to climb, four full seconds after ignition. Its eight engines, generating 1.3 million pounds of thrust, propelled it to a peak altitude of 84 miles and a speed of 3,607 miles per hour before it impacted, as planned, 215 miles down range. Its remarkable first-time success heralded a new era in American rocketry.

Dr. Brainerd Holmes, then director of NASA's Office of Manned Space Flight, was ecstatic. "This firing," he said, "was one of the most complete successes in the history of experimental rocket testing. Every part of this most complex rocket stage thus far attempted by the United States performed well." And, he had a pat on the back for the launch team he had seen work so smoothly in the blockhouse: "The entire 12-hour countdown that preceded the firing was conducted without a single technical interruption."

The next two Saturn I vehicles, SA-2 and SA-3, were more of the same. Their launches, on April 25 and November 16, 1962, were both successful and spectacular. Each rocket carried 95 tons of water in its upper stages—to simulate the weight of the fuels these would carry when live stages were placed atop the booster. A couple of minutes after liftoff, at respective altitudes of 65 and 104 miles, these stages were purposely exploded in a side project called "High Water." By this time, of course, the prime objectives of the shots, flight tests of the booster, had been achieved. Scientists felt a bonus objective could be obtained with the water experiment, for they wanted to observe the effect of this large mass of water on the upper region of the atmosphere or lower ionosphere. To spectators at the Cape and on the beaches, it was a thrilling sight.

On March 28, 1963, SA-4 was launched. One hundred seconds after liftoff one of the eight booster engines was intentionally cut off. Engineers wanted to see what effect, if any, it would have on the flight. It had none.

It was 10 months before the next big Saturn flew, this time with a live second stage. To handle the double-barreled rocket, another new complex was carved out of the wilderness a mile directly north of the pad at 34. Launch Complex 37 was built on a 120-acre tract and had two pads instead of the usual one. Again, the dominating landmark was the service structure, this one 328 feet high and weighing an even seven million pounds. It came equipped with fixed platform levels and adjustable service platforms to provide access to the space vehicle at all levels. Two 268-foot-tall umbilical towers were erected, one at each pad.

More than 3,290 yards of concrete and 400 tons of steel were used to mold the blockhouse. Inside it, over 300 launch team members could work in comfort, without crowding each other. Huge cylindrical propellant storage tanks, similar to those at 34, ringed the new complex.

Two months before the first launch took place at 37, there was a distinguished visitor at the Cape: John Fitzgerald Kennedy. He received a thorough briefing on progress in the manned lunar landing program inside 37's blockhouse, then he stepped outside and squinted into the sun while looking at the towering, 163-foot-tall SA-5 vehicle on its pad. He was impressed with what he saw. It was his third visit to the Spaceport in 21 months. He had flown in to greet returning Mercury astronaut John Glenn in February, 1962, and came back that September. Kennedy later boarded the USS *Observation Island* and witnessed the launching of a Polaris missile from the submerged nuclear submarine *Andrew Jackson* off Canaveral.

Before departing, and after shaking a number of hands of workers at Complex 37, JFK told Kurt Debus, "I have found this visit most informative. It has been a great help to me and will aid me in assessing our space programs."

The young President was highly popular at Canaveral, for employees could sense his sincere interest in the work they were doing. A couple of days later he expressed this interest again in a speech. "There will be setbacks and frustrations and disappointments in

Rocco Petrone of NASA briefs high government officials on the Saturn program at the Spaceport, September, 1962. Seated, front row, left to right, are NASA Administrator James E. Webb; the then Vice President Lyndon B. Johnson; Dr. Kurt Debus, now Director of the John F. Kennedy Space Center; President John F. Kennedy; and Major General Leighton I. Davis, then Commander of the Air Force Missile Test Center. (NASA Photo)

space," he said. "And there will be pressures for our country to do less and temptations to do something else. But this research must and will go on. The conquest of space must and will go ahead."

Six days after his Cape visit, Kennedy was dead, the victim of an assassin's bullet in Dallas, Texas.

The first launch at 37 occurred at 11:25 A.M., January 29, 1964. About 48 miles up, after almost two and a half minutes of flight, the booster engines, which had each been uprated to 188,000 pounds thrust, cut off and the big S-I stage separated and fell back into the ocean. Seconds later, while everyone in the blockhouse crossed his fingers, the S-IV engines ignited on schedule, burned for about eight minutes, and shoved the entire second stage and payload into an elliptical orbit around the earth. At 19 tons, it was the largest object ever to break the earth's bonds, and it more than realized even the most optimistic expectations. That night, 20 miles south of the pad in Cocoa Beach, there was one of the most joyous postlaunch celebrations ever held. The U.S. had matched Russia's heavy booster capabilities and then some.

On the morning of a Saturn launch, and most of the I-class vehicles were flown between 8 A.M. and noon, there is a steady swirl of activity. Motion is everywhere, from the blur of controlled action in the blockhouse to the liftoff and flight itself. The night before launch, however, is a striking contrast of dark stillness and quiet. Here is an eyewitness description of what Complex 37 was like 12 hours before the scheduled liftoff of SA-6, May 28, 1964:

"The blockhouse is empty, and the silence is, in this case, deafening. A lone technician checks out a phone line, as all around him the great array of complex equipment is quiet and still. Not a light is flashing, not a machine humming. There is virtually no motion anywhere. It is like the eye of a hurricane, the lull before the storm. It is almost impossible to visualize at this time the activity, the tense, exciting drama that is to unfold here within a few short hours when the countdown is resumed.

"Off in the distance, under the blockhouse's main floor, someone turns on a portable radio. Music flows for a moment, then stops, and the silence sets in again. At the pad, a thousand lights, from small bulbs to giant floods, give the service structure and encased Saturn an eerie, luminous effect. There is a soft breeze blowing off the ocean, and all is serene, save for a single generator's monotonous hum.

"At the top of the boom high over the service structure, more than 325 feet up, a flashing red light winks its warning to any aircraft, but there are none in the skies. Every so often a NASA shuttle taxi makes its round from the blockhouse to the pad and back. It has few passengers. It is 9:30 P.M. Mosquitoes seem to be the only form of live movement. Then, a lone security guard slowly makes his rounds. All is quiet.

"At the main gate to 37, a fire truck, its beacon cutting a red swath across the inky blackness, drives up. Near the pad apron is a tersely worded sign. Its message, 'No vehicles allowed beyond this point without spark arresters,' is mute testimony to the fact the giant Saturn booster is already fueled.

"Fifteen minutes later a liquid nitrogen truck drives up the pad and the stillness is broken. Into the blockhouse men enter, one by one, carrying with them thick notebooks, headsets and lunch bags. They wear freshly pressed launch jackets of their employers: NASA, Douglas, Chrysler, North American, and IBM. The cycle of activity, which will slowly build during the early morning hours to a roaring tempo leading to launch, has begun anew.

"The rocket and the night are no longer alone." *

* From an article written by the author for *Spaceport News,* NASA house publication at the John F. Kennedy Space Center.

Both SA-6 and SA-7, which followed on September 18, 1964, scored successes, and the Saturn I was declared an operational vehicle three flights early. Said one frequent launch witness, Congressman George Miller of California, Chairman of the House Science and Astronautics Committee: "This confirms our faith in the Saturn and in the competence of the scientists and technicians behind it."

Due to a numbering sequence change, SA-9 flew before SA-8, but the 8 and 9 vehicles, and SA-10, last of the Saturn I's, ran out an unprecedented string of triumphal flights for the program: ten launches, ten successes. Each of the last three birds carried a scientific payload into earth orbit: Pegasus satellites I, II, and III. They were designed to measure the number, force, and direction of meteoroids in near-earth space.

Without question, the flight of SA-8, launched May 25, 1965, was the most spectacular of the series. It was the only one that took place at night. Gulping three tons of propellants per second, the rocket trailed a blinding golden flame, like a great, elongated sun, that illuminated the entire eastern horizon as it arced spaceward. It was seen for hundreds of miles.

SA-10 flew on July 30, 1965, three years and nine months after SA-1. There wasn't a single hitch in the countdown. Launch crews of NASA and contractor personnel, many of them greenhorns at the start, had matured under fire. Results of their work could not have been better. Saturn I was a far cry from some classic failures in the Cape's past.

During the early days of Saturn testing, there was a major NASA reorganization at the Cape. It was triggered in November, 1961, with the activation of the Office of Manned Space Flight at NASA Headquarters in Washington. This office observed the rapid expansion taking place at the Spaceport, and decided it was time to establish a separate field center there. Up to this point, the Launch Operations Directorate had been the test firing wing of the Marshall Space Flight Center in Huntsville.

On July 1, 1962, the Launch Operations Center (LOC) was created. Dr. Kurt H. Debus was named Director. The fledgling Center was given the responsibility of serving all NASA projects at Cape Canaveral, and consolidated all NASA operating relationships with the Air Force. There were no public ceremonies commemorating the

All eyes are on the TV monitors in the Complex 37 blockhouse during the launch of SA-8, May 25, 1965. In center, pointing, is the Director of the John F. Kennedy Space Center, Dr. Kurt Debus; to his left, Dr. Wernher von Braun; between them, in foreground, Dr. Hans Gruene. (NASA Photo)

transition, since the formation of LOC was the result of organizational realignments of responsibilities involving no change in physical location, but only functional transfers of personnel. Still, it was a happy day for the local launch crews. The importance of their growth and work over the years had been formally recognized.

Not all NASA elements at the Cape were included in the initial transfer. G. Merritt Preston's spacecraft checkout teams, for instance, were still, organizationally, under the Manned Spacecraft Center in Houston, and unmanned satellite and space probing launches were directed by Robert H. Gray and a complement of personnel attached from the Goddard Space Flight Center, Greenbelt, Maryland.

Seventeen months after being designated a Center, LOC had a new name. It came in the form of an executive order in early December, 1963, only a few days after the assassination of John F. Kennedy. The order read:

"Whereas President John F. Kennedy lighted the imagination of our people when he set the moon as our target and man as the means to reach it; and

"Whereas installations now to be renamed are the center and symbol of our country's principal assault on space; and

"Whereas it is in the nature of this assault that it should test the limits of our use and grace, and strength and wit, and vigor and perseverance—qualities fitting to the memory of John F. Kennedy,

"Now therefore, by virtue of the authority vested in me as President of the United States, I hereby designate the facilities of the Launch Operations Center of the National Aeronautics and Space Administration and the facilities of Station #1 of the Atlantic Missile Range in the State of Florida, as the John F. Kennedy Space Center; and such facilities shall be hereafter known and referred to by that name."

The order was signed by Lyndon B. Johnson.

There was some initial resentment at changing the Cape's name. Canaveral has historic origins dating to the 16th century. In fact, the town of Cape Canaveral, which separates the launch pads from Cocoa Beach, voted to retain its name despite the controversy. But President Johnson explained that the change in the name of the Cape itself was made to "honor John F. Kennedy's memory and the future of the works he started. His dream of conquering the vastness of space was one of the nation's major goals which had been vitalized by his drive and dedication."

No one at the Spaceport could dispute that.

Chapter 9

UNMANNED OPERATIONS

When NASA inherited Project Vanguard in 1958, it also acquired the nucleus of a fine, experienced launch team. The Vanguard launch director was a native of Meadville, Pennsylvania, who had early been captivated by the exciting and limitless potentials of space exploration. Robert H. Gray is both a dynamic leader who can inspire his men to work to the maximum of their capabilities, and he is a cool, technical-minded engineer who can perceptively diagnose a rocket's condition before flight.

After Vanguard closed out, Gray and a staff of about 80 key engineers and technicians formed the Field Project Branch of NASA's Goddard Space Flight Center. Their job: to launch various unmanned satellites and spacecraft for a number of foreign nations, government agencies, and other NASA divisions. Essentially, three rockets have been used over the years to boost a wide variety of space-probing payloads into earth orbit and to the far reaches of the solar system. They are Delta, Atlas-Agena, and Atlas-Centaur.

Launch complexes for the Delta and Agena programs were already constructed—Air Force Thor pads 17 A and B, and Atlas ICBM pads 12 and 13. Major modifications were made to the facilities, particularly to the service structures, to handle the delicate spacecraft these birds would be called upon to fly. A new complex, 36, was built just south of ICBM Row for Atlas-Centaur. It is complete with two 210-foot-tall gantries and two pads, A and B.

For the smaller payloads, mostly satellites designed to orbit earth, NASA chose a booster that had long since proven its reliability at

Canaveral: the Air Force-developed Thor. Of course, Thor was no stranger to space. In addition to its lengthy development program as an Intermediate Range Ballistic Missile at Canaveral, the Air Force also used it as the booster for the first two Pioneer flights. This version of the vehicle was called Thor-Able, and it also launched Explorer 6, a paddle-wheel satellite, and Transit 1A, an all-purpose experimental payload.

The Thor-Able Transit launch figured in one of the Cape's weirdest incidents. It involved a red-bellied woodpecker, and of all the many stories of wildlife at the Spaceport, none can match this one. It caused one of the knottiest engineering problems in missile history.

It all began, harmlessly enough, about three weeks before launch, when the bird landed on the Thor-Able's umbilical cable. This was a maze of wires, wrapped in aluminum foil, that supplies power to operate subsystems in the Thor prior to flight. "Woody" roamed about the cable, gradually working his way upward, until he found a cozy niche about 80 feet high in the launch platform. He then began pecking merrily away, and hollowed right into the cable's core, where he constructed a nest. Air Force officials and employees of Douglas, the manufacturers of Thor, held hurried consultations on how to remove the unwanted tenant. A loud horn failed to disturb the bird. Ringing bells were tried, and seemed not to bother but to soothe him as he pecked deeper into the cable. Launch crews were becoming frantic.

Electrocution attempts failed. Discharge of firearms is prohibited at the Cape, so that was ruled out. An entomologist was called in. He placed a carbon dioxide bottle near the nest, but this, too, was unsuccessful. More consultations were held. Florida Power and Light Company representatives were queried as to what methods they used to keep woodpeckers from boring into their utility poles. They used a mixture of arsenic and creosote, but this was termed inadvisable since it would not adhere to the slippery aluminum surface that wrapped the cables.

Finally, in sheer desperation, engineers devised a special countdown procedure entitled, "Elimination of Woodpecker." A high pressure air bottle was fastened beneath the bird's hole, with a lanyard extending to the missile tower's seventh deck. As Woody unsuspectingly approached his perch for another stint of pecking, the men began their count, 5-4-3-2-1, and yanked. The resulting jet stream of air pressure sent the bewildered woodpecker high into the atmosphere in a southeasterly direction, the same route most missiles take. The bird disappeared from sight and was never seen again. Engineers patched the hole and fired the Transit satellite on schedule.

Today, visitors at the Cape take a long second look when they tour pad 17-B. On the north side of the stand are stenciled rocket impressions representing successful firings. And, in the upper left hand corner, is a picture of a red-bellied woodpecker with a cross beside it—indicative of a perfect launch.

With a Vanguard system as its second stage and a small solid propellant third stage, the new NASA Thor vehicle was given the name Delta. When NASA signed a contract with the Douglas Aircraft Company in 1959 for a dozen Deltas, there were no plans for any beyond them. But by July, 1967, the space agency had launched 50 of the relatively inexpensive rockets, and the end was still not in sight. In fact, 50 percent of all unmanned satellites launched by NASA since 1960 have been with Delta.

The first flight was May 13, 1960, and to say the vehicle had an inauspicious debut would be an understatement. It carried an Echo passive communications satellite, but the rocket failed enroute to orbit. Three months later, with early troubles cleared up, Delta number two orbited Echo I, a 100-foot-in-diameter, balloonlike satellite. Because of its bright appearance as it moved in the night sky, Echo I for years served as the most tangible evidence of the U.S. space program to peoples around the globe for whom "satellite" was otherwise only a word. They could see Echo pass like a slow moving star across the horizon. In fact, it was probably seen by more people than any other man-made object. Newspapers printed timetables of its nightly runs. Many called it America's most influential space ambassador.

Delta number two started a successful launch string that lasted two and a half years and included 22 consecutive orbits: a performance of unprecedented reliability. There were many milestones covered enroute. Several Tiros (*T*elevision *I*nfra*R*ed *O*bservation *S*atellite) flights, for instance, were included. During the first five years of the program, Tiros satellites snapped nearly half a million cloud pictures, and transmitted them to ground stations for immediate use in weather forecasting. These pictures enabled meteorologists to issue more than 2,400 storm bulletins and have helped give advance warning for almost all hurricanes. Pictures from Tiros 3 were taken in time to make possible the largest mass evacuation ever to take place in the United States. More than 350,000 persons were able to flee the path of Hurricane Carla in September, 1963, and deaths were held to a minimum.

Delta 8 launched the first Orbiting Solar Observatory (OSO) on March 7, 1962. Before this, the sun, which is earth's closest star, could be studied only from land-based observatories, through the distorted haze of earth's atmosphere. Today, advanced OSO's send daily information on phenomena such as solar flares and radiation, which will help scientists determine how variations on the sun affect the environment here on earth.

Delta 9 had another important payload. It carried the first truly international satellite into orbit April 26, 1962. Ariel I, a joint United Kingdom-United States venture, contributed much to man's basic knowledge of the ionosphere, an electrified region of the atmosphere extending from about 40 miles to several hundred miles above earth.

Telstar I, the famed communications satellite, was orbited aboard Delta 11, July 10, 1962. It transmitted for the first time live television over intercontinental distances between Andover, Maine, and stations in France and England. Long distance telephone calls were also transmitted during the first week of orbit.

Two more communications satellites, Relay I and Syncom I, were flown on Deltas 15 and 16, December 13, 1962, and February 14, 1963. Relay studied effects of space on experimental wide band communications between widely separated ground stations. Many transmissions of telephone, TV, and data were accomplished over intercontinental distances. Relay also beamed John F. Kennedy's funeral services to millions of mourners in Japan and Europe; transmitted an English patient's brainwaves across the Atlantic to American neurologists for diagnosis; and carried, live, the coronation of Pope Paul VI.

Syncom (*Syn*chronous *Com*munications Satellite) was the forerunner to an operational communications satellite system. By placing as few as three spacecraft into 22,300-mile-high orbits, spaced equidistant around the equator at roughly the same orbital speed as the earth's revolution, they would remain "stationary," and could thus provide global service.

Also included in the string of 22 successful launches, which wasn't broken until Delta 24 failed March 19, 1964, were several Explorer scientific satellites, of odd shapes and sizes. Basically, this series of probes studies the space environment and upper atmosphere surrounding the earth, including such phenomena as radiation fields, cosmic rays, micrometeoroids, temperature, magnetic fields, solar radiation, ionospheric studies, air density, solar plasma, and gamma rays.

The Delta launch team began a new series of successes with the flight of Syncom III August 19, 1964, on vehicle number 25. Following this, Explorers 21 and 26, Tiros 9 and OSO II were orbited in order. Then came Delta 30 and another pace-setting mission: Early Bird. The date was April 6, 1965. It was the world's first commercial communications satellite. It linked Europe and North America via television transmissions, presaging the day of truly international TV.

Another highlight was reached February 3, 1966, when Delta 36 orbited ESSA I. This was the first of the operational Tiros system satellites. NASA launched it for the Environmental Science Services Administration, which soon after began providing regular and continuous cloud photographs of the entire sunlit portion of the earth to subscribing ground stations at least once a day.

The work of ESSA satellites orbiting earth, enabling meteorologists to prepare accurate long-range weather forecasts and give advance warnings of approaching storms, is a great boon to mankind. President Johnson estimated some cost savings based on the accurate prediction of weather only five days in advance. These include:

—$2.5 billion a year to agriculture.
—$45 million to the lumber industry.
—$100 million to surface transportation.
—$75 million to retail marketing.
—$4 billion to water resources management.

The saving in human life cannot be precisely measured, but it, too, would be substantial. NASA associate administrator Dr. Homer E. Newell has said the day when it may be possible to plan a picnic, fishing trip, or any other outing weeks in advance and know almost for sure that it will not rain on that day is not far off.

The first Biosatellite was carried into orbit by Delta 43, December 14, 1966. It carried a payload that included pepper plants, wheat seedlings, frog eggs and amoebae, and was designed to provide answers to questions about a large number of basic biological processes, particularly the effects of the space environment on various life processes.

The 50th Delta vehicle launched an Interplanetary Monitoring Platform into orbit July 20, 1967. Of the first half hundred flights, only three failed to carry out their mission. Reflecting on this re-

Overall aerial view of ICBM Row, on Cape Kennedy, looking north.
(NASA Photo)

Technicians mating a BIOS-B biological satellite to its launch vehicle at Cape Kennedy, August, 1967. (NASA Photo)

markable record, NASA engineers cited one of the prime reasons for the success as the stick-to-itiveness of the launch crews, both contractor and government. Most of the team that began with the Echo failure in 1960 were in the blockhouse 50 launches later. Their experience under fire, and their strict attention to detail, including extra inspections, certainly are important factors in the Delta story at the Spaceport.

Many improvements have been made in the basic vehicle over the years. Most important was the upgrading of the third stage engine and the addition of strap-on, solid-propellant rockets to the booster to give it more kick. With these strap-ons, the booster's thrust was upped from 170,000 to 333,550 pounds. This Thrust Augmented Improved Delta (TAID) stands 92 feet tall, and weighs 75 tons at liftoff.

Using a Thrust Augmented Improved Delta launch vehicle, NASA sends a Pioneer spacecraft into orbit around the sun, August 17, 1966. (NASA Photo)

Though there have been few problems encountered with the Delta launch vehicle, there was a single tragic incident involving one of its payloads. On Tuesday morning, April 14, 1964, technicians inside a building near the eastern tip of the Cape were running a series of tests on an Orbiting Solar Observatory and the Delta third stage engine, prior to their mating with the booster at pad 17. The final check to be run was called a spin test. The third stage and OSO spacecraft were to be placed on a large turntable and brought to a high spinning rate to insure proper balance. This spinning would be necessary during flight to keep the payload from tumbling through the airless void in space. It was considered a routine test. A number of similar ones had been run without incident.

During the actual spin-up, the 11 men making final preparations were to move to a safe position, behind concrete protectors. They had only a few minutes more work to do when there was a sharp crack, then another, then a sizzling noise. Within seconds, hell broke loose. Unexpectedly, the third-stage rocket's solid propellants had been set off—*inside* the building! With 3,000 pounds of thrust power, the rocket blasted off the turntable and spun around the room, spewing savage flames in all directions. For some of the men, there was no escape, no place to go. They were enveloped in fire. Others dived into a pit in the center of the room or huddled behind tables and chairs. A concussion wave, created at ignition of the motor, hurled men across the large room. One technician was lifted out of his shoes. As the berserk rocket continued to lash about uncontrollably, the smoke and flames became blinding. Those who reached the door found they couldn't open it, for too much pressure had built up inside. The temperature soared over 3,000 degrees!

Finally, mercifully, the pressure became too much for the building's structure, and the main door blew out. Huge clouds of curling black smoke poured forth, blotting out the bright morning sunshine. And then came the men, running, crawling, screaming. They rolled on the ground, trying desperately to beat out the flames that covered their seared bodies. Three of them died from the burns they received, and others were hospitalized for varying periods of time. It was later believed that static electricity had triggered the third stage's igniters. It was, at the time, the Spaceport's worst disaster. And it proved once again how potentially dangerous the business of rocketry is. No matter how stringent the safety precautions, there is always hazard involved.

While Delta has many advantages as a launch vehicle—reliability, versatility, inexpensive cost, to name a few—it is somewhat restricted in the size of the payload it can orbit. It is mostly used for small earth satellites. For heavier satellites and space probing craft, NASA chose a beefier booster. It, too, had been time tested by the Air Force at Canaveral, and had long since been declared an operational system. The vehicle selected was Atlas. The uprated booster had a liftoff thrust capability of over 360,000 pounds; powerful, but not quite enough for the bulk lifting jobs NASA required of it. Thus, a second stage, the Lockheed-built Agena, was added. It uses inhibited red fuming nitric acid and unsymmetrical dimethyl-hydrazine as propellants to generate 15,000 pounds' thrust, a strong enough in-space kick for the missions it was to be assigned.

The two-stage combination resulted in a 97-foot-tall bird that could launch a 3,500-pound payload into a 300-nautical-mile earth orbit, hard land 800 pounds on the moon, or boost a 570-pound payload on an interplanetary flight. Atlas-Agena was to be assigned some of the most glamorous space missions ever conceived by man. Former Air Force ICBM Launch Complexes 12 and 13 were transferred for NASA use.

One of the rocket's first tasks was of Herculean proportions. It was to send a Mariner spacecraft past earth's sister planet Venus, more than 36 million miles away. The Mariner program was managed for NASA by the Jet Propulsion Laboratory of the California Institute of Technology. The first flight attempt was made July 22, 1962, but it ended in failure five minutes after liftoff when the rocket strayed off course and was destroyed by the Range Safety Officer.

A little over a month later, another Atlas-Agena, carrying a backup spacecraft, was ready for a second try. This one left earth August 27. After a week, when Mariner II was more than one million miles out in space and speeding toward its target at over 60,000 mph, ground controllers sent it a vital command. A lunar or planetary mission has too great a range and too small a target to be accurately guided solely from the brief initial powered flight. Thrust must also be applied from a small spacecraft motor earlier than the midpoint of the flight to increase possible accuracy. Thus, the spacecraft was ordered to execute a complex midcourse maneuver that changed its trajectory from one that would have reached no closer than 230,000 miles to Venus to one that would brush within 22,000 miles of the planet.

On December 14, 1962, 109 days after launch, Mariner II sailed past Venus at a distance of 21,648 miles, giving man his first relatively close-up observation of the cloud-shrouded planet. The successful flyby climaxed an epic space flight experiment that greatly advanced the world's knowledge about interplanetary space and contributed to planning for astronauts' eventual journeys to the moon and to other planets.

From the many experimental devices aboard, Mariner found that the temperature of Venus may be as hot as 800 degrees Fahrenheit, hot enough to melt lead. This confirmed what scientists had long believed: no life as is known on earth could survive on Venus. The spacecraft also detected no openings in the dense cloud mass that envelops the planet. In all, Mariner II transmitted about 90 million bits (from *b*inary dig*it,* meaning a unit of information) to earth. Radio contact was lost January 3, 1963, when the 449-pound craft was nearly six million miles beyond Venus and almost 54 million miles from earth.

In addition to the invaluable information it gathered and tele-metered home, Mariner proved the feasibility of sending deep space probes on an accurate course. It was the world's interplanetary trail-blazer, and added reality to the dreams of men who envisioned the day when man would first fly by and later land on other worlds in the solar system.

Another intangible benefit from Mariner II was the confidence it gave launch and spacecraft crews. They would need it, for the next Atlas-Agena mission in this program was even more difficult, com-plex and longer than the Venus flyby. The assignment was the most challenging yet handed Bob Gray's Atlas-Agena team, headed by Harold Zweigbaum: to launch a new Mariner past the surface of Mars! The curving flight distance alone would be 350 million miles, nearly twice that of Mariner II. Some 138,000 components in the unmanned spacecraft would have to function 6,500 hours in space to achieve the objectives.

Because the flight was such a long shot, the Cape crews were to be given two cracks at it. They needed both. Mariner III was launched from Complex 13 November 5, 1964, during a month when Mars would be in a favorable position in relationship to earth. It was doomed within minutes of liftoff. The cylin-fiberglass-honey-comb nose shield, designed to protect the craft during the smashing thrust up through the atmosphere and then to be jettisoned, failed, and could not be properly ejected. Flight controllers made vain at-tempts to correct the problem, but the precise trajectory necessary to reach the distant planet had been missed, and only a few hours after launch, Mariner III's batteries ran out of power.

Ground crews worked around the clock to ready the second Atlas-Agena and Mariner IV in time before Mars passed out of favor-able range. They made it with a liftoff at 9:22 A.M., November 28. After the big Atlas booster had done its job, an improved Agena's 16,000-pound-thrust engine kicked Mariner into orbital velocity of 17,500 mph, then shut down and coasted for over 40 minutes, swing-ing around earth to line its sights on the target. Agena restarted and propelled the spacecraft toward Mars at better than 25,000 mph on

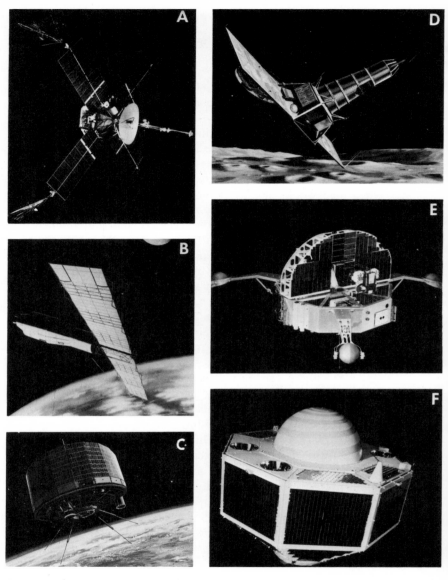

Unmanned satellites: (A) Mariner IV, which flew past Mars in July, 1965. (B) Pegasus, used for collecting micrometeoroid data. (C) TIROS (Television Infrared Observation Satellite). (D) Ranger VIII, which photographed the moon's surface before impacting on it February 17, 1965. (E) OSO II (Orbiting Solar Observatory). (F) GEOS I, used for more precise mapping of the earth. (NASA Photos)

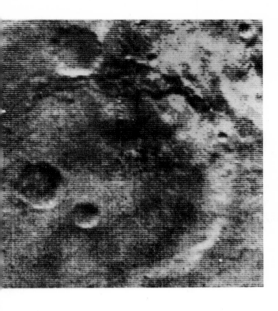

One of the finest of Mariner IV's fantastic photographs of the surface of Mars. (NASA Photo)

a path that would take it within 150,000 miles of the surface. The launch operations crew had threaded the needle. Mariner IV was on its way.

Later, its solar panels were deployed to draw power from the sun. Then, a week after launch, the delicate midcourse maneuver was made, changing the angle of flight only a quarter of a degree, and the speed of the craft only 37 mph; minute figures, but, because of the vast distance to be traveled, enough to steer Mariner on a line that would send it much closer to Mars.

The long journey lasted seven and a half months. Mariner IV reached its destination July 14, 1965, and passed within 6,118 miles of the Martian surface. During the eight and a half hour flyby, its camera snapped 21 fantastic photos and sent them back to earth, climaxing a truly historic mission. The pictures, the most remarkable of the space age, surprisingly revealed the face of Mars was pitted with craters, and may not have changed much in billions of years.

Among Mariner IV's other accomplishments:

—Measured radiation and surveyed magnetic fields along a 418-million-mile journey through space, but found no radiation belt or magnetic field around Mars.

—Gave new and more accurate information on the planet's size, gravity, and path around the sun.

—Showed that the planet's atmosphere is so thin, perhaps one percent as dense as that on earth, that astronauts would need pressure suits to survive there.

—Revealed that on Mars, as on earth, an ionosphere will, under certain conditions, make radio communications possible between distant points on the planet.

Scientists were still gleaning valuable information two years later on the 21 photographs taken. The pictures, after thorough analysis, indicated that craters and other surface features on Mars showed a striking similarity to the surface of the moon.

Mariner IV did not find out whether there was any form of life on Mars. It had not been designed to. That would come in time from more sophisticated spacecraft. Two years after launch, the long-distance record setter had traveled 1.3 billion miles from Cape Kennedy, and was still operating well.

It was a long way, in just 17 years, from the flight of Bumper 8, which had lasted only a few minutes.

On June 14, 1967, Mariner V was launched from Complex 12 for a four-month flight to Venus. The firing team achieved one of the highest accuracies ever, so precise, in fact, the spacecraft would have passed by the planet within four hours of the scheduled flyby time—even without a midcourse maneuver. Primary mission objective was to obtain scientific information on the origin and nature of Venus and its mysterious environment. The pass occurred October 19, 1967, when Mariner V brushed within 2,500 miles of the planet's surface, after traveling more than 217 million miles in an arcing flight, and began relaying reams of important scientific data back to earth. Jet Propulsion Laboratory scientists spent months deciphering data on the planet's atmosphere, ionosphere, temperatures, and surface qualities. Flight controllers said the spacecraft's sensitive instruments performed flawlessly during the 19,000 mph flyby. After the Venusian pass, Mariner V streaked on into space, eventually going into solar orbit averaging 54 million miles from the sun.

Among Mariner V's major findings:

—Venus glows, eerily. Something, possibly chemicals burning in the atmosphere, or electrical storms far more intense than those on earth, causes the night side of the planet to glow with an ashen hue.

—Venus' atmosphere is extremely dense and is largely composed of carbon dioxide. This denseness acts like a giant lens, bending light waves around the planet, and causing great distortion.

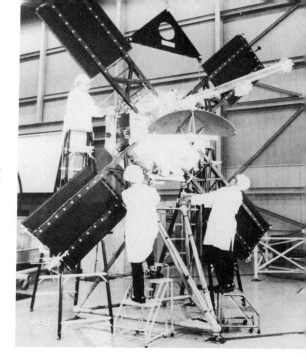

Engineers checking the Mariner V spacecraft at Cape Kennedy preparatory to launching on four-month flight of more than 217 million miles in which it passed only 2,500 miles from the planet Venus. (NASA Photo)

—The outer fringe of the atmosphere is about 700 degrees Fahrenheit. No oxygen, earth's life-giving element, was found in the upper atmosphere, though hydrogen was detected.

—Tracking of radio signals from Mariner V as it swept behind Venus showed the planet is virtually spherical, compared with earth's slightly pear shape.

Under Project Ranger, also designed and built for NASA by JPL, Atlas-Agena was given another tough assignment—to hit the moon dead center with a camera-carrying spacecraft. Hitting the moon today with Surveyors or circling it with orbiting satellites doesn't sound like too difficult a job. It is taken for granted. Space technology advances that rapidly. In 1961, when Ranger I was being prepared for flight from Canaveral, however, the mission looked nearly impossible. Here were some of the prime reasons:

—The earth was rotating on its axis, making one complete turn every 24 hours. The launch site, being in Florida, approximately 30 degrees north of the equator, turned through space at a speed of nearly 1,000 mph.

—The lunar target orbited earth at 2,000 mph.

—Escape velocity can only be reached safely outside the earth's mantle of atmosphere.

In effect, it meant the launch crews had to fire their rocket at a target only one fourth the diameter of earth, but nearly a quarter of a million miles away. This would be complicated enough if the target were stationary. It was not. The Atlas-Agena would have to be shot ahead of the moon, so aimed to hit a point in space at the same time the moon arrived at that point in its earth orbit. This called for accuracy of the greatest magnitude.

Ranger itself weighed over 800 pounds. Its camera was to take man's first close-up photographs of the lunar face. Not only would these pictures add immeasurably to the world's knowledge of the moon, but they would be used to help determine landing sites for following generations of spacecraft, both manned and unmanned. The first two Rangers, launched August 23 and November 18, 1961, were developmental flights to prove the spacecraft concept, and make deep space scientific measurements. Although the launch vehicle didn't place them in the desired orbit, the tests of the spacecraft were considered successful.

Ranger 3 was to be the first to photograph the moon during its final minutes of flight before crash landing on the lunar surface. It left earth January 26, 1962, but the Atlas-Agena boost was too strong, and it arrived ahead of the moon and missed, soaring into a solar orbit.

Ranger 4, three months later, was given a perfect ride and impacted on the hidden portion of the moon's leading hemisphere. The mission had to be declared unsuccessful, however, because the spacecraft's control clock failed and no pictures were taken or received. Ranger 5 also missed the moon after a failure in the switching and logic circuitry of the power system. It was launched October 18, 1962. At this point, the program was in trouble. Five of the expensive spacecraft had flown and not one had fully achieved its objective. Congressmen demanded to know why. Confidence at Canaveral ebbed to a low point and some project reorganizations were made.

Ranger 6, hopefully, would put the program back on the tracks. It carried six television cameras to obtain high resolution photographs of the lunar surface, and was launched under near-perfect conditions January 30, 1964. As the spacecraft neared its target 68 hours after liftoff, scientists crossed their fingers. It was dead on target, and would hit the moon in the Sea of Tranquility within 17 miles of the aiming point. This was a remarkable navigation feat in itself, but photography was Ranger's primary mission. Hope died as the craft smashed into the lunar terrain without transmitting a single picture. The camera systems had completely failed.

Ranger was now in very real danger of cancellation, but after much debate, it won another chance. Launch and spacecraft teams, given the reprieve, redoubled their efforts. Ranger 7 was ignited at 11:50 A.M., July 28, 1964. Thirteen minutes before it was to smack into the moon, the cameras were turned on. They worked! The spacecraft returned 4,316 pictures of exceptional quality. The resolution was 2,000 times better than any photograph of the moon made by earth telescopes. Craters less than three feet across were visible in the final pictures. The textbook mission was a spectacular success. It had, admittedly, been a long time coming, but the results justified the wait. It was a giant step forward in the advancement of space technology, and it brought this country closer to the national goal of landing men on the lunar surface.

Rangers 8 and 9 followed 7's triumph. Launched February 17 and March 21, 1965, both worked perfectly and sent back nearly 13,000 more close-up photos of the lunar terrain. After a near-fatal beginning, Ranger finished like a champion. Scientists are still studying the more than 17,000 photos that were received from the last three spacecraft in the series, and much new knowledge has been gained about the moon.

Lunar Orbiter was a follow-on project, planned to continue the efforts of Ranger, to acquire knowledge of the moon's surface to support the manned lunar landing, and to enlarge scientific understanding of earth's nearest neighbor. Unlike its predecessor, however, the 850-pound, Boeing-built Orbiter was not planned to crash into the moon—rather, to fly around it and snap pictures. It was a veritable flying photographic laboratory.

The first in this series, which was under the direction of NASA's Langley Research Center in Virginia, was launched aboard an Atlas-Agena August 1, 1966, and promptly demonstrated its incredible versatility. It photographed about two million square miles of the lunar surface, and provided the first detailed scientific knowledge of the lunar gravitational field and topographic and geological information of direct benefit to those planning future astronaut landing sites.

Lunar Orbiter 2 followed on November 6, and flew an even more successful mission, providing wide angle and telephoto coverage of

Setting a new mark of 29 consecutive successes for the launching team, an Atlas-Agena booster lifts off carrying Lunar Orbiter 4 on its way to the moon. (NASA Photo)

more than 1.5 million square miles of moon surface. The third flight in the series was one that will be long remembered by Cape "bird watchers." It was launched at 8:17 P.M., February 4, 1967, on a cool, clear night. The flaming rocket was visible to the naked eye for several minutes. Some observers could follow it for 400 miles down range before losing sight.

The Lunar Orbiter 4 flight was also noteworthy. It was the 329th Atlas launched, and as the big bird lifted off, blockhouse personnel were unusually quiet. They had a string of 28 consecutive successes going. It was the second time they had reached 28. On the previous run, the 29th vehicle blew up. When Orbiter 4 made it through the earth's atmosphere and on its way to the moon, there was a collective sigh from the launch crews. It was also the 78th success in the last 81 Atlas flights.

The fifth Lunar Orbiter closed out the series. Like all others, it scored a perfect launch and flight. The five spacecraft collectively photographed millions of square miles of the lunar surface, providing much new information about the dynamic processes which shaped the moon. Dozens of potential manned landing areas were also recorded on film. As a bonus, Lunar Orbiter I sent back the first photograph of earth—a sensational view—taken from the vicinity of the moon.

Orbiter 2's shot of the crater Copernicus (below), showing a deep, flat valley with rugged, high cliffs in the background, has been called by many the "picture of the century." As a plus, Orbiter helped in the first extensive chart made on the moon's far side. More than 85 percent of the photos used in the map were snapped by the five spacecraft in the series. All pictures, both wide angle and telephoto, showed lunar surface details with great clarity. The telephoto

Lunar Orbiter 2's close-up photograph of the crater Copernicus, one of the most prominent features on the face of the moon, has been called "the photograph of the century." When the view was taken, Lunar Orbiter was 28.4 miles above the moon's surface and about 150 miles due south of the center of Copernicus. Horizontal distance in the portion of the photo shown here is about 17 miles; from the horizon to the base of photo is about 150 miles. The 3,000-foot mountain on the horizon is the Gay-Lussac Promontory. (NASA Photo)

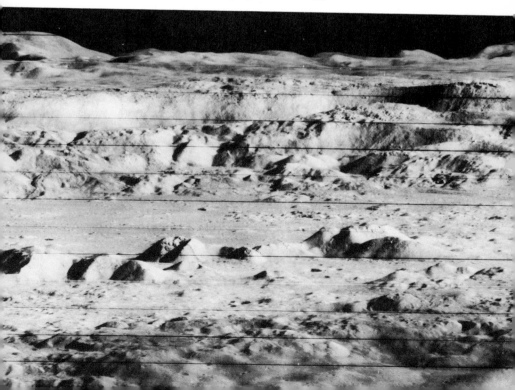

shots clearly revealed objects less than three feet in diameter, exceeding all mission requirements. As a result, scientists could easily eliminate some potential manned landing sites and concentrate their studies on the best-looking ones.

The five launches in the program were close to dead on target; all were in the "one sigma" range. In engineering vernacular, this means about as close to hitting the mark as can be expected after allowing for the element of chance and anticipated in-flight errors. If the bull's-eye was to achieve a circular orbit 400 miles up, for example, a three sigma designation would be set. This could be, say, anything within 25 miles of the 400-mile target, plus or minus. On a normal flight with everything working as planned, 99 percent of the time three sigma would be obtained. Two sigma would be an aiming point a little closer to the 400-mile figure, which is hit 95 percent of the time if all goes well. Either one of these is acceptable to carry out the mission. Any major deviation might cause trouble.

To win the sharpshooter score, however, requires a one sigma shot, which in the case of the 400-mile orbit would be within plus or minus eight and one third miles. Again, if everything worked as planned, this can be hit 67 percent of the time. Theoretically, this could go down to zero sigma if an exact 400-mile orbit was hit, but in reality, there is no such thing as a perfect flight.

There are many variables, Engine performance, velocity, roll, pitch, guidance—all this adds up. A pitch bend 1/100th of a degree off, for instance, will be compounded as more flight factors become involved. All this is taken into consideration, and around it an aiming point is calculated. Many Cape engineers believe anything better than one sigma is luck; that one sigma is the best possible performance that can be expected of the rocket, and well above the acceptance average.

All five Atlas-Agena launch vehicles carrying Lunar Orbiters were well within one sigma range. Any individual shot would have been considered good, not exceptional. But all five hitting the needle's eye was a significant accomplishment. Only minor midcourse maneuvers had to be made on each flight, allowing the spacecraft more working room to do a better job while circling the moon. The launch crews had done their work well.

Following Orbiter 5, NASA associate administrator Dr. Homer Newell sent a wire to the Kennedy Space Center: "The receipt of the final photographs from Orbiter 5 signals the climax of one of the most successful programs in NASA's history. The data returned from

The Lunar Orbiter 5 spacecraft, training its telephoto lens on the sunlit side of the earth, made this first photograph of the nearly-full planet from 214,806 miles away. Cloud cover overlies some of the features identified by the superimposed names, but many, such as Italy, Greece, Turkey, the Suez Canal area, the Red Sea, the Arabian Peninsula, and the entire east coast of Africa are clearly visible. The time was 5:05 A.M., Eastern Daylight Time, August 8, 1967. (NASA Photo)

the five successful missions represent a scientific advancement which far exceeds our initial objectives. An entire new base for exploration of the moon has been established. The success of Lunar Orbiter is due to large measure to the team spirit and cooperation that existed across the board among the many government and industrial activities involved. You have set an outstanding example for future programs to follow. Congratulations and best wishes for the future to the many individuals who played a role in this magnificent achievement."

In addition to lunar and interplanetary spacecraft, Atlas-Agena has been called upon by NASA to carry other heavy scientific payloads into earth orbit. One is the Orbiting Astronomical Observatory. At 3,900 pounds, it was the heftiest payload carried by the reliable launch vehicle. It is also the most electronically complex unmanned spacecraft ever developed in the United States. OAO contains more than 440,000 separate parts and 30 miles of electrical wiring.

Its job is to study stars and other celestial objects from an orbital vantage point, free from the obscuring and distorting effects of the earth's atmosphere. Prior to its maiden flight, April 8, 1966, the total amount of direct scientific observation in the ultraviolet, X-ray, and gamma ray spectral regions was less than an hour. This had been obtained from sounding rockets and balloon flights above the atmosphere. Thus, the potential offered by OAO in expanding man's knowledge of the universe rank it, in many respects, with the invention of the telescope.

Another in the series of scientific payloads is the Orbiting Geophysical Observatory (OGO). This 1,135-pound package was designed to study the relationship between the sun and the nature of the earth's environment. This includes such phenomena as the solar wind, solar flares, terrestrial magnetic field and ionospheric disturbances, radiation belt particle populations and aurora and polar cap events, ionization and variations in atmospheric density.

OGO-1, launched September 4, 1964, was only partly successful, as was the second spacecraft, but together they achieved all technological objectives. Later shots in the program fared better and added much new lore to scientific storehouses. It is hard to cite direct advantages or material benefits of some of these data, but to scientists ever curious about the earth we live on and the universe it revolves in, each bit of information gained is a new piece fitted into the master jigsaw puzzle.

One of Atlas-Agena's last jobs was to orbit an 815-pound Applications Technology Satellite (ATS). The first spacecraft in this project was launched December 6, 1966. Lessons learned from ATS flights are intended to improve spacecraft technology, develop long-life control systems, advance in-space communications, and improve long-range weather predictions; just about something for everyone.

NASA's use of Atlas-Agena as a space booster ceased after March 1, 1968. The decision was not a slap in the face of the launch teams. On the contrary, the vehicle was one of the most successful work-horses in the stable. It was partly a matter of economics and partly the fact that the number of programs it could support had dimin-ished. Ranger and Lunar Orbiter were completed, and Mariner flights were very infrequent. It was expensive to maintain Launch Com-plexes 12 and 13 for the tapering workload, so officials decided another rocket system could handle the rest of Atlas-Agena's mis-sions, along with its own.

That rocket, which also used an Atlas booster, was Centaur. Atlas-Centaur had a turbulent early history at the Cape.

First stage of the vehicle caused no major problems. It was a mod-ified version of an Atlas booster that initially developed 367,000 pounds' thrust. It was the second, or Centaur, stage that was the troublemaker. It was to be the first United States rocket to use liquid hydrogen for fuel. Centaur design called for powering by two rocket engines capable of developing 15,000 pounds' thrust each. These were also to be able to shut down and then reignite in space to allow for a coast period. This feature would permit Centaur to wait until its target or intended flight path was in the most advantageous position before resuming powered flight. Like the booster, Centaur's stainless steel skin was to be no thicker than a dime and have no internal framework. Slight pressurization inside the propellant tanks would maintain its shape and provide necessary strength. One fact sheet compared the vehicle to a football, which is extremely light but has great strength. The entire configuration stood 113 feet tall and weighed 300,000 pounds at liftoff.

The headaches involved the use of liquid hydrogen as a fuel. This was a giant step in the advancement of the rocket propellant "state of the art," or progress to that point. It had never been done before. One main reason was the difficulty of handling it, for to remain a liquid, hydrogen must be maintained at a temperature of minus 423 degrees Fahrenheit. If it rises above that it vaporizes to gas. It is a highly desirable fuel, however, for it can give the rocket a high-energy kick of much greater proportions than conventional propellants. Liquid hydrogen, in fact, provides about 40 percent more energy per pound; enough to lift 8,500 pounds of scientific equipment into earth orbit, more than a ton to the moon, and 1,300 pounds to Mars or Venus.

Centaur was assigned the job, after proving itself as a reliable rocket, of shooting a Surveyor spacecraft to a soft landing on the lunar surface. By the time the first Atlas-Centaur was ready for flight from Canaveral, engineers weren't sure whether they had mastered liquid hydrogen technology or it had mastered them. The bird sat on the pad for endless months as checkout tests ran far behind schedule. There was even some fear the salt spray from the nearby ocean would rust out its insides before it could get off. The whole Centaur program was lagging and received considerable criticism in Congress, the press, and elsewhere.

The initial launch on May 8, 1962, it was hoped, would quiet the critics. It did just the opposite. The booster lifted off perfectly, but 55 seconds later a weather shield came off the second stage and Centaur exploded into a brilliant fireball high over the ocean, just off Canaveral's shoreline. Drastic reorganizational steps were taken to straighten out the program.

It was more than a year and a half before the next launch, but it was worth the wait. Atlas-Centaur 2, on November 27, 1963, became the first rocket to fly with a hydrogen-oxygen propulsion system, a pioneering landmark of rocketry of such significance that it perhaps will only be accurately measured by future historians. The entire second stage was placed into an earth orbit. Some of the new technology gained was immediately applied to the development of the Saturn I's second stage, the S-IVB.

But Centaur was not completely out of the woods. The third flight, June 30, 1964, was only partially successful, and the fifth launch attempt was a total disaster. It exploded and burned on the pad, threatening for a time a blockhouse full of technical personnel. Despite the frustrating setback—no success comes easy at the Spaceport—efforts were renewed, and the next few flights put Centaur back in good repute.

Centaur 9, for instance, demonstrated for the first time the restart capabilities of a booster fueled with liquid hydrogen while under the weightless conditions of outer space. It achieved a parking orbit above earth, the engines were shut down, and, while weightless, they were successfully restarted to hit a lunar trajectory. Though little publicized at the time, this event represented a significant advance both for the Apollo manned lunar landing program and for future deep space missions. Without a proven restart capability, launch operations involving liquid hydrogen-fueled boosters would experience four or five months per year during which there would be no lunar launch window, due to the moon's distance and relative position. (A "window" is a time period during which the vehicle will have to get off, or it will miss its target.) With the restart capability, at least one satisfactory launch window is assured every month.

Not all activity at Launch Complex 36 had to do with the development of Centaur birds. Preflight test operations were abruptly halted one morning for a highly unusual reason. An excited voice announced over the area loudspeaker: "There's an alligator on the pad!"

Unbelieving engineers and technicians filed double time out of the blockhouse and, sure enough, were greeted by an angry, snorting, nine-foot-long saurian, who had mistakenly crawled through a drain pipe into the launching area. Pan American security policemen gingerly lassoed the unbadged intruder and escorted it to a less-populated region, where it could roam freely without disturbing the missile men.

Many believe it was the same 'gator who had, a year or so before, periodically slipped into the Centaur's liquid oxygen dump pond—a man-made pool into which excess rocket oxidizers are sometimes poured, at a temperature of minus 297 degrees Fahrenheit. His luck ran out one day when he was caught snoozing in the pond as fuel mechanics were dumping a load of the liquid oxygen. Eyewitnesses reported that when the super-cool substance hit the water, the alligator took off like a runaway rocket, nursing what perhaps might have been the only frostbitten 'gator tail in Florida history.

On Memorial Day, 1966, Atlas Centaur launched Surveyor I. The spacecraft, built by Hughes Aircraft under the management and direction of the Jet Propulsion Laboratory of California's Institute of Technology, carried a single scanning television camera to photograph the moon's surface and crushable pads on two of its three triangular landing legs, to find out how deeply the pads would sink into the lunar soil upon impact. The 2,194-pound Surveyor was to soft land on the moon, not smash upon contact as Ranger did. Such a landing technique would have to be perfected before man could follow machine to the dead world circling earth.

Retrorockets would brake the spacecraft's descent from 6,000 miles per hour to about three and a half mph. Even optimists gave the mission one chance of success out of five. It was that difficult a task! Following an accurate launching. Surveyor sped to its moving lunar target. The flight lasted just over 63½ hours, and when time came to fire its retros and slow the speeding craft down, the world looked over the shoulders of mission controllers. With astonishing precision, everything worked as had been planned. Surveyor 1 settled gently in the mare known as Oceanus Procellarum (Ocean of Storms), touching down within nine miles of the selected landing site!

Over the next two weeks it performed almost flawlessly and responded to nearly 100,000 commands from earth. The television camera scanned the lunar landscape and transmitted 10,338 close-up and long-range photos of high resolution back to the United States before the spacecraft systems were shut down during the long lunar night, when temperatures dropped 250 degrees below zero. As an added bonus, the camera was again turned on July 6, and 812 more photos were received.

Commenting on the amazingly successful flight, Congressman Joseph Karth of Minnesota, Chairman of the House Subcommittee on Space Science Applications, said: "Surveyor has traveled a very rough and rock-strewn road to success, but maybe when a program has traveled this kind of a treacherous road, in the final analysis success is so much sweeter."

To the tired but happy launch crews at the Cape and to the spacecraft teams in California, these words rang home. Surveyor I sent back much vital data. Foremost was the fact, now proven, that man would one day be able to land safely on the lunar surface. He would not sink in or cause irreparable damage to the spaceship.

The countdown for the launch of Surveyor 2, September 20, 1966, ranks as one of the most dramatic ever held at Cape Kennedy. As already indicated, on all lunar and interplanetary flights, and on a lot of other orbital shots, the launch vehicle, in order to connect with its target, must be counted down so liftoff will occur through a flight "window." These windows vary from a few seconds up to several hours. For Surveyor 2, the time frame or deadline the crews had to meet was about 30 minutes.

Here is a re-creation of the final minutes:

As the green countdown clock methodically ticks off precious seconds, the checks continue without interruption. There are no problems. At T minus five minutes a built-in hold is announced. When the count is picked up, the launch vehicle test conductor (TC) asks for status reports. They come in staccato fashion:

"Atlas propulsion?"

"Go."

"Centaur propulsion?"

"Go."

"Guidance?"

"Go."

Down the line all answers are affirmative.

"Spacecraft?"

"Go."

Suddenly, there is a jolting halt.

"Launch Director?"

"TC, we're no go at this time," Bob Gray replies. "We have a low reading indicated on the hydrogen peroxide temperature. We will hold while we evaluate the problem."

The hold is declared. Time in the launch window ticks steadily on. Meanwhile, telemetry data is stripped out and the temperatures are found to be okay. The count is recycled to T minus five minutes and picked up. Because of the hold, the flight azimuth is changed to 96.998 degrees. Status checks begin anew.

"Range safety commands to internal."

"Guidance to flight mode."

"Atlas inverter on."

"Start flight pressurization."

At this point a terse "standby" is called. Seconds later the TC announces the count has again been held at T minus five minutes. There are now less than 25 minutes remaining in the window. A lox boiloff vent valve did not close, and consequently the Atlas could not be pressurized. For long, dragging minutes there is silence on the communications channels as technicians try to isolate and solve the problem. Time in the launch window drains uncomfortably low. It is now a crucial factor.

The voices break in again. The TC explains the valve probably stuck because moisture collected on it. It is now working properly, and the count is picked up once more at T minus five minutes. Only now the time in the launch window is also five minutes—exactly. There is no more leeway. There can be no more holds.

A new flight azimuth of 114.361 degrees is set. But now there is another problem, a more pressing one. During the interim while the valve was being fixed, liquid oxygen boiled off in the Atlas booster stage. It is now below flight level and must be replenished. The TC does not know if there is enough time left to do it.

"Let's pick up the count and take her down as far as you can," the Launch Director says. The countdown is resumed. It is going to be a real cliff-hanger. The TC runs through status reports once again. In between, every few seconds, he checks the lox level with his systems engineer. Each time there is a negative response. The lox pumps are running wide open, but if the tanks do not reach flight level in time, the launch will have to be scrubbed. There is no alternative now. The window is closing fast.

Someone shouts "pump, pump!" and the tension is broken for a second. The count goes on. Then, the engineer suddenly breaks in:

"I've got a blinking light on the panel. We're nearing flight level. We may get there."

A chorus of sighs arises in the blockhouse. At the critical go or no go point in the count the TC asks about the lox.

"How does it look? Are we going to make it?"

Everyone holds his breath.

"Believe we will!"

"Roger, bring her in."

The crisis is passed. It is T minus 90 seconds. The count now snowballs.

"Range clearance to launch?"

"Go."

"Verify launch azimuth."

"Centaur to arm. Atlas to arm."

"T minus 10 seconds and counting . . . five . . . four . . . three . . . ignition . . . two . . . one . . . zero . . . we've got a release!"

Outside, in the brilliant sunshine, the great metallic bird thunders off its pad and rises straight and true into the pale blue sky. Onlookers are oblivious to the tense drama that preceded its flight. The comments now are all positive:

"She's on her way!"

"Guidance and propulsion look very good at this point."

"A smooth plot all the way."

"Data looks fine, the bird looks good. Nice and steady."

"It looks textbook from here."

Inside the blockhouse there are handshakes and backslaps and smiles. The window closed at 7:32 A.M. The liftoff occurred at 7:31:59.765. There was less than one second left! Ironically, 60 seconds after liftoff there was a short power outage in the blockhouse. Had it come a minute earlier, the launch would have been scrubbed.

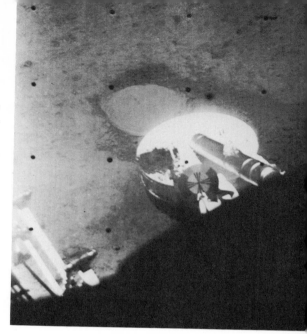

As Surveyor III rests on the surface of the moon, its sampler extends its scoop arm. On top of one of the spacecraft's round, podlike feet, a pile of lunar material has been deposited by the surface sampler. (NASA Photo)

It seems almost sacrilege to add that the launch team's valiant efforts under the greatest of pressures were in vain. The mission failed when one of the three vernier engines did not ignite during the critical midcourse maneuver.

Surveyor III, however, scored a resounding success when it soft landed on its lunar bull's-eye on the east wall of a 650-foot-diameter crater in the Ocean of Storms, April 19, 1967. In addition to providing additional photographs, this craft carried a specially designed scoop shovel to dig into the lunar surface for soil characteristic studies. Upon commands from earth it did just that, digging four narrow trenches, and then depositing some of the loose soil on its own foot pod. Cameras then photographed this and transmitted it back to anxious scientists who began extensive studies to evaluate the soil's composition further. It appears to be quite earthlike.

Though Surveyor IV failed, the fifth spacecraft in the series got off to an excellent start from Complex 36 September 8, 1967. KSC's Unmanned Launch Operations' team and Atlas-Centaur's major contractor, General Dynamics Astronautics, achieved the most accurate injection of a craft on a lunar trajectory yet made. (Development of the launch vehicle was under the direction of NASA's Lewis Research Center in Cleveland.) The rocket performed flawlessly, yet a malfunctioning helium pressure regulator valve threatened to destroy the mission as Surveyor V headed for the lunar surface.

Though most experts now wrote off a successful landing as a 1,000 to one shot, Jet Propulsion Laboratory scientists nevertheless worked frantically in the final hours of the flight and devised an alternate route of descent. The spacecraft touched down at 8:45 P.M., September 10, bounced a couple of times, and came to rest on a sloping wall inclined at an angle of almost 20 degrees. Despite the rough landing, all systems worked well, and over the next two weeks, 18,000 photographs were transmitted to earth, more than the combined total received from Surveyors I and III.

Surveyor V also carried a special instrument which provided truly historical data: the first direct measurements of the composition of an extraterrestrial body. It determined the relative abundance of chemical elements on the moon. Lunar soil turned over by this instrument looked incredibly like clods of dirt and rock fragments found on earth.

Surveyor VI scored another success following its launch November 7, 1967, and landing two and a half days later. Scientists described pictures transmitted to earth from the moon by this spacecraft as "magnificent," and "the best yet." Nine days and 12,764 photographs later, JPL scientists rang up still another precedent by firing Surveyor VI's engine, causing it to "hop" about 10 feet from its original landing position. It thus became the first object from earth to lift off the lunar surface.

This highly successful program was closed out early in 1968 with the January 7 launch of Surveyor VII. It, too, landed on lunar target and performed brilliantly with camera, scoop shovel and a chemical soil analyzer.

Though each Surveyor flight began with less than a 50-50 chance of succeeding, five of the seven spacecraft made it, adding immeasurably to the nation's increasing storehouse of lunar knowledge, and assuring astronauts they would indeed be able to land safely on the moon's surface.

On October 1, 1965, all NASA operations at the Florida launch site were consolidated. This was finalized with the transfer of Bob Gray's 100-man team, the Launch Operations Division of the Goddard Space Flight Center, to the Kennedy Space Center. Thus, KSC became responsible for the supervision, checkout, and launch of all NASA launch vehicles except the small, solid-propellant Scout rockets which are developed and launched by the Langley Research

Center, Hampton, Virginia. These flights take place at Wallops Island, Virginia, and the Western Test Range near Lompoc, California, 150 miles north of Los Angeles on the Pacific coast. Facilities there are shared with Vandenberg Air Force Base.

Deltas and Thor-Agenas are also launched at the Western Test Range, under KSC direction. These vehicles boost such spacecraft as ESSA and Nimbus weather satellites, some Explorers and Orbiting Geophysical Observatories, among others. Any spacecraft that will perform best from a polar orbit is launched from California, because such an orbit is easier to obtain there. From Cape Kennedy, a more complicated, "dogleg" flight over Cuba has to be achieved to place a satellite into polar orbit, and although this has been successfully done a number of times, it is easier, more convenient, and without the potential dangers when done at the Western Test Range. Once, when fragments of an off-course rocket fell on the Cuban mainland, Fidel Castro tried to explode it into an international incident ranting that a farmer's cow had been killed by the falling debris.

NASA uses a number of facilities at Cape Kennedy to carry out its unmanned launch operations. In addition to the rocket pads at 17 (Delta), 12 and 13 (Atlas-Agena), and 36 (Atlas-Centaur), a number of buildings and hangars have been converted for spacecraft checkout and testing. Jet Propulsion Laboratory personnel prepare Surveyor, Mariner, and other lunar and interplanetary craft in the AO Building, and operate a control room during launches which is directly linked with their headquarters in Pasadena, California, and with their deep-space tracking stations.

Satellites carried by Delta rockets are prepared for flight in Hangar AE. There is also a Mission Director's Center here where much of the prelaunch and countdown activity is centered. Adjacent building AM is used for final checkout of observatory-type satellites, Pioneers, and other advanced technology satellites. And Hangar S, of Mercury fame, was modified to handle Lunar Orbiter and Biosatellite spacecraft. Dust-free rooms, where the delicate payloads are worked on in surgically clean areas, are located in most of the buildings.

The addition of Gray's unmanned launch team to Kurt Debus' organization gave it still more experience and professional knowhow. With the earlier transfer of G. Merritt Preston's spacecraft checkout crews, it gave NASA's Kennedy Space Center an unequalled expertise and competence in all phases of rocketry missions—under one roof.

Chapter 10

STEP TWO: GEMINI

The second, or intermediate, step to landing astronauts on the moon—Mercury had been the first—was called Gemini, after the third constellation of the zodiac, featuring the twin stars, Castor and Pollux. It was so named because Gemini was to be a two-man spacecraft.

NASA announced plans for the new project December 7, 1961. An ambitious set of goals was involved. Mainly, Gemini was to accomplish rendezvous and docking or the linking of two spacecraft in earth orbit, and to test the effects of long-duration flights, up to two weeks, on astronauts. Both objectives would have to be met before man could be sent to the moon. A third and more daring task was to send one man out of the capsule in orbit for a "space walk." Two-man crews were desired so the astronauts could spell each other during longer flights.

Although work was begun soon after the program was announced, it was not until astronaut Gordon Cooper splashed down in the Pacific Ocean May 16, 1963, thus ending Project Mercury, that full attention could be focused on Gemini. Even then, it was nearly two years between Cooper's recovery and the first two-man spacecraft flight.

McDonnell Aircraft, builder of the Mercury capsule, was also selected by the government to create the new design. Naturally, it was considerably larger than the original, one-man craft: 7,000 pounds to Mercury's 4,000, and 11 feet high and seven and a half feet in diameter to Mercury's nine-foot by six-foot measurements. One of the major system changes was the configuration of Gemini so astronauts could control it during their flights. Mercury, being primarily a research and development vehicle, had been designed to provide automatic control from the ground, although it had some built-in capabilities for switchover to pilot control. There were, of course, many other changes and refinements, the majority of them developed from Mercury-gained experience.

To lift the heavier capsule into orbit, a more powerful booster than Atlas was needed. NASA, after surveying the field, again chose a vehicle that had already passed its testing program at the Cape with high marks: the Air Force's Martin-built Titan II Intercontinental Ballistic Missile. Its twin booster engines provided 430,000 pounds' thrust at liftoff, and the single second-stage engine added another 100,000 pounds at its ignition altitude, about 40 miles up.

A number of major modifications were made to "man-rate" Titan II. Most of them were aimed to beef up reliability and safety factors. A Malfunction Detection System (MDS) was installed, for instance, to sense trouble in any of the vital launch systems, and instantaneously transmit this information to the astronaut crew.

Complex 19, the Gemini launch site, underwent some face-lifting too. One of the major additions here was the construction of a large "white room" high in the Titan's gantry. This fitted around the spacecraft, allowing technicians and astronauts easy access to Gemini after it was mated to the launch vehicle. The 102-foot-tall umbilical tower was redone to better service the booster and capsule. More than 800 miles of wiring ran from the blockhouse and test stand to this tower.

Hangar S also became obsolete. New astronaut quarters and an elaborate complex of spacecraft checkout facilities were constructed across the Banana River from the Cape on Merritt Island. Modern bachelor apartments were built for the pilots on the third floor of the huge new Manned Spacecraft Operations Building. Included in their elaborate "home away from home" were a small gymnasium, lounge, and kitchen, conference room, and a fully equipped medical clinic for the exhaustive pre- and post-flight examinations that would be given each Gemini astronaut.

North of this building arose a small technical "city" called the Fluid Test Complex. Incoming Gemini spacecraft, fresh from the plant in St. Louis, would undergo rigorous inspection, checkout, and testing in these facilities.

Each Gemini, after arrival at Cape Kennedy's skid strip, would be put through a thorough checkout cycle at the new complex of sites on Merritt Island. Only after it had passed stringent inspections and been outfitted with ordnance and other items was it okayed for the trip across the Banana River for mating with the launch vehicle at Complex 19.

The maiden Gemini flight, with a spacecraft shell aboard Titan II to test structural compatibility and dynamic loads, was made April 8, 1964. Everything worked fine, but program directors wanted one more tune-up before they committed men to board the new machine. Gemini 2 was set for launch December 9, 1964. The countdown progressed normally, and at zero, with several astronauts looking on, the stage-one engines ignited. Even then, there was no liftoff. The Malfunction Detection System sensed trouble from a hydraulic pressure loss and automatically shut down the engines at T plus one second. It was a near-repeat of the abortive Mercury Redstone 1 launch attempt. The vehicle was rechecked and successfully flown January 19, 1965. All systems, from liftoff to reentry and parachute deployment, worked as planned. The heat shield fended off temperatures up to 2,000 degrees during reentry.

With the success of Gemini 2, officials announced the next spacecraft would be manned. Astronaut Virgil (Gus) Grissom, veteran of the *Liberty Bell 7* Mercury suborbital flight, was named command pilot, and Navy Lieutenant Commander John Young, a member of the second group of nine astronauts selected, was named pilot. Actually, they had been in training for several months, and had virtually lived with their capsule, following it from St. Louis, after it had been completed, to the Spaceport during its checkout cycle.

When they were not working directly with Gemini 3, Grissom and Young spent more than 100 hours "flying" their route again and again in a simulated spacecraft in the Cape's Mission Control Center (formerly Mercury Control). The simulator was equipped to do everything but leave the ground. It was outfitted with instrumentation identical to the flight capsule, and in it, astronauts could be drilled on every conceivable condition they might encounter in orbit.

Engineers could program any one of 600 different spacecraft malfunctions during a simulated run to test the astronauts' reaction time and ability to solve the unexpected problem. In fact, some of the pilots' roughest flights were flown in the simulator rather than in space. It was realistic training under the toughest of conditions, and it was to pay off repeatedly in the flights to come when a number of demanding situations developed, requiring quick, cool response from the crews.

Grissom and Young, their booster and spacecraft, were ready to fly March 23, 1965. Theirs was to be a short mission, only three orbits, but an important one. The astronauts would be controlling much of their own flight. There was a new team in the blockhouse. Launch director was Air Force Lieutenant Colonel Jack Albert, chief of the Gemini Launch Vehicle Division for the Air Force's 6555th Aerospace Test Wing. It was his responsibility to pull the entire launch vehicle crew together, to assure that the Titan II was thoroughly checked out so it would perform with maximum in-flight reliability.

Colonel Albert worked closely with a long-time veteran of manned space flight, G. Merritt Preston. Following his transfer to the Kennedy Space Center, Preston was named deputy Gemini Mission Director for Launch. Preston and his associate of years, John J. Williams, supervised the overall spacecraft checkout operations.

As Gemini 3's launch date approached, Colonel Albert expressed a candid opinion about flight readiness: "You have the feeling you've done all you possibly can," he said. "It's like training a football team. It can be the best-coached team ever, but still the game must be played. If it is apprehension we feel when the vehicle lifts off, this is offset by our confidence in knowing we've done our jobs as best as is humanly possible."

The support team for Gemini 3 and all following spacecraft in the program, a team stationed at sites around the world, numbered in the tens of thousands. Tracking stations down the Air Force Eastern Test Range (formerly Atlantic Missile Range) and communications stations in NASA's worldwide tracking network were geared up. Mission Control was jammed with personnel. At the Cape, in the Atlantic, and at other global points, 10,000 Army, Air Force, Navy, Coast Guard, and Marine servicemen were deployed in alert recovery forces. They manned aircraft carriers, destroyers, smaller ships, aircraft, helicopters, and land and amphibious vehicles—17 ships and 126 aircraft in all. Heading up this vast and talented task force was Lieutenant General Leighton I. Davis, former Commander of the Air Force Missile Test Center (now the Eastern Test Range), and now Department of Defense Manager for Manned Space Flight Operations.

Not since John Glenn's orbital shot in *Friendship 7,* more than three years earlier, had such excitement hit the Cape as it did the morning of March 23, 1965. More than 750 newsmen, many from foreign nations, crowded the press site, a scant two miles from Launch Complex 19. All three major U.S. television networks sent their ace newscasters to record the event live for millions of Americans at home.

Grissom named his ship the *Molly Brown* after the hit Broadway play and movie, *The Unsinkable Molly Brown*. He was obviously referring to his unscheduled swim following *Liberty Bell 7*'s splashdown and sinking. Debbie Reynolds, star of the movie, sent Gus the old-fashioned bloomers she had worn during its filming.

At 9:24 A.M., *Molly Brown* lifted off, after minor technical problems had delayed the countdown only slightly. The booster shot up unfalteringly, and placed Gemini 3 into earth orbit. For the next five hours, Grissom and Young set precedents. On the first pass over the United States, for example, the astronauts fired rockets of the orbital attitude maneuvering system and changed orbits. Such a maneuver, never tried before, was a necessity for the rendezvous and docking of two objects in space that would come in later flights. Grissom and Young performed a number of other key functions during the three orbits they were up, and then became the first pilots to control their craft manually through the reentry phase.

They touched down in the Atlantic at 2:17 P.M. and were soon picked up, though Grissom was on the water long enough to get seasick. Their 81,000-mile flight had been a total success, almost without incident. Aboard the recovery aircraft carrier *Intrepid,* the new space heroes received a telephone call from the White House. "We're very proud of you," President Lyndon Johnson said, "and very grateful for your return." He told them he had followed every minute of their flight, and he also paid tribute to the "heroes on the ground as well as in space" who had made the successful mission possible.

The astronauts returned to the Spaceport two days later for a national news conference in Cocoa Beach, before a heartwarming reception from tens of thousands of happy, proud Americans. Spirits were high at the conference, and there was even time for a quip or two between the two space pilots. When a newsman asked Grissom if the cabin light in Gemini was left burning following their landing in the Atlantic Ocean, Gus, the command pilot, couldn't recall. Young, however, jibed, "The light was out, but Grissom wouldn't know because, contrary to normal shipboard procedure, the first guy to leave the *Molly Brown* when it got in the water was its captain!" Grissom, who was in a hurry to be picked up by the recovery helicopter after getting seasick, quickly retorted, "I made you captain when I left."

Gemini 3 had not been without its lighter moments before liftoff and in orbit, too. On launch day, for instance, backup pilot Wally Schirra greeted Grissom and Young as they came out for the trip to the pad. He was wearing a faded, undersized space suit that had been torn in dozens of places. Wagging a crooked gloved finger at the two astronauts, he told them he was ready if they weren't. It broke them up.

Schirra also had another gag cooked up for Gus. He smuggled a jumbo corned beef sandwich to Young before he entered the space-craft, and John hid it inside his suit. After they were in orbit, when they broke out their nibble-size rations, most of them dehydrated, Young asked Grissom if he would like a corned beef sandwich.

"Sure," the veteran pilot replied, "but where are you going to find one up here?"

"Here," Young retorted, trying to keep a straight face, "try this!"

The sandwich caper made all the newspapers and magazines, and had repercussions clear to Washington. Stiff-collared congressmen complained that crumbs from the sandwich could have fouled up delicate spacecraft instrumentation. The astronauts were ordered not to take any more food of their own, and from that point on, they had to log all personal effects they carried aboard.

But despite the censure, it didn't dim their senses of humor, and that is a significant point. Far from being cutups, the astronauts take their mission seriously. A more sincere, dedicated team couldn't be found anywhere. But in the grim business of orbital flight, where a pilot error or mechanical malfunction could be fatal, the spacemen have never failed to "stay loose," to maintain their wonderful, well-balanced senses of humor.

Their longtime nurse and close friend, Dee O'Hara, once said: "They always seem to relieve tensions during the countdowns when actually they're the ones who should be getting help." It is, in fact, well known that the calmest people at Cape Kennedy on the morning of a big launch are the very astronauts destined to be shot into space. Gordon Cooper was so relaxed in the waning moments of his *Faith 7* Mercury countdown that he even snoozed in his capsule for a brief spell.

If the astronauts, through their absolute confidence in the space program and its people, and their calm, contagious self-assurance, can cut the binding cords of tension for rocket and spacecraft engineers and mechanics, they are also the ones best suited to keep their fellow space pilots relaxed. Alan Shepard exemplified this natural ability when he said, as Gus Grissom was preparing to be launched on his first flight in July, 1961, "Hey, Jose, don't cry too much up there." Shepard was referring to a comedy routine popularized by José Jiminez, a character portrayed by comedian Bill Dana. In the routine,

José, dressed as an astronaut, is asked what he plans to do in space, and he mournfully replies, "Well, I plan to cry a lot."

Grissom could only laugh.

When Gemini 3 splashed down in the Atlantic and its occupants were recovered, it marked the end of an era at the Spaceport. It was the last manned flight to be directed from Cape Kennedy's Mission Control Center. For the rest of Gemini and other programs to follow, control would be maintained at NASA's new Manned Spacecraft Center in Houston, Texas. There, on what had been cow pastures only a couple of years before, vast electronic complexes arose. The Cape would still carry out the launching phase of each mission, but everything else now reverted 1,200 miles west to the Texas site.

Mission Control at the Cape was not completely phased out, however. It still served as one of the key worldwide manned tracking network stations. Radar, telemetry, command and air-to-ground real-time data during the flight, acquired at the Cape and over the Air Force Eastern Test Range, was now to be passed on to the Manned Spacecraft Center.

Two of the newer group of astronauts, James A. McDivitt and Edward H. White, were selected to fly Gemini 4. Both the planned

First American astronaut to leave his spacecraft while in orbit, Edward H. White floats into space, secured to the Gemini 4 spacecraft by umbilical and tether lines wrapped together with gold tape to form one cord. (NASA Photo)

length of their flight and the tasks they were to perform in space were the most ambitious yet assigned. What turned out to be a four-day mission began sharply at 10:16 A.M., June 3, 1965. As the craft sped across the Pacific Ocean at five miles a second, White opened the capsule hatch and stepped outside to begin his historic walk in space. He performed it brilliantly, and seemed to enjoy himself so much McDivitt almost had to order him back in. He floated about for 23 minutes, maneuvering back and forward, up and down, with a hand-held pressure "gun." White's success outside the cabin proved that it would be practical, with more development and practice, for an astronaut to work in space if necessary, to make spacecraft repairs or carry out experiments. Although the Russians had earlier performed a more abbreviated "walk," White gave the United States a big boost in prestige, as well as demonstrating technological progress, with his stroll. It was another well planned and rehearsed step, and a spectacular one.

Gemini 4 fell 50 miles short of its intended recovery area; still the two astronauts were safely on board the carrier *Wasp* less than an hour after hitting the water. NASA officials were elated that they were in such good physical condition following 98 hours in space. Plans proceeded for a long-duration flight on Gemini 5.

There was one humorous footnote to the McDivitt-White mission. A young girl from Hobart, Tasmania, wrote the Spaceport with a pertinent query: "Can you tell me how the astronauts go to the bathroom?" she wanted to know. "I asked my teacher this and she said that's why Ed White took a walk in space!"

More space records were set by Gemini 5, piloted by veteran astronaut Gordon Cooper and rookie Charles Conrad. Following their launch August 21, 1965, the two covered 3,312,993 miles over the next eight days as they circled in orbit 100 miles above earth. They shattered the previous long-duration flight of Russian cosmonaut V. Bykovsky, established two years earlier.

A low fuel-cell power rating early in the flight knocked out some of the mission objectives, but one of the prime factors officials wanted to learn was how man and the Gemini machine would fare after such a long ride. To anyone at Cape Kennedy's skid strip August 30th, there was no question as to how the astronauts felt. The jaunty Cooper and Conrad had a spring in their step and a grin on their faces as they were greeted by launch team members and press representatives before crossing over to Merritt Island for debriefings and physical examinations. Later, Cooper said the Gemini Titan booster was like riding in a Cadillac compared to his Mercury Atlas flight 27 months earlier.

One of the prime objectives of the Gemini program was to attempt rendezvous and docking of two spacecraft in orbit; a technique that would have to be perfected before three Americans could be sent to the moon and returned safely. First crack at the tricky rendezvous, the most difficult step yet attempted in the manned space flight program, was assigned to old pro Wally Schirra of *Sigma 7* and balding Tom Stafford, at six feet even the tallest astronaut.

The plan called for a dual launch at the Cape. This would involve complicated simultaneous countdowns at two different complexes— something never before tried. The astronauts were to be preceded in orbit by an unmanned capsule, Agena. Its booster would be an Atlas. For these rendezvous flights, Mercury Atlas Complex 14 was reactivated and updated. The Atlas-Agena was to be launched first, and as it flew around the earth the first time, Schirra and Stafford, aboard their Gemini 6 spacecraft, would be boosted into orbit at a time to coincide closely with Agena's first pass over the Cape. They would then, according to the flight plan, maneuver their capsule in close to Agena, to catch up with it in space.

Such a formidable mission called for unexcelled efforts by both launch and flight crews. As the days to liftoff grew closer, one of the largest support operations ever assembled at Cape Kennedy went through practice countdown after countdown to spot, recognize, and solve problem areas before the real thing got under way. The closest of coordination was demanded of Air Force, NASA, and contractor personnel. Never before had the Eastern Test Range, despite its vast resources of manpower and equipment, been so heavily taxed. One major launch commanded everyone's attention; two would require something extra. There would be only 95 minutes difference between the Atlas-Agena and Gemini 6 liftoffs. Not only that, but if Schirra and Stafford didn't hit a precise window, that is, unless they got off within seconds as Agena flew overhead, they would fall too far behind it to catch up. Actually, to achieve success, six major elements would have to function perfectly: the Gemini 6 spacecraft, the Agena target vehicle, the Titan II booster, the Atlas booster, the Mission Control Center in Houston, including the manned space flight tracking network, and the Air Force Eastern Test Range. A problem with any one of these could scrub the entire mission. It would be, obviously, a massive task of coordination, one that had been in planning at the Spaceport for more than a year.

Once in orbit, Gemini 6 would pick up Agena's trail by means of radar beacon. Test runs of the two spacecraft had been made at a radar site on Merritt Island during the long weeks of checkout preceding launch day. Everything was finally brought to a prime state of readiness on October 25, 1965. The astronauts were sealed in their capsule at Complex 19 when the Agena-bearing Atlas blasted off. After what seemed like a perfect launch, however, signals from the target vehicle were lost. It had apparently failed to enter orbit. It was a bitter disappointment to a lot of geared-up people, both in and outside the Gemini 6 spacecraft. There was nothing left to do but cancel the mission.

Several weeks later NASA officials came up with a revised flight plan, one far more elaborate and exciting than had originally been scheduled. Now, Schirra and Stafford would rendezvous with a live target—the Gemini 7 spacecraft of astronauts Frank Borman and Jim Lovell. The 7 mission was to run 14 days in orbit and provide a final, hard look at the effects on man of long-duration space-flight exposure. Gemini 6, it was hoped, would be placed on the pad after 7 had lifted off, and be checked out and launched within that two-week period, so Schirra and Stafford could catch their buddies while circling earth. Again, it was a precedent-setting program of exacting dimensions.

Because Complex 19 was the only one adapted for the modified Titan II booster, no other pad could be used. Launch crews would have to clean up after 7's liftoff, erect the Gemini 6 rocket, mate the new spacecraft, and get the whole package ready for flight within a few days. Though nothing like this had ever before been conceived, much less attempted, there was a strong feeling of confidence that it could be done.

At this point in the program, five launch vehicles and five Gemini capsules, three of them manned, had flown. Checkout and test techniques had been refined and the time cycle from assembly area to pad shortened considerably. The Air Force-Martin Company launch crews and the NASA-McDonnell spacecraft teams would get their vehicles as close to flight ready as possible before mating them at Complex 19. Then, if no major problems were encountered on the pad, they felt they could get two birds off within the tight two-week deadline. At least they would try as best as was humanly possible.

Further, Gemini 6 had been through all the tests associated with buildup, checkout and systems integration. When the 6 vehicle had to be taken down from the stand, it was placed in bonded storage. Then immediately following the Borman-Lovell launch, Gemini 6 was rushed to the pad. Since it had already been checked out for its original firing date, only abbreviated tests were needed to verify integrity of the entire system.

Borman and Lovell lifted off at 2:30 P.M., December 4, 1965, and made orbit without a hitch. Almost before the pad had cooled, technicians swarmed over it, ripping out burned cabling and other debris, so the Gemini 7 booster could be erected. It was raised into position less than 12 hours after the Borman-Lovell launch. In another 12 hours the spacecraft and rocket had been mechanically mated. Everyone pointed toward a second shoot on December 12, during Gemini's eighth day in orbit.

The countdown continued uninterrupted to a liftoff time of 9:54 A.M. At that instant one of the tensest moments in Spaceport history occurred, one that chilled the hearts of millions and came frighteningly close to a national disaster. Engine ignition came on schedule, but there was no motion on the pad. The engines automatically shut down 1.2 seconds later. Inside the Gemini cockpit, Wally Schirra and Tom Stafford had a life-at-stake decision to make. In effect, they were now sitting on top of a live bomb, thousands of gallons of hypergolic fuel, that could explode into a prodigious fireball at any time.

The gloved hands of both pilots reportedly gripped the twin D-rings, or "chicken switches," as the astronauts called them. When pulled, they would trigger ejection seats that could catapult Schirra and Stafford 400 feet into the air, where, so the manual said, parachutes would open; then they would calmly float back to earth. However, if they pulled the D-rings, the mission would be lost; there would be no chance whatsoever of catching up with Borman and Lovell in orbit. Secondly, although the ejection system worked fine on paper, it had never been tried during a live launch. In fact, in previous tests, some plastic dummies had been badly battered while being thrown out the capsule's small hatches.

Gemini's entire escape system differed sharply from that of Mercury, which had a small rocket tower atop the spacecraft that could pull it free of the booster if trouble was sensed at any point during powered flight. Ejection seats replaced this system on Gemini, and there were many who doubted the wisdom of this change.

The alternative to pulling the chicken switches was for the spacemen simply to sit tight and sweat out the terrifying possibilities of a launch site explosion. With the icy nerves of a true professional, this is what Schirra, the command pilot, elected to do. He based his decision on instinct, for on the instrument panel the trip clock had

Astronauts Tom Stafford (left) and Wally Schirra in their Gemini spacecraft during a simulation test. They risked death when in a tense moment in Spaceport history, on December 12, 1965, their booster engines suddenly shut down on the pad, leaving them in effect sitting on a live bomb. (NASA Photo)

started, indicating there had actually been a liftoff. Schirra gambled the clock was lying, banking his decision on the experience of his previous Mercury flight, three years earlier. If the rocket had lifted off, he and Stafford would have been pushed downward into their couches by acceleration forces. Also, their red abort lights in the cockpit had not flashed.

With cool deliberation, Schirra began reading off the all-important fuel pressure figures. From 186 miles overhead, Frank Borman, in Gemini 7, called down that he had seen Gemini 6 light up and then die. By the time technicians could get to the pad, wash down fuel that had leaked, and drain the Titan's tanks, Schirra and Stafford had been sealed on top of the "bomb" for more than three and a half hours.

An immediate investigation was called to determine the cause of engine shutdown. Embarrassed technicians found that a two-cent dust cover, which should have been removed during prelaunch inspection, had been left in the rocket, and had obstructed the oxidizer inlet line of a gas generator. Insignificant as it was, the tiny dust cover emphasized a mighty large point: that no matter how much care, dedication and extra effort are put into a program, so long as human beings are involved, there is always a chance for human error. Minimizing that element of chance to an infinitesimal figure was the goal of everyone at Complex 19.

Three days later, on December 15, the potential catastrophe was turned into a resounding success when Schirra and Stafford, on their third try, made it. Soon after, they were hot on the orbital trail of Gemini 7. On the first spin around earth, Gemini 6 was 730 miles away, but phasing and plane-changing maneuvers quickly cut the distance. A successful rendezvous was effected five hours and 50 minutes after the 8:37 A.M. liftoff from Cape Kennedy, when Schirra reported to Mission Control in Houston that the two spacecraft were but 120 feet apart. A joyous wave of elation swept through launch and flight crews. In the MCC, everyone unfolded a small American flag and fastened it to his console.

It was another high moment that would leave a deep notch in the American history of space flight, another unparalleled technological achievement. From two frustrating scrubbed missions, Gemini 6 had emerged magnificently triumphant. Rendezvous was one of the most difficult program objectives of Gemini. That it had been achieved in such spectacular fashion by two manned spacecraft was especially satisfying to all involved. It also spotlighted the benefits of flexible planning. Originally, rendezvous had been designed to be made between a manned craft and an unmanned target vehicle. It took quick and courageous thinking even to attempt the dual Gemini 7-6 flights. But of such stuff are the Spaceport's people made. They, like the astronauts who carry out the plans, are true pioneers of a new horizon.

Though docking of the two capsules high above earth was not to be tried, Schirra and Stafford jockeyed Gemini 6 to within a foot of their sister spacecraft, proving that this next important step could be taken with relative ease following initial rendezvous. Gemini 6 then performed an in-plane fly-around maneuver, circling Gemini 7, and the four astronauts flew in formation side by side for four revolutions around the world.

A few hours before Gemini 6 was scheduled to retrofire and return home, Schirra broke in with a report that aroused the curiosity of people everywhere. "We have a mysterious object sighted," he said. "It looks like a satellite, going from north to south, up in a polar orbit. He's in a very low trajectory. Looks like he may be going to reenter pretty soon. Stand by, it looks like he's trying to signal us." Smiles broke out in Mission Control when Schirra added, "seems to be a man with a red suit and a white beard, and he has eight objects in front, propelling him." Then the veteran astronaut broke out with a spirited rendition of "Jingle Bells" on his harmonica, accompanied by Stafford with bells, and millions of people listening to the transmission from space suddenly had lumps in their throats.

Gemini 6 came down December 16th, and 7 followed two days later. After 14 days in space, Borman and Lovell were still in excellent physical condition, adding to the proof of man's ability to survive long-duration missions in space without ill effects. The 14-day mission, covering 5,129,400 miles, eclipsed all previous distance records for a manned flight. The dual mission's outstanding success made a nice Christmas present to thousands of Spaceport personnel who had labored hard for months to help pull it off.

With rendezvous accomplished, docking was the next stepping-stone, and it was the primary objective assigned to Gemini 8 pilots Neil Armstrong and David Scott. The mission again called for maximum efforts at the Cape. One hour and 41 minutes before Gemini 8 lifted off March 16, 1966, an Agena target vehicle was launched. The astronauts were to catch up to it in space and physically link the two craft. For nearly seven hours the textbook flight followed the script of the mission plan. Armstrong and Scott sighted the Agena target vehicle after six and a half hours, closed in, and after receiving permission from the control center, edged up and made the delicate docking operations while both craft were hurtling around earth at better than 17,500 mph. It was another milestone event of major significance, but on this occasion there was precious little time for celebration.

A short circuit in a key electrical system locked an orbital attitude maneuvering thruster in the open position, causing it to splatter flame and send Gemini 8 whirling into a violent series of rolls. The astronauts found the cause of the trouble quickly enough, but they couldn't close the thruster. Within minutes, they were in real trouble. The spacecraft roll rate was now screaming well past the red lines of safety. There was imminent danger of the pilots' blacking out. Remaining cool under fire, Armstrong and Scott disengaged Gemini from the target vehicle. Still the rolling increased.

As they entered range of their next communications station, they described the situation, adding that they weren't sure how much longer they could hang on. The decision didn't take long: they were told to break out the reentry control system to stabilize the berserk spacecraft. In doing this, they would have to come down, aborting the mission two and a half days short. And while thousands of rescue specialists waited in the prime Atlantic Ocean recovery area, they would now have to splash down in a remote part of the Pacific, after reentering the earth's atmosphere over Red China. But there was no other choice. It was that or black out in space, possibly never to regain consciousness!

As millions of anxious spectators listened, the astronauts landed. Thirteen minutes later, Air Force pararescuemen jumped into the waters beside them and placed a safety flotation collar around Gemini 8. The pilots were shaken but safe. Another near-calamity had been narrowly averted. Almost lost in the bold headlines of the dramatic reentry and recovery was the fact that docking in space had been achieved. The U.S. was another step closer to the moon's surface.

There was a touch of tragedy to the Gemini 9 mission. Astronauts Elliott See and Charles Bassett had originally been assigned to fly it, but they were killed February 28, 1966, in an airplane crash near the spacecraft manufacturing site in St. Louis. The backup team of Tom Stafford, who had been Gemini 6 pilot, and Gene Cernan then stepped in. There were no new precedents to be set on this particular flight. Rendezvous, docking and extravehicular activity (EVA—walk in space), had all been carried out by now, but these operations would have to be perfected to build up confidence in astronaut performance capabilities before man could be committed to flying to the moon. So, all three objectives were part of the Gemini 9 flight plan.

Hardluck Stafford, who with Schirra had been grounded twice before finally getting off the ground in Gemini 6, ran into another string of difficulties on this flight with Cernan. On May 17, an Agena target vehicle was launched from Pad 14 while the astronauts awaited their turn. It didn't come. Two minutes and 10 seconds after Atlas liftoff, all signals from the target vehicle ceased and the mission had to be scrubbed. Stafford's widely quoted comment was, "Aw, shucks." A backup craft, an Augmented Target Docking Adapter (ATDA), was put aboard another Atlas booster and launched June 1. This one made it into orbit, but this time Gemini 9 missed its critical liftoff "window," and again the mission was postponed. Stafford and Cernan got off two days later, but they were to suffer more annoying frustrations in space. Rendezvous was effected routinely; however, the pilots found the shroud on the nose of the ATDA had not separated cleanly.

"We have a weird-looking machine up here," Stafford radioed. "Both the clamshells of the nose cone are still on, but they are open wide. It looks like an angry alligator out here rotating around."

Nearly 50 hours into the flight, Cernan became the second American to walk in space. He moved outside the cabin and began a series of planned maneuvers. He found, however, that any time he exerted effort, his helmet visor fogged up. For this reason, he did not accomplish all his assigned tasks while outside the capsule, a fact that caused planners to reevaluate future workloads during EVA activity. But Cernan did remain alone in space for over two hours, setting a new record. Practically everything on Gemini 9 seemed to have been bugged up to reentry. But the astronauts landed only two miles from the carrier *Wasp* and were quickly recovered.

As for mission objectives, it was more of the same on Gemini 10, launched July 18, 1966: rendezvous and docking and EVA. Pilots were Gemini 3 veteran John Young, and Mike Collins. The Atlas-Agena target vehicle was launched on schedule and the blockhouse

The Augmented Target Docking Adapter with fiber glass cover still attached, as seen from the orbiting Gemini 9 spacecraft during the flight of Stafford and Cernan. Below is the Caribbean Sea, with one of the Islas Los Roquez at top of the photo; Caracas, Venezuela, is at lower right, below cloud cover. (NASA Photo)

Astronauts Tom Stafford (left) *and Gene Cernan, in their Gemini 9A spacecraft, wave to the crew of the approaching U.S.S. Wasp. Stafford and Cernan splashed down in the Atlantic Ocean 345 miles east of Cape Kennedy the morning of June 6, 1966. (NASA Photo)*

crew at Complex 19 had only a 37-second window to work with, but they got Young and Collins off precisely on time. Not only did they rendezvous and dock with Agena 10, but after performing several maneuvers while in tandem, they unhooked, and then pursued and caught up with the target vehicle that Gemini 8 had docked with in March. Collins, during an EVA period, also retrieved an experiments package that had been placed on Agena 8. The reentry and recovery of the astronauts three days after liftoff was without incident.

In addition to the new list of accomplishments in space, Gemini 10's launch and capsule crews had established some precedents also. Only a month and a half had elapsed between the liftoffs of Gemini 9 and 10. "This is an excellent demonstration of on-time launch capability," said Dr. George E. Mueller, NASA's associate administrator for Manned Space Flight. "We're pleased with all the crews." The six weeks turn-around time on the pad was a long progressive step from the early Mercury days when each flight was separated by several months.

Gemini 11 astronauts Charles Conrad, who had joined Gordon Cooper on the eight-day Gemini 5 flight, and Richard Gordon, flew higher than any other men in the history of civilization. They also executed one of the most difficult feats in the entire program when they rendezvoused with the Agena target vehicle on its first orbital pass overhead. On previous flights it had taken astronauts several hours and hundreds of miles to catch up with the target, which is launched 90 minutes or so before the Gemini vehicle.

To pull this spectacular off, crews had to hit the tightest liftoff window ever imposed at the Spaceport—two seconds! If the count-down slipped any more than that, this part of the Gemini 11 plan would have to be chucked. Remarkably, they made it, and the clock started at 9:42:26 A.M., September 12, 1966. Less than an hour later they had caught their quarry. Docking and undocking exercises followed, then on the second day up, Gordon went outside for an EVA experiment. He came back in, exhausted, after 33 minutes in space.

Forty hours into the flight, while docked, the Agena primary propulsion system kicked the two craft into an elliptical orbit which had a high point above earth of 741.5 miles and a low point of 156.3 miles. For the next two revolutions of the world, the two pilots stayed busy taking hundreds of photographs from this never-before-attained altitude. Said Conrad at the postflight press conference: "We just had the impression that we were looking down at the ground while going straight up. We saw some of the most amazing sights that man has ever seen. The photographs do some justice to what we saw, but you can't do justice to what you actually see with your eyes."

As the beginning of their third day in orbit neared, Gordon again left the confines of the spacecraft, this time standing up in his seat, his upper body outside the hatch, for two hours and eight minutes. Gemini 11 also performed a successful tether operation with the Agena target vehicle, flying a series of maneuvers while the two were connected with a long line. After 71 hours and 17 minutes, Conrad and Gordon landed one and a half miles from the prime recovery ship, the USS *Guam*.

On the twelfth and final flight in Project Gemini, and the tenth consecutive manned one, liftoff from Pad 19 at Cape Kennedy came at 3:46 P.M., November 11, 1966—within one half second of the scheduled liftoff time. Aboard were astronauts James Lovell, who had been Gemini 7's pilot, and Edwin "Buzz" Aldrin. Several primary objectives were assigned to and carried out by Gemini 12. Among them:

—Rendezvous and docking with the Agena target vehicle.

—Three separate space walks by Aldrin.

—A tethered-vehicle station keeping exercise, as was done on Gemini 11.

—Successful conducting of scientific experiments.

—Performance maneuvers using the Agena primary propulsion system to change orbits.

By making good use of planned rest periods during work outside the spacecraft, Aldrin was able to accomplish most of his EVA tasks without the fatigue and fogging-up difficulties encountered by his predecessors. Experience was paying off.

Fourteen scientific experiments were attempted on Gemini 12; these were similar to ones tried on all manned flights in the program. They included: manual navigation sightings, synoptic terrain photography, synoptic weather photography, libration regions photography, ion sensing attitude control, tri-axis magnetometer, beta spectrometer, and Bremsstrahlung spectrometer. Also: frog egg growth, Agena micrometeorite collection, sodium vapor cloud, airglow horizon photography, micrometeorite collection, and ultraviolet astronomical camera.

At 2:21 P.M., November 15, 1966, the last Gemini spacecraft had landed and the astronauts were safely aboard the USS *Wasp* less than 30 minutes later.

Eight days afterward, an awards ceremony was held at NASA's Manned Spacecraft Center in Houston. Spaceport workers were well represented during the activities. Group achievement awards were presented to:

—The Kennedy Space Center's Gemini spacecraft launch crew, "for outstanding team effort in conducting spacecraft test and check-out operations for all Gemini flights to insure systems reliability and astronaut safety within the constraints of tight schedules and short launch intervals."

—The Gemini launch operations and range support team, United States Air Force, "for outstanding teamwork by the 6555th Aerospace Test Wing in conducting launch operations, and the Eastern Test Range team for range support for Gemini space flight missions."

Public service awards were presented to officials of all prime Gemini and Titan contractors, and outstanding leadership medals were given to:

—John J. Williams, Kennedy Space Center Director of Spacecraft Operations, "for technical direction of spacecraft operations at KSC, and for his significant contributions to the completion of the Gemini program."

—Major General Vincent G. Huston, Commander of the Air Force Eastern Test Range, "for his significant contributions in directing the efforts of the U.S. Air Force range in providing the critical launch and operations support, and in coordinating and directing the total efforts of the Department of Defense operational support forces for the Gemini program."

An exceptional service medal went to Colonel Jack Albert of AFETR, "for directing the checkout and launch operations of Gemini launch vehicles, especially for directing launch vehicle operations in support of Gemini 7-Gemini 6."

What had been learned from Gemini? Where did the U.S. manned space flight program stand now that Gemini had been completed? Perhaps the words of Dr. Robert C. Gilruth, Director of NASA's Manned Spacecraft Center, best summed it up:

"To go to the moon," he said, "we had to learn how to operate in space. We had to learn how to maneuver with precision, to rendezvous, to dock, to work outside the spacecraft in the hard vacuum of outer space, to learn how man could endure long duration in the weightless environment, and to learn how to make precise landings from orbital flights. This is where the Gemini program came in. We have rendezvoused, I believe, 10 times, using different techniques and different orbits. We have docked and we have worked outside the spacecraft. We have demonstrated a system which can make precise landings."

Gemini flight director Chris Kraft added: "At the end of Mercury we had not maneuvered in space, and this is fundamental to the Apollo program. You have to make very large scale maneuvers. And, in injection to the moon, you have to make midcourse corrections to rendezvous at the moon. You have to orbit around the moon and you have to rendezvous at the moon. All these things require precise measurements, precise computing. We have done this in Gemini, and it is directly applicable to the lunar flight."

The United States had successfully taken the second of three steps to the moon with Gemini. Mercury had been the first. The next would be Apollo.

Chapter 11

A MIGHTY ROAR: TITAN III

While NASA was busy with its Mercury and Gemini manned programs, and with its variety of unmanned projects, the Air Force had been equally active on the drawing boards, designing a new bird that would be powerful and versatile enough to carry out a number of missions, both with and without men aboard. As a foundation for the launch vehicle, the reliable veteran, Titan II, was again chosen. But it was destined for a major face-lifting, uprating of its engine boost capability, and a new name—Titan III. Though the system was based upon technology and hardware developed in Air Force ICBM programs, it was also the first launch vehicle to be developed for the Department of Defense from the outset as a space booster.

Titan III offered many advantages: it could boost heavier payloads into space, it would have an increased launch rate, and it would be economical, through savings made by simplifying certain characteristics of the rocket and its supporting facilities. There was nothing particularly impressive about Titan III's initial statistics. Its 124-foot height certainly was still well within Saturn I's shadow, as was its 10-foot diameter. Nor is there anything dramatically different about its three main stages, all liquid fueled, which produce, in successive steps, 430,000 pounds, 100,000 pounds, and 16,000 pounds' thrust. The booster's 430,000 pounds is at sea level. This jumps to 470,000 pounds when ignited in space. The flexible third or trans-stage allows for multiple restart capabilities in space and can transfer from a parking orbit to a higher one, or to a deep space trajectory. It can also change the plane of an orbit, or establish a synchronous orbit.

Where Titan III gets its Sunday punch is with the addition of two five-segment solid rocket motors, each 10 feet in diameter, and each capable of producing more than one million pounds' thrust. These motors are strapped onto the sides of the booster. With them and the three stages, this triple-thronged vehicle has more than 2.5 million pounds' of thrust muscle, over one million more than the heavier, more expensive Saturn I.

Major contractors include the Martin Company, booster manufacturer and airframe assembly, test and system integration; Aerojet General Corporation, liquid propulsion systems for the first, second, and third stages; and United Technology Center, solid strap-on rocket motors.

Without these strap-ons, the configuration is called Titan III-A With the solids, it is Titan III-C, which is capable of orbiting payloads from 5,000 to 25,000 pounds and of propelling 5,400 pounds on deep space or lunar missions.

To accommodate the new vehicle, a strikingly different complex of facilities was designed and constructed on what had been part of the Banana River, west of Cape Kennedy's industrial area. The idea behind the design was to build a faster launch capability. In the research and development programs of the past, this had not been needed. But now the Air Force asked itself if a launch vehicle which must stand on the pad for six weeks or more of preflight checkout offered any real military capability.

It was reasoned that if existing launch pads were tied up for weeks at a time, it would not take long for them to become saturated, requiring more to be built. And the Air Force was running out of real estate at the Cape. The growing trend toward larger, more exotically fueled, and thus more potentially dangerous boosters increased safety zone distances on land sites that were already at a premium. Still, there was no area in the world that could provide the unique launch support offered by Cape Kennedy and the Eastern Test Range. Thus, looking ahead, planners foresaw the need to change the style of rocket operations, to increase launch rates, and provide for greater flexibility should a mission requirement change or a bird explode on site.

Against this background of thought, the Air Force's $150 million-plus, Integrate-Transfer Launch (ITL) facility was born. It consists of nine major elements and a railway network. Included are: a segment arrival storage area (SAS); motor inert components assembly storage building (MIS); segment receipt-inspection building (RIS); segment ready storage building (SRS); vertical integration building (VIB); solid motor assembly building (SMAB); a propellant tank car storage area; and two new launch complexes—40 and 41, located at the extreme north end of the Cape. Each of these has its own mobile service tower, umbilical tower, aerospace ground equipment building, fuel and oxidizer holding areas, a gas storage area, and an exhaust duct.

Though all the names bewilder the mind, the ITL facility, over-simplified, is much like an industrial assembly line. Titan III is the end product and is received, inspected, assembled, and delivered ready for flight at the end of the line, at one of the two launch pads.

To make room for such elaborate new furnishings, over 4.75 million cubic yards of fill, more than required in concrete for the Hoover Dam, were pumped up from the bottom of the Banana River and molded into a man-made island. The dominating structure at the south end of the facility is the Vehicle Integration Building. Standing 23 stories tall, this impressive edifice has four bays where the liquid fuel core sections of Titan III are assembled in an upright position. Folding work platforms in each bay wrap around the booster during assembly, allowing technicians convenient access to any part of the vehicle. Base of the booster rests on a launch pedestal and tower. The core's three stages and payload are delivered to the VIB and then stacked one atop another in one of the checkout cells, or bays, on a rail transporter, a mobile launch platform spanning 40 feet.

Heart of the VIB, and, in fact, of the entire complex, are the two control centers in the northwest corner of the building. Unlike the conventional blockhouses of the past, these centers are more than three miles from the pads. Flights are directed by electronic means. Also inside the VIB are four spacecraft control rooms and an instrumentation station. Surrounding the building are various storage areas.

Directly north of the VIB, between it and the twin launch pads, is the huge, 235-foot-tall Solid Motor Assembly Building. In this, the 86-foot-long, half-million-pound solid propellant rocket motors are built up and mated to the Titan III-C core. The solid motor segments are received at ITL on specially modified railroad flatcars. Then they are transported to the segment arrival storage area, later go to the Segment Receipt Inspection Building for readiness checkout, and then are housed in the Segment Ready Storage Building until assembly time.

There are seven miles of railway tracks, five of them double tracked, connecting the VIB, SMAB, and the two launch complexes. Once Titan III has been inspected, assembled, and checked out in the two buildings, it is then transported in a vertical, flight ready position on a mobile launch platform. This is powered by two parallel-controlled, 110-ton diesel locomotives. At the pad, a 170-foot-tall stationary umbilical tower provides rollout platforms at 13 levels, to permit access at each elevation for servicing or maintenance functions. The transporter and umbilical masts are sheathed with a ceramic material for protection from engine exhaust at liftoff.

Vans housing aerospace ground equipment are attached to the transporter. Electrical equipment in the vans remains connected to the booster from the time it is erected and assembled, through launch. The vans are also equipped with railroad wheels, which permit them to travel on the ITL tracks, and to move as a unit with the transporter-borne vehicle.

Thus continuity of all checkout and launch equipment is maintained from assembly through liftoff, greatly reducing the probability of delays at the pad due to remarriage of the rocket to ground equipment. This is a radical departure from the "fixed" launch concept that had been used at the Cape since the days of Bumper 8.

Titan III arrives at the pad in a vertical position, and the mobile launch platform is precisely positioned and locked in place. Umbilical tower platforms are then extended, and the mobile service tower is brought into position around the rocket and its payload. Next come brief vehicle verification tests and a final combined systems test, before fueling begins. The bird is then ready to fly. The 25-story-tall mobile service tower is rolled 600 feet away from the pad to a safe parking position. Each launch pad has a 145-foot-long concrete exhaust duct leading from the flame deflector, providing an escape path for the tremendous volume of exhaust gases emitted by the strap-on solid propellant rockets.

The Integrate-Transfer-Launch facility makes it possible for the Air Force to launch up to 30 Titan III's a year if necessary. To date, however, the flight rate has not neared this maximum. The system is also designed to permit launch of a Titan III within two seconds of a preselected liftoff time and to permit a readiness condition close to launch to be held for up to a month.

Under the new concept, the Air Force could, for the first time, completely assemble all stages of a large space booster, integrate them with the payload, a mobile transporter and specially designed ground support equipment, and check out the entire system in a controlled, factorylike environment. Everything needed to fly the bird, except storable liquid propellants, moves as a single item to the pad.

Before ITL was finished, however, Titan III-A rockets were test launched from modified Complex 20 at the Cape. This was formerly a Titan II ICBM site. First flight was made at 10 A.M., September 1, 1964. Though the third stage shut down prematurely, nullifying achievement of orbit, most primary and secondary test objectives were met. A little more than three months later, on December 10, a second Titan III-A repeated the flight plan and made orbit.

The launch was made under a new commander at the Air Force Eastern Test Range: Major General Vincent G. Huston, who took over August 12, 1964. Earlier in the year Brigadier General Harry J. Sands, Jr., had assumed command from Major General Leighton I. Davis, who was promoted to head the National Range Division, Air Force Systems Command. This included AF missile bases at the Cape and at Vandenberg AFB, California. Previously, Sands had served as deputy to Davis. An electrical engineering graduate, Huston had been assigned to Headquarters, Pacific Air Forces, Hickam AFB, Hawaii, as Assistant Chief of Staff, Matériel. Official designation of the Air Force base had been changed from Atlantic Missile Range to Eastern Test Range in January 1964.

On February 11, 1965, a Lincoln Experimental Satellite was placed atop Titan III-A number three, and launched at 10:19 A.M. A planned earth orbit 115 miles up was hit, and from there, the trans-stage reignited twice. Again, the shot was a success. All launch vehicle, and 95 percent of the satellite's goals were met.

Fourth and final Titan III-A tune-up flight left the Cape May 6, 1965, with a dual payload: another Lincoln Satellite and a radar calibration sphere. This time the trans-stage was ignited four times, and the satellites were placed into planned elliptical orbits. Everything worked exactly as the books read. The Air Force was now ready to strap on its twin solid-propellant motors and attempt to fly the most powerful rocket yet developed by the United States: Titan III-C.

Veteran bird watchers at the Cape have long disputed which vehicle is the most exciting to watch at liftoff. To some, it was the Saturn I without question. The sheer ponderousness of its bulk, straining to clear the pad at a snail's pace while building up its powerful thrust, added drama to every launch. For others, the sleek, solid-fueled ballistic missiles, which scream to life and climb a stairway of smoke at a highly accelerated pace, seemed more spectacular.

Certainly, any rocket flight from the Spaceport is a momentous sight to witness, and no one, no matter how many flights he has seen over the years, is immune to the flash and rumble. Of all the hundreds of launches that took place up to the introduction of Titan III-C, two stand out in everyone's memory. One was a Titan II that was flown at dusk. As it peaked over the horizon and staging action took place, the sun, hidden from ground observers, caught the bird in a brilliant glare high over the Atlantic Ocean. Atmospheric conditions were perfect that evening, and the missile was seen by hundreds of thousands of people all along the southeastern coast of the United States, from North Carolina to the southern tip of Florida. The other memorable flight was the eighth Saturn I launch. It occurred at 3 A.M. in the morning. It was as if dawn had come three hours early. Newspapers could be read by the spectacular orange-yellow light of the giant rocket's engine flames.

But even Saturn I could not compare to the super-splashing pyrotechnics display ignited by each Titan III-C launch. There is no sight comparable. It is one that holds all viewers in reverent awe. The twin solid motors kick the bird off the ground with a force that shakes the land for miles around. Thick tongues of flame lick back 300 feet, and as the fire-snorting, metallic monster rises, it trails large inverted

An incomparable spectacle: liftoff of Titan III-C. This aerial view also shows the Integrate Transfer Launch Complex area of the Spaceport, with the Vehicle Integration Building in middle foreground. (U.S. Air Force Photo)

funnels of smoke all the way to the pad. The fire is so bright, on-lookers must shield their eyes. On a clear day, III-C can be seen for hundreds of miles. After the solids burn out, high over the Atlantic, they are jettisoned and tumble back into the ocean, as the core, or main stage, ignites and soars ever upward. It is a sight that becomes indelibly etched in the mind.

Maiden flight of this new bird occurred June 18, 1965, and all programmed events took place as scheduled. A ballast payload of more than 29,000 pounds was placed into orbit. A follow-up launch occurred October 15, again with successful results. Though a malfunction in the third stage attitude-control system resulted, preventing a circularization of orbit on Titan III-C number three, most mission objectives were realized on its December 21, 1965, flight. The following June, vehicle number four in the series made it a quadruple success when it orbited seven communications satellites and one gravity gradient test satellite. All systems of the trans-stage performed flawlessly through three burns and two orbital plane changes.

If Titan III-C is spectacular during a normal launch, it is virtually indescribable when it explodes in midair. And that's exactly what happened to the vehicle launched August 26, 1966. Eighty-two seconds after liftoff, the rocket nosed down due to loss of the payload fairing and destroyed itself in a tremendous fireball. Huge fragments of flaming metal showered down into the Atlantic, leaving long smoke streamers hanging in the sky. It was an expensive fireworks exhibit.

Air Force and contractor teams put their all-powerful space vehicle back on course, however, with three successive orbital shots following the failure. By July, 1967, Titan III-C had placed 22 operational satellites into a synchronous-equatorial corridor. Nineteen of these were for the Department of Defense global military communications network. Robot sentries, called Velas, designed to do detective work under the international nuclear test ban treaty, were also orbited.

Final stages of Titan III development at the Cape were supervised

After lifting the Titan III-C to an altitude of approximately 25 miles, the spent solid-propellant motors are ejected and the three-stage liquid-propellant center core vehicle takes over to complete the mission. Photo sequence (bottom to top) was taken from a specially equipped KC-135 jet photographic aircraft flying at 40,000 feet. (U.S. Air Force Photos)

Major General William L. Richardson
HQ AF Div., Joint Long Range Proving Ground /
HQ Joint Long Range Proving Ground
10 April 1950 — 31 July 1954

Major General Donald N. Yates
Air Force Missile Test Center
1 August 1954 — 4 May 1960

Major General Leighton I. Davis
(Presently Lieutenant General)
Air Force Missile Test Center
31 May 1960 — 1 January 1964

Brigadier General Harry J. Sands, Jr.
(Presently Major General)
Air Force Missile Test Center /
Air Force Eastern Test Range
2 January 1964 — 16 July 1964

Major General Vincent G. Huston
Air Force Eastern Test Range
12 August 1964 — 5 May 1967

Major General David M. Jones
Air Force Eastern Test Range
5 May 1967 —

Air Force commanders at the Spaceport. (Respective commands and dates are given under each officer's name.) (U.S. Air Force Photos)

by Major General David M. Jones, who succeeded Major General Huston as Commander of the Air Force Eastern Test Range on May 5, 1967. Jones had been deputy associate administrator for NASA's manned space flight program. His background is rich in color and in research and development work. He participated in the Doolittle raid on Tokyo during the early phases of World War II, and was later shot down and captured in North Africa. He became director of the B-58 test force when it was organized in February, 1958, and flew more hours testing the B-58 aircraft than any other USAF pilot.

Though Titan III-C launches were initiated and the bird was developed at Cape Kennedy, the vehicle is destined to make its boldest headlines 2,500 miles away, on the western coast of the United States. For there, at Vandenberg AFB, the Manned Orbiting Laboratory (MOL) project, approved by President Johnson July 25, 1965, will be carried out. It is to solve a long-debated question: can man do a useful military job in space?

The Air Force will use Titan III-C to boost two military astronauts into orbit in a thermos-shaped craft for 30 day flights. Above earth, MOL will provide the platform from which man can experiment to determine the armed forces' role in space. First manned flight is set for about 1970, considerably behind original schedules. Five flights are planned, and what is learned from them will determine whether there will be follow-on projects.

By June, 1967, the Air Force had selected 16 astronauts for the MOL training program. Much of it is secret. All manned launchings will be made from Vandenberg rather than Cape Kennedy so MOL can be launched into a north-south polar orbit, a path on which it can fly over every area of the world. This is a necessity for military operations. At the Cape such an orbit would require a difficult, dogleg flight that would take the rocket over land masses. From California, however, polar orbit can be more easily obtained without any safety fears.

In the program, two astronauts will man a modified Gemini capsule—a "blue Gemini," blue for Air Force. This will cap a 41-foot, 19,000-pound laboratory. Once in orbit, the pilots will crawl through a hatch into the lab, shed their space suits, and work in a shirt-sleeve environment. At the end of the month-long flight, they will reenter Gemini, detach it from the lab, and reenter the earth's atmosphere for landing.

In many ways, the work the astronauts perform will help settle long-nagging questions that aerospace scientists have argued for years: primarily, can man do a better job in space than a machine? Specifically, Air Force astronauts will help decide whether man is more effective at performing communications, reconnaissance, surveillance, navigation, and mapping tasks that are now performed by unmanned satellites. Pilots will maneuver outside their craft. They will attempt maintenance and repair chores, work with laser beams, which could be developed as communications tools or weapons, and they may test devices for escaping from a disabled capsule.

Proponents of a strong military space program foresee the day when America's global striking force may be controlled from a huge maneuverable command post in orbit. They also envision large military installations in space with elaborate communications facilities, sophisticated observation systems, repair workshops, and stations for refueling and rearming space battleships.

But all such concepts must be proven, and the first step is to send man up to perform from a military list of assignments. MOL is completely separate from NASA's Apollo program of landing American astronauts on the moon, but it is likely information gained under each project will be usefully exchanged. MOL launches will be counted down in California, but the basic roots of the program—the development of the Titan III-C rocket—took place in Florida. It is a colorful chapter in the Spaceport's history.

The book on Titan III-C may not be altogether closed at the Cape even without MOL. The versatile rocket has many possible future applications. Among them:

—To boost scientific payloads into earth orbit and into lunar and interplanetary trajectories.

—To boost manned spacecraft into earth orbit.

—To boost manned orbiting space stations.

—To transport a unit to supply and service space stations.

These and other uses are the subjects of extensive long-range studies, both by NASA and the Air Force. There are many advantages to be derived from reactivating the bird at the Cape. It is economical, costing only about half what a Saturn IB does. It can be readied for flight quickly, and in a controlled environment. And, perhaps most important, the ITL facility and two launch complexes are intact and ready to pick up operational activity where the development program left off.

Chapter *12*

BIRTH OF A SPACEPORT

"In a very real sense, the road to the moon is paved
with brick, steel and concrete here on earth."
—*James E. Webb,* NASA Administrator

Man has dreamed of landing on the moon for centuries,
probably since the beginnings of civilization. The huge yellow orb
that hangs in the sky has been an inviting target for eons; enticingly
close, yet unreachable. At the start of the sixth decade of the 20th
century, however, man, for the first time, felt he could break down
the impregnable space barrier that separated the two worlds. Wernher von Braun and others had long considered a lunar landing goal,
since the late 1930's and early 1940's, but their dreams had to wait
while they developed missiles for military use, first for Germany, and
later for the United States.

With the flights of Russia's *Sputnik I* and America's Explorer I in
the late 1950's, it became obvious to everyone at the Spaceport that
it would be only a matter of time and national interest before the
U.S. could acquire the technology needed to send man to the moon.
President John F. Kennedy, on May 25, 1961, announced the goal of
landing astronauts on the lunar surface before the end of the decade
and returning them safely to earth. By then, the technology was already well in development.

To those in the rocket launching business, a clear evolution would
have to take place. First, to propel men to the moon by conventional
means, that is without using a nuclear or other exotic type stage, a

giant vehicle, unlike anything before ever designed, would have to be built. This would be necessary simply to lift a heavy spacecraft above the earth's gravitational pull and then insert it into a proper trajectory for the 225,000-mile flight to the moon. Nothing on the pads in 1961 could begin to do the job, not even Saturn I.

Secondly, an entirely new concept in launching operations would be needed to support a national lunar landing program and other ones that would follow it. Men of vision had long foreseen the day when the "fixed pad concept" used at the Cape since 1950 would become outmoded. That day was fast nearing. There were many obvious disadvantages to such systems.

A major one was the length of time a vehicle must remain on the pad, exposed to the elements. It took approximately two months to completely check out a Saturn I, for instance, and another month to rehabilitate the pad after launch for the next bird. This limited the facility to but four flights a year, a low utilization rate for an expensive complex. Also, since the rockets would, of necessity, get larger as the space targets they shot for became more distant and difficult, it would require larger towers to service the vehicles, and this becomes a tremendous expense.

Blockhouses, too, would have to be bigger and fitted with more complex and sophisticated equipment, and their cost would become prohibitive if the launch rates increased substantially. Another unavoidable expense would be the necessity of remating the vehicle to ground equipment. The removal of umbilical cables and connections in the assembly area makes it necessary to mate the rocket again to all checkout and launch equipment at the pad. When an umbilical connection is broken, all related data becomes invalid and the checkout of involved gear must be resumed from the beginning.

There were many other disadvantages to continuing launch operations under the fixed concept. Higher explosive equivalences of the future giant family of vehicles would require greater pad separation distances to prevent interference during hazardous tests. This would consume vast amounts of land for safety reasons alone. Established launch techniques would also require multiple crews of experienced personnel, and there just weren't that many veterans to go around.

Weighing all these and other factors, Spaceport engineers set to work to develop a new concept in launch operations. They faced monumental problems, not the least of which was to provide long-range planning in a rapidly expanding, comparatively young technical field.

Some initial requirements of this new approach were obvious. For one, new facilities would be needed to support and fly a rocket several times larger and more powerful than anything ever before launched at Cape Kennedy. Because of the size of the vehicle, its cost and the importance of its mission, the highest standards of reliability would be imposed. And, whatever facility was designed, it would have to stand up to the test of time. It must sustain not only the manned lunar landing program, but the equally or more ambitious projects that would surely follow conquest of the moon. Plans for assembling spacecraft or space stations in orbit would make it necessary to have facilities for short-interval, successive launches. Standby rockets would be necessary; thus the requirement for a faster launch rate.

In January, 1961, four months before the Mercury flight of Alan Shepard and President Kennedy's announcement of the lunar landing goal, Dr. Kurt H. Debus met with some of his key long-range planners to discuss new concepts for launching heavy space vehicles. He asked his colleagues to think in terms of designing sites for rockets of between five and ten million pounds thrust.

No one man is responsible for what has become, since then, the nation's first and only operational Spaceport. There can be no individual credit taken for the new concept of launching super-sized rockets that has evolved. As with the flights themselves, the working out of this new approach was a product of teamwork. A series of in-depth studies was made, using some of the nation's finest aerospace brainpower. The planning centered on one key factor: the new concept would have to rely on mobility. Cornerstone of this idea would be that preflight checkout and the launch would be carried out in separate areas, and the giant rocket would be transported between the two.

In March, 1961, Dr. Debus sketched some penciled drawings showing an assembly building and launch control center, where rockets could be checked out in a protected environment some distance from the launch pads. For a mode of transportation from the assembly area to the launch site, he drew a flatbed type railroad car with the rocket horizontally strapped atop it.

Though the final design of what was to become world famous as the "mobile launch concept" had not yet fully developed, the need for a tract of land several times larger than Cape Kennedy was apparent from the first. Before facilities could be designed and built, a site for the Spaceport would have to be selected. A worldwide survey for such a site was begun in June, 1961, headed by Debus, representing NASA, and Major General Leighton I. Davis, then Commander of the Air Force Missile Test Center, representing the Department of Defense.

After intensive study, the search was narrowed to eight locations: in the mid-Pacific, on the California and Texas coasts, an island off the coast of Georgia, at White Sands, New Mexico, islands in the Caribbean, and Merritt Island, adjacent to the Cape. There were advantages of an island launching base that had to be seriously considered. Safety was one important plus. No land masses would be endangered by exploding or falling rockets. Yet it would be difficult to maintain a technically oriented population at a remote site. There would be need for schools, shops, churches—all the conveniences of a modern community. And, because of the scientists and engineers who would make up a considerable portion of the lunar landing task force, schools of higher learning would have to be accessible.

Climate was another prime element to be weighed in the final site selection. The base would have to be operational 12 months a year. And it would have to be on or near water, for some of the moon rocket's stages would be so large they could only be transported from the manufacturing plant to the launch area by sea.

After a thorough examination of all potential sites, Debus and General Davis settled on recommending Merritt Island. More than any other specific area, it met all requirements. The semitropical weather would pose no major problems, other than an occasional in-season brush from hurricanes. But facilities could be windproofed. There was enough acreage on the island not only to take care of rockets to reach the moon, but also anything larger that would follow them in time and space. Engineering studies determined that there was sufficient area on Merritt Island safely to launch vehicles of 35 million pounds thrust: far greater than anything presently planned by the United States.

And this section of Florida is surrounded by several towns that could offer all the services and facilities of a normal community. The state also announced it would build a large technological university within easy driving distance of the Spaceport.

Perhaps the overriding factor behind the Debus-Davis recommendation, however, was the nearness of Merritt Island to Cape Kennedy and the vast resources of the Air Force Eastern Test Range. Tracking instrumentation and support areas already developed could be easily and economically adapted to support NASA's lunar landing goals.

Only on the island could NASA consolidate all its major launch activities, both manned and unmanned.

Satisfied with their choice, Debus and General Davis submitted their report on July 31, 1961, to James E. Webb, NASA Administrator, and to Robert S. McNamara, Secretary of Defense. It didn't take long for Washington to confirm their recommendation. The final decision was announced less than three weeks later, August 18, 1961, and Congress subsequently authorized the National Aeronautics and Space Administration to initiate land acquisition.

This began in 1962, and NASA eventually bought 87,763 acres of North Merritt Island for $74 million. There were relatively few inhabitants, so relocation of homes and condemnation proceedings presented no major problems. In addition, the State of Florida granted NASA the right to use 53,553 more acres of submerged lands, most of which were north of Cape Kennedy, separated from the ocean by a narrow strip of beach on the east, and connected with the Indian River on the west by the Haulover Canal, which bisected the island. Total property investment today is about $80 million, and the Spaceport, not counting Cape Kennedy or the range, presently totals 141,316 acres. The Air Force retained ownership and control of the Cape and the series of down-range island tracking stations.

The land runs north and south for 30 miles, stretching from a point parallel to the southern tip of the Cape to a boundary just south of New Smyrna Beach. Most of the site is bordered on the east by the Banana River, and, further north, the Altantic Ocean. The Indian River runs along the western perimeter. Not counting submerged property, NASA's overall holdings are roughly six times the size of Cape Kennedy.

With the neighboring Cape, the history of Merritt Island can be traced far back. Indians made their homes here possibly as early as 2,000 or 3,000 B.C. Several sites have been discovered on the northern half of the island that can be assigned to that time frame, the Pre-Ceramic Period of Indian life. At the sites are mounds, called middens. These are veritable islands of clamshells; mealtime refuse piles. Archeologists know, from examining these middens, that they date prior to 1,000 B.C., because no pottery was found in them.

The Indians made tools of shell, and spear joints were chipped out of flint. Their homes were temporary shelters of the windbreak type. Staples of their diet were oysters, clams, coquina, and various other shellfish, in addition to the wildlife and waterfowl that still abound in the area. By the 16th century, white men had sighted, explored, and settled on Merritt Island. The Indians were not friendly to the Spanish and French, however, and it was another 100 years before they could coexist satisfactorily.

In 1818, Colonel Thomas Dummitt, who 11 years earlier had fled his plantation on Barbados, arrived on Merritt Island, bearing some budwood from Spanish orange plantings found near St. Augustine. From these, he began growing an orange that was to become world famous. His first groves are located in the heart of the Spaceport's 88,000 acres. By 1869, with an annual production of 700,000 oranges, the groves were recognized as the largest in the state.

After Dummitt died, an Italian nobleman, the Duke of Castellucia, acquired the property in 1872 and soon after built a huge home with twin gables for his new bride. Guests from all over the world came to fish, hunt, ride horses, and play tennis at the Villa Castellucia. The surrounding woods were full of birds, deer, and bear, and the waters were brimming with fish. The mansion became a hunting lodge near the turn of the century.

A hard freeze hit Florida in 1895, and the Dummitt trees were among the few in the state that survived. They had been protected by the warm waters of the Indian and Banana rivers which flank Merritt Island. The groves were productive until 1916, and were then left unattended for years. Wild oranges still grow there today. The Duke's mansion was also standing when NASA bought its property. In the interests of local historical preservation, NASA made an arrangement with civic officials to have the building transported, intact, off government property for possible restoration.

One of the most interesting yet least known attractions at the Spaceport today lies well hidden at the edge of a swampy area, surrounded by palmetto scrubs. Here are the ruins of an 18th-century English sugar mill. All that remains is a six-foot-high wall, 28 feet long. It was constructed of small slabs of broken stone held together by crude mortar. Crumbled brick ruins lie nearby.

Historians believe this mill was built between 1763 and 1783. During this period sugar mills flourished along the Florida coast. The raw cane was washed and shredded. It was crushed and squeezed until the juice was extracted. It was then diluted with water and heated. The resulting product was poured into evaporation tanks and the juice crystalized. The thick, syrupy substance was used for molasses. Records indicate that one of the old mills in the area was rebuilt in the second half of the 19th century by American settlers. It was complete with boilers, engines, rolls, and evaporating pans.

Improved means of transportation in the late 19th century opened the Spaceport area to growth and prosperity. In the 1880's, for instance, a regular steamer service was begun on the Indian River. Fruit could then be shipped faster, supplies obtained more easily, and tourists began to arrive. On February 6, 1893, Henry Flagler's first train rolled through the county. Early settlers on the island either farmed or started citrus groves, many of which still abound today. Beans, tomatoes, eggplant, pineapples, and sugar cane were grown at sites where giant rockets are today readied for flight.

There were no bridges to the island until 1916. Sailboats and gasoline launches were used to commute to the mainland for supplies and mail. With the addition of the first wooden bridge came more growth. Still, the island did not become thickly populated until long after the space boom arrived in 1950. When NASA announced its manned lunar landing program and the need for 88,000 acres, North Merritt Island, except for scattered houses, orange groves, and one main paved road, remained an essentially undeveloped tract of land. Most early residents settled on the south end of the island.

Within the new federal reservation are 185,000 citrus trees which produce some of Florida's finest oranges and grapefruit. NASA immediately established a good-neighbor policy with the former grove owners. Since the land on which these trees stood would not specifically be needed for construction of facilities, an agreement was drawn up whereby the citrus men could lease back their groves from the government for an annual fee. Beekeepers, too, were granted a similar arrangement to maintain hives within the groves, since pollination is essential to fruit production.

As had happened at the Cape more than a decade earlier, the newly acquired property included some burial sites. NASA gives relatives visiting privileges to these areas at any time they desire them. The Air Force at the Cape follows the same policy, though one wry spokesman pointed out that the most popular visiting periods invariably coincide with the launch time of big rockets.

The land acquired in 1962 also included miles of fine white beachfront that had been used for recreation by residents of the area for years. NASA left this shoreline open to residents during the summer, when the county provided lifeguards.

An open door policy was also extended to hunters and fishermen. The Spaceport contains some of the finest freshwater bass and bream streams and canals, and is also a haven for waterfowl. Fishermen and hunters are allowed access to their favorite grounds during the season.

As at Cape Kennedy, wildlife thrives on Merritt Island. The major portion of government property is undeveloped, in the same natural state as in the days when Indians called the land home. There are bobcats, armadillos, opossums, raccoons, deer, snakes, alligators, otters, and various other creatures that today coexist with the Free World's largest, most powerful rockets.

The bird population on Merritt Island is legendary. Each year Audubon Society members are allowed to enter the Spaceport, wearing special badges, to take the bird census as part of their national count. During an average 24-day operation they spot 90 or more different species in the shadows of the moon rockets. Working for the Audubon Society is not without its occupational hazards, however. One member had set up a camera with a telephoto lens on a tripod in the middle of some dense underbrush and was all set to snap pictures of a scarce Wilson's plover when he was suddenly confronted by a squadron of security police. He had to do some fast talking to convince them his bird-watching intentions were genuine.

Among the many attractions at the Spaceport today is a huge eagle's nest, located just off one of the main roads leading to the lunar launch pads. Three eaglets were born and raised in the nest a few years back, and were greeted with almost as much attention as a rocket flight.

Because a good portion of NASA's land on the island was not immediately needed for clearance and construction, the space agency arranged an agreement with the U.S. Bureau of Sport Fisheries and Wildlife. As a result, the Merritt Island National Wildlife Refuge, managed by the Bureau, was established in August, 1963. It covers nearly 58,000 acres. This action is in keeping with the Bureau's program to develop the recreational potential of national wildlife refuges where such use is compatible with the management objectives of each area. The program also furthers the Kennedy Space Center's policy of affording controlled public access without interference with operations.

Once the Spaceport site had been finally selected and the land acquired, vast armies of architects, engineers, and construction workers—7,000 of them at the peak of employment—were assembled to begin building the unique and immense launch facilities for the manned lunar landing program. There were to be two main areas of activity. All supporting operations, plus those directly involved in premate testing of the Apollo spacecraft, would be in an industrial area six miles south of the lunar launch site itself.

By this time the spacecraft and launch vehicle contractors had been selected, and the rocket and Apollo capsule designs had been approved. Manufacturing work began. Once these final sizes and shapes had been determined, designing of the launch support facilities could be completed. It was decided that only those activities essential to the checkout, mating, erection, and launch of the moon vehicle would be located in the general pad area. This would include the assembly building, the pads, the launch control center, and all other instruments and facilities needed in direct support of flights. This area would be called Launch Complex 39.

While the rockets would be put together and checked out in an environmentally controlled structure on Merritt Island, the actual launch pads would be three and a half miles east, a few hundred feet from the Atlantic. This point of land is not on the island, nor is it on Cape Kennedy, which lies to the south. This fact has caused some confusion, particularly to newsmen's datelines. Many reporters contend their stories on Apollo/Saturn V launches should begin with the familiar Cape Kennedy dateline, because this is best known to world audiences. NASA officials, however, prefer Kennedy Space Center.

North of Launch Complex 39, the land has remained virtually untouched. This portion of the Spaceport is reserved for future programs of either NASA or the Department of Defense. To the south, NASA helped finance the construction of a new lock at Port Canaveral, linking the Indian and Banana rivers with the ocean. This was necessary to allow entry of barges carrying the huge Saturn boosters and second stages from their manufacturing plants to the assembly building where the giant rockets would be inspected, tested, and readied for flight.

Congress allotted more than $800 million for construction of the Spaceport, in annual increments. Compared to the cost of earlier, individual launch complexes at the Cape, this is a staggering figure. But in long-range terms it was a sound investment that will continue to save American taxpayers money in years to come. The many advantages of the mobile launch concept—greater launch rate, protection of the rocket during assembly, etc.—well justify the high initial expense for construction of facilities.

Because NASA is in the space exploration business, it chose another government agency, a specialist in its field, to act as the central agent responsible for directing the design and construction of the Kennedy Space Center on Merritt Island. That organization, the U.S. Army Corps of Engineers, already had years of experience in molding launch facilities at Cape Kennedy. Corps employees had, in fact, been on the scene at the Cape since the flight of Bumper 8 in July, 1950, and had served as NASA's supervisory design and construction agent in the area since the inception of the National Aeronautics and Space Administration in October, 1958.

The scope of the building project on Merritt Island was of such vast dimensions that the Corps created its first new district in more than a decade. Sole function of this Canaveral District, located on Merritt Island, was aerospace construction in the Cape-Spaceport area.

Colonel William L. Starnes, former district engineer, summed up the Corps' role when he said: "To say we build nothing is another way of saying what we are, really, are managers, administrators, inspectors and coordinators. We are the design and construction agency for the Department of Defense and NASA. The using agency, NASA, the Air Force, the Army or the Navy, tells us what it wants built. We supervise the design and then we see the project through construction to the finish. We contract out most of the design to architect-engineering firms, and all of the building to construction firms. We supervise the work—insuring its quality and on-time delivery—and we administer the contracts."

The number of Corps employees at the Spaceport reached 600 at its peak. In late 1967, with most of the major Spaceport facilities completed, the Corps announced plans to move its headquarters to Patrick AFB as an economy measure.

Heart of the Spaceport's industrial area is the Manned Spacecraft Operations Building (MSOB). This was the first major structure to be built on Merritt Island. Ground was broken for it with informal ceremonies January 23, 1963. Much of the final checkout and testing of the Apollo spacecraft, before its marriage to the launch vehicle, is carried out in this building. Flexibility was built into the MSOB, for planners knew checkout operations on Apollo would change as the state of the art advanced. The building contains 600,000 feet of office, laboratory, and assembly area.

A high bay 224 feet long and 100 feet high and an adjacent 251-foot-long low bay accommodate the three-man Apollo capsules. In the high bay are two immense tanks. These are identical altitude chambers, each 55 feet high, 33.5 feet in diameter, and capable of housing the complete spacecraft configuration, including the command and service modules and the lunar module. Inside the tanks, pressurized

The Manned Spacecraft Operations Building on Merritt Island. (NASA Photo)

"flights" up to 250,000 feet in altitude can be run to simulate actual mission conditions.

One chamber is equipped for testing the command and service modules of the Apollo spacecraft. The second one has been outfitted to hold the lunar module. A manned mission in these tanks simulates a flight from liftoff through reentry. Here the seal of the spacecraft is verified along with breathing, cooling, and electrical systems. Here the astronauts practice maneuvers and experiments required in actual space flight. Two other tests are performed before the manned runs under vacuum conditions. First, the pilots check out Apollo under normal atmospheric attitudes. This is followed by an unmanned altitude test in which the chamber is "pumped down to ultimate altitude," simulating a flight at a height of more than 40 miles. Only after the command and service modules meet the specifications of the spacecraft test conductor is a manned mission at altitude permitted.

Offices and laboratories occupy most of the MSOB's first floor. These include malfunction investigation facilities, a lunar module radar and communications lab, and an Apollo guidance and navigation lab. On the second floor are Apollo electrical power and sequential labs, a biomedical and flight experiments lab, instrument calibration, and buildup facilities, instrument checkout equipment lab, and the lunar module environmental control system lab.

Astronaut crew quarters are located on the third floor. Pilots occupy these modern, well-furnished apartments for periods up to three months while their spacecraft are being checked out at the Kennedy Center. The fourth floor is mainly taken up with ACE (Acceptance Checkout Equipment) computers and monitoring systems for Apollo.

There is also a Weather Bureau station and room for Apollo flight experiments support equipment. Weather is of paramount importance at the Spaceport. It has direct effect not only on rockets in the launch area, but also in recovery zones, particularly involving the pickup of manned craft. Both the Air Force and NASA have meteorological stations at the Center. The Air Force operates out of Patrick Air Force Base. NASA's branch of the U.S. Weather Bureau is on Merritt Island.

Lightning, thunderstorms, winds, and tropical storms present the greatest dangers. Full protection from lightning cannot be afforded. Attempts can be made for only grounding. Rockets are especially vulnerable when the service structures are rolled back, leaving them naked on the pad. Complex 19 was once struck by lightning during prelaunch checkout of a Gemini-Titan II vehicle, and the flight had to be delayed weeks for repairs. Lightning doesn't have to score a direct hit to cause damage at the pad. It creates surges in power and raises havoc with electronic circuits. For these and personnel safety reasons, all pads are cleared of workmen when a thunderstorm is within five miles of the launch complex.

Winds, both at ground level and several miles up, are also critical to rocket flights, as was evidenced in the delays in the launching of America's first satellite, Explorer I, in January, 1958.

In addition to normal weather facilities and services, meteorological balloons and small weather rockets, which probe winds, temperatures, and pressures up to 200,000 feet, are sent up from the Cape on a regular basis. No one at the Spaceport takes weather for granted. It is an important element to be considered on every flight schedule.

Keeping an eye on seasonal hurricanes that often blast across Florida is another important function of the weathermen at KSC. Though the storm season starts in June, it is usually late August or September before the big winds blow in from the Atlantic. Some pads at the Cape, notably Saturn I Launch Complexes 34 and 37, have been designed to withstand full force hurricanes with a rocket in the service structure. On others, the bird must be taken down and stored if a storm is predicted to hit the Spaceport.

Several hurricanes have sideswiped the area, some delivering wind gusts above 75 miles per hour, but there have been no direct hits, and consequently no great property damage to buildings or complexes. Still, each storm bears close watching from the moment it is detected until is has cleared the Florida coastline.

Many storms have hit hard at some of the Air Force Eastern Test Range tracking stations, however. Here, thanks to early warnings and advanced battening down preparations, life and property losses have been held to a bare minimum. Early information on the spawning of tropical hurricanes is transmitted from earth orbiting satellites launched from Cape Kennedy. Today, ESSA weather eyes in the sky can detect a newborn storm within hours of its development, and alert personnel so proper precautions can be taken.

Several smaller buildings south of the MSOB directly support spacecraft checkout work. Key facilities include:

—A Pyrotechnic Installation Building, where ordnance items ranging from mortars to deploy parachutes and explosive bolts to separate the launch escape tower, are installed on Apollo.

—High pressure and liquid oxygen testing of Apollo's environmental control systems are performed in the Life Support Test Facilities.

—Spacecraft fluid test systems are component tested in the Fluid Test Support area.

—At the Hypergolic Test Facility, spacecraft stabilization and attitude control systems, orbital maneuvering, and reentry control systems are tested and verified.

Just off the southwest corner of the MSOB is the Flight Crew Training Building. Some of the most intensive training for manned flights takes place here. On the main floor are three full-sized simulators, two of the Apollo command module and one of the lunar module. As with the Mercury and Gemini simulators on the Cape, astronauts can practically "fly" their entire missions in these land-locked, electronically controlled machines.

Crew members are able to look out the command module simulator's windows and see cloud formations above the earth below, or they can observe stars along the celestial sphere. When the flight plan calls for rendezvous and docking with the lunar module, they are able to see it come into view, and they can maneuver their controls to link the two craft. Later, when two of the men have "transferred" to the LM, they can view the moon below as they "orbit" around it, and then, as they descend, they see the surface "come up" to meet them. On their way home to earth after "landing," they make celestial fixes with a sextant.

All these scenes are created in the simulation room by elaborately designed infinity imaging systems, in which lenses are placed outside Apollo's windows. Optics create the illusion that the images of earth, moon, and stars are varying distances away at different points in the simulated flight. It is like having a personal planetarium, and it provides a realistic touch to the astronauts' training programs.

Also, as with Mercury and Gemini, the Apollo simulators each have their own operator instructor station, which allows engineers to monitor the flights and to program impromptu malfunctions. Crewmen are tested on how well and quickly they solve these problems. In fact, for each hour of flight astronauts spend in space, they log dozens more in the simulators. Every conceivable condition they might encounter in earth orbit or on the way to or from the moon is covered in these grounded spacecraft time after time, until the pilots' reactions are rehearsed to the point of automatic reflex. Their toughest flights are often flown in the simulators.

Immediately west of the MSOB is the Kennedy Space Center Headquarters Building, housing administrative offices of NASA personnel. From his fourth floor windows, the director, Dr. Debus, can view the Launch Complex 39 area six miles to the north. In addition to his suite, the Headquarters Building houses the offices of the technical support, design engineering, administration, reliability and quality assurance, safety, and security sections, and of the chief scientist and legal, financial, contract procurement, and other staff functions. Offices of personnel more directly involved in launch operations are in the MSOB.

The heartbeat of Saturn rockets is measured in the Central Instrumentation Facility, just west of the Headquarters Building. With a variety of odd-shaped dish antennae adorning its roof, CIF is probably the most modernistic-looking structure in the Industrial Area. Inside it is an electronic storehouse of computers and equipment all calibrated and tuned to gather and record prelaunch and launch information on the lunar rockets. Specifically, measurements are received during flight of temperatures inside and outside the rocket, of propellant flow rates, engine temperatures, wind pressures, and other pertinent data on vehicle performance.

Telemetry, in-flight television and prototype tracking and data processing stations are housed in the CIF. A new technique allows six different time plots of telemetry data to be requested simultaneously on six different systems and displayed within one second. This system can sort through millions of bits of telemetry data and display only that which is vital to engineers' questions. It is a far step from early instrumentation days at Cape Canaveral. On the Redstone missile, for instance, only 116 telemetered measurements were made and processed. More than 2,150 are made on Saturn V.

Raw telemetry data comes from the antennas on the CIF roof and from sources on the Air Force Eastern Test Range. Engineers in the CIF building are responsible for processing and dispatching all Apollo spacecraft data to NASA's Manned Spacecraft Center in Houston, and launch vehicle telemetry information to the Marshall Space Flight Center in Huntsville, Alabama. This data is, of course, invaluable for flight controllers to measure the space vehicle's performance.

During flights, rocket and spacecraft system engineers man the CIF's Data Presentation and Evaluation Room, where there is enough space to spread out documentation and analyze any problems that arise. This room, in many respects, serves as a second, or backup, launch control center. Closed circuit television cameras at the launch pad are connected to large screen projectors here, so propellant engineers can get a close-up view of any trouble areas.

The Manned Spacecraft Operations Building, Central Instrumentation Facility, and Headquarters Building are the most impressive sites in the KSC Industrial Area. But there are many other structures too, nearly 50 in all. It is like a small, self-supporting city, complete with cafeterias, a hospital and medical staff, fire stations, security police force, post office and bank, supply warehouses, motor pools, power stations, utility buildings, and other facilities.

Running the Spaceport on Merritt Island today is much like running a municipality of 23,000 people, only there are many unusual, demanding requirements that far exceed those placed on a community of the same size and population. Launch operations are dependent upon electricity—for checkout, to operate computers, communications equipment, and many other systems, from the launch control center to the rocket and spacecraft. Backup power systems for launch-related equipment are thus essential, should there be an outage at a critical point in a countdown or flight. Excessive water demands must be met, particularly during the moment of liftoff, when tens of thousands of gallons of water are pumped onto the pad to cool it from the rocket's exhaust to help hold down damage to the site.

As can be imagined, communications are vital at the Spaceport. Systems in use include operational and administrative intercoms, closed circuit television, data transmission, public address and paging, mobile radio, telephones, carrier, teletype facsimile, tape recorders, audio and video, and wide band transmission. On a normal workday, 10,000 phone calls are made at the Kennedy Space Center. On a launch day this figure zooms upward.

Supply alone is a tremendous operation that can be effectively handled only through automation. Everything from tiny transistors to huge spare parts for the Saturn rockets is stocked at the Center— up to 42,000 different items, mostly electronic.

Firemen stand guard during every major prelaunch test and actual flight. Theirs is a difficult and potentially dangerous profession, for they must not only be able to control conventional fires; they must know how to handle highly toxic and flammable exotic propellants as well. Doctors and nurses must also be knowledgeable in the area of what injuries a rocket explosion would be capable of inflicting. Safety personnel must plan accordingly, for every possible contingency when a bird is being worked on. And, explosives specialists must stay abreast of the latest developments in the safe handling of the many diverse ordnance items at the Center that must be stored and installed on space vehicles.

Chapter   13

THE MAMMOTH BUILDING

To accommodate the world's largest rocket, it soon became evident that a building of colossal proportions would have to be constructed. The Saturn V was to be 36 stories high, which itself was taller than any structure in Florida. To make room for the assembly and checkout of the various stages of up to three or four vehicles at one time would require a facility enclosing a tremendous amount of space.

Designers had their work cut out. Fairly early in the game it was decided to have four large bays, or checkout cells, big enough to handle all stages of the Saturn V and spacecraft in a "stacked" configuration; that is, completely assembled in an upright, launch-ready position. Space flight needs as far into the future as could be foreseen did not show the necessity of working on more than four rockets at one time. More bays could be added later if the requirements changed.

As early as 1961, Dr. Debus had penciled a sketch of the building's shape. It was in the form of a crucifix, with a high bay at each of four points on a cross. Later, this idea was modified in favor of a narrow, rectangular structure having the four bays on one side, facing east, toward the launch pads. The low bay area would run adjacent to the high bays on the west side of the building. NASA finally discarded this approach, however. Its slablike shape would have necessitated a stiffer and more expensive structure. Also, a bridge crane would have been needed for each individual bay.

The final design NASA chose was a boxlike building with a back-to-back bay arrangement. Two high bays would face east and two west, with the low bay area, where rocket upper stages would be brought in in a horizontal position and checked out in special cells, located on the south end of the building.

There were drawbacks even to the design finally selected. For example, the six towers—four on the corners and two on the sides—which are the main support columns of the building and which form the high bays would have to be tied together at their bases for structural stability. The resulting framework extends up 190 feet on each side of the center aisle, through which the rocket stages enter the high bay area. Thus, they must be lifted up and over this structural steel truss before they can be lowered into position in the bay.

But overall, the advantages of the back-to-back system outweighed the disadvantages to a greater extent than had been the case with earlier designs. For one thing, only two overhead cranes would be needed instead of four, because each one would roll back and forth on a track beneath the roof of the building to service the two bays facing each other across the aisle. Also, with this concept, there would be a roomy transfer aisle for easier off-loading, handling and positioning of rocket stages in their checkout cells. There would be, additionally, plenty of area left in each tower for office space.

By November, 1962, plans were far enough along to turn over the detailed architectural design work to a contractor. The overwhelming size of the project called for an engineering task force of major proportions. Four New York firms joined efforts to tackle the job. Their combined venture was called Urbahn-Roberts-Seelye-Moran. Managing partner of the group was Max O. Urbahn, an architect of international reputation. Structural design, civil, mechanical, and electrical plans and specifications, and foundation analysis and designs were farmed out to the other organizations who had joined Urbahn. More than 200 engineers began preparing the plans and specifications for what was to become the world's largest building.

To Urbahn, it was the challenge of a career, and he and his people took it on with spirited enthusiasm. As can be imagined by the sheer size of the structure, and the complexities of the work to be performed inside its walls, this space-age hangar for moon rockets presented some awesome problems to those who were building it on paper. Urbahn noted some of them at the time:

"As an architectural structure, the building will be little more than a slick polished box, covering eight acres. Inside the box it is somewhat more interesting, with whole buildings hanging from its sides, some of them moving up and down and in and out like suspended file drawers, mating with one another to form still other buildings within buildings to house the space vehicles.

"Still, as an architectural creation, it is very little different from other buildings. But we have solved some intriguing technical problems created by the monstrous size. For instance, more than 50,000 tons of structural steel will be needed in the VAB's [Vehicle Assembly Building's] framework, enough for more than 30,000 automobiles. The heaviest members we designed will weigh 734 pounds per linear foot and are larger than any steel sections ever rolled before. Launchings can create acoustical pressures of up to 145 decibels on the skin surfaces of the building, and the skin must resist it.

"We were faced with the fascinating possibility that the shape of the building might make it react like an immense box kite, and it could blow away in a high wind. We had to design pile foundations that would prevent that.

"Inside the building we had to find ways not only to get at and work on vehicles many hundreds of feet high, but to provide work areas that could be air conditioned and sealed against dust. We devised moveable work platforms that are, in effect, small self-contained buildings, some three stories high, that move around and enclose the vehicle. The compartments move vertically and horizontaly. The tolerances, when they meet and join together, are three sixteenths of an inch.

"But these were merely technical problems. What was difficult was the administrative problem of allowing for smooth and continuous communication between several hundred professional architects, engineers and designers, each of whom was working on a small, interlocking part of the whole.

"The job was completed within nine months. The paperwork alone was monumental. Approximately 2,500 separate drawings were submitted. The final specifications drawn up and duplicated for the firms who bid on construction took a carload to deliver from the printer.

"What we learned from this endeavor was the new and challenging technique of designing structures for optimum efficiency as machines, as well as for people. The structure is not so much a building to house a moon vehicle in construction, as a machine to assemble a moon craft."

Site clearing for the VAB began in November, 1962. More than 1.5 million cubic yards of soil were pumped up from a channel just southeast of the area, raising the land to an average height of seven feet above sea level. In this channel, rocket-bearing barges bring Saturn stages to the front door of the structure in which they are assembled.

Florida turf is not noted for its stability. Under the construction site were layers of sand and compacted shell. Obviously, some form of beneath-the-earth support was necessary, otherwise the building, with all its thousands of tons of steel framework, would literally sink into the ground. About 120 feet down there was a three-foot-thick layer of limestone shelf. Below this was stiff clay and silt running down to solid limestone bedrock at about 160 feet. It was decided to pile drive steel tubings to this bedrock and anchor the concrete foundation of the building over these tubings. For months, workmen pounded these steel roots—4,225 of them—into the ground. In all, 680,000 linear feet (128 miles) of the hollow tubings were driven, and filled with sand to within a foot of the top. Concrete caps were built around clusters of six to 20 pilings. The pilings served not only to keep the building from sinking, but also to anchor it in the high winds that frequent the Spaceport area, particularly during hurricane seasons.

More than 30,000 cubic yards of concrete were poured into the foundation of the VAB, covering eight acres. This was necessary when designers discovered, following wind tunnel tests, that the entire structure might blow over during a tropical storm if more conventional building methods had been used. Pile driving and foundation work was done by the Blount Brothers Corporation, Montgomery, Alabama.

Next came the framework. The skeleton of the VAB consists of 60,000 tons of structural steel. There are more than 45,000 separate pieces of steel welded in the building, each weighing from 150 pounds to 72,000 pounds. These members are fastened with over one million high-strength bolts. It took nearly a year just to get the steel delivered to the Spaceport. It had to be shipped to the port at Tampa, on Florida's west coast, and laboriously trucked across state.

To mold the Spaceport, literal armies of construction tradesmen were assembled. Some of the nation's most skilled iron workers were recruited by the American Bridge Division of U.S. Steel for the erection of the steel framework, which began in January, 1964. These men were human flies as they lifted, bolted, and welded steel beams higher and higher, until the workers looked like mere specks against the sky. High winds blew and hot sun beat down upon them. It was, at times, a dangerous job to straddle a thin ribbon of steel 300, 400,

500 feet up. There were injuries and deaths. A few workmen fell. Others were hit by falling objects. But onward and upward they pushed, until the last beam was in place and the building was topped out in April, 1965.

Paneling of the VAB, exclusive of its doors, includes 23 acres of insulated aluminum siding and 70,000 square feet of light-emitting plastic panels. This siding is designed not only to stabilize thermal effects, but also to reduce the sound pressures created by the launch of a moon rocket.

Statistics on just the doors of the Vehicle Assembly Building are enough to defy imagination. They form the outer wall to each of the four high bay areas, as well as the entranceways to the north and south ends of the VAB. Each high bay door is 456 feet in height, taller than St. Peter's Cathedral in Rome or the Los Angeles City Hall. They are shaped in the form of an inverted "T," and each one has seven leaves, or sections. It takes 45 minutes to open or close one high bay door.

Inside each high bay there are five pairs of extensible work platforms which serve much the same purpose as the service structure or gantries do at Cape Kennedy on fixed launch complexes. In the VAB, these platforms provide air-conditioned areas for technicians

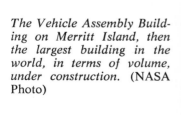

The Vehicle Assembly Building on Merritt Island, then the largest building in the world, in terms of volume, under construction. (NASA Photo)

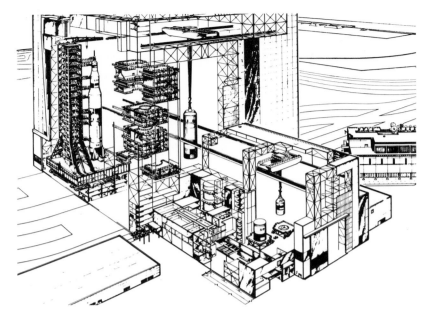

Cutaway view of the Vehicle Assembly Building. To the left is the high bay area, with facilities for assembly and checkout of Saturn V stages; instrument unit and Apollo spacecraft. The low bay area contains eight stage preparation and checkout cells. (Courtesy of NASA)

conveniently to reach any part of the assembled rocket and space-craft. They are 60 by 60 feet, one, two, and three stories tall, and are both vertically and horizontally adjustable to encircle the Saturn V.

There are 141 various lifting devices in the building, running from one-ton hoists to the two huge, 250-ton bridge cranes which lift the heavy rocket stages into place from hook heights of 462 feet. Contract specifications stated that the large cranes must hold a load for up to 30 minutes without moving it more than 1/32nd of an inch. Such close tolerances are required for proper mating of Saturn V stages and the Apollo spacecraft. Operators have become so adept at handling the cranes, they can lower a load weighing several tons so as to touch the top of a raw egg without cracking the shell!

There are 17 elevators in the VAB, including two enclosed in glass paneling. There is also enough air-conditioning equipment—10,000 tons of it—to cool the 800,000 square feet of floor area in the building, including offices and extensible work platforms. This amount of air conditioning would suffice for more than 3,000 homes. A utility annex houses air-conditioning, water, and electrical equipment.

The VAB is so large that designers had to consider the possibility that clouds could form inside, causing condensation and fogging, if not rain. To prevent this, a gravity ventilation system effects a complete change of air every hour through 125 ventilators on the roof. More than 3,000 white collar workers occupy the tiers of offices that have been built into the VAB.

Construction of the building, under the joint venture firm of the Morrison-Knudsen Company, Inc., Perini Corporation, and Paul Hardeman, Inc., South Gate, California, was essentially completed early in 1966. Its final measurements were almost beyond immediate comprehension. Overall, the VAB is 525 feet high, 716 feet long, and 518 feet wide. It encloses 129,482,000 cubic feet of space, and has 343,500 square feet of floor space. By comparison, the Pentagon encloses 77 million cubic feet, and the Great Pyramid of Cheops, Egypt, 90 million. Four football games could be played on the floor of the building simultaneously, with room left over. There are 60,000 tons of steel in the Empire State Building. The VAB has 98,590 tons, with 60,000 tons in structure framework alone. The building is just 30 feet shorter than the Washington Monument.

Despite its vastness and boxlike appearance, the structure is completely hurricane proof, capable of withstanding winds up to 125 miles per hour. By nature of its design and dimensions, the VAB sways in strong gusts of wind. It can sway up to 12 inches in a full-bore hurricane.

The VAB does not appear to be the massive facility it is. From a distance, it looms large on the horizon, but certainly does not impress visitors as being the largest building in the world, which it was when construction was completed. Rather, from five or 10 miles away, it appears to be just an oversized building. But once inside, there is no longer any doubt as to its immensity. From the floor of the transfer aisle, one peers up at the seemingly endless steel crossbars until the neck is tilted straight back in a horizontal position.

There is an impression, as architect Max Urbahn said, that the building is more nearly a machine. There is life inside its great walls; there is action, motion, noise, vibration, activity. There is never silence. Cranes swing, elevators bob, work platforms move, phones ring, girders groan, paging systems blare, air-conditioning equipment hums; there is sound and motion everywhere. Rocket stages are

Apollo 4, first space vehicle in the Apollo/Saturn V program, leaves the Vehicle Assembly Building for erection at Pad A of Complex 39. The 363-foot, three-stage rocket and spacecraft, on its mobile launcher, is being moved by the transporter over the special crawlerway to the launch pad. (NASA Photo)

hoisted and swung into place. They are mated together and tested and retested.

In round figures, the VAB cost more than $100 million to build, but it is an investment that will pay the United States dividends in space for decades to come. For within its confines, man's most advanced creations will be prepared for exploration of outer space.

The VAB can no longer lay claim, however, to being the world's largest building. That distinction now belongs to one constructed for the Boeing Aircraft Company, with headquarters in Seattle, Washington. To manufacture the largest jet airliner, the 231-foot-long 747, Boeing built an entire new plant complex at Everett, Washington, 30 miles north of Seattle. The huge structure, in two sections, encloses a volume of approximately 160 million cubic feet—over 30 million more than the Vehicle Assembly Building. The structure is only 115 feet high, however.

The brain of the mobile launch concept is the Launch Control Center. It connects with the VAB on the southeast over a long hallway. In itself, the LCC is an impressive architectural structure, but it is almost lost in the shadow of the Vehicle Assembly Building. Construction began in March, 1964. Exterior walls at the first floor level are recessed to form an arcade around the LCC. Walls are sheathed in precast architectural concrete panels surfaced in dark granite strips. Remainder of the building is surfaced predominantly in exposed cast-in-place architectural concrete. The design of the Launch Control Center was as advanced as are the missions performed inside it. The LCC, in fact, won the 1965 Architectural Award for the Industrial Design of the Year. It is a four-story structure, 378 feet long, 181 feet wide, and 76 feet high, covering 213,900 square feet. The building includes a number of offices, shops, laboratories, and supply areas. Like the Vehicle Assembly Building, the LCC was designed by Urbahn-Roberts-Seelye-Moran, and construction was under the direction of Morrison-Knudsen, Perini, and Hardeman.

Heart of the LCC and of all Saturn V launch operations is on the third floor. There, in a row, are four nearly identical firing rooms, each 80 feet by 140 feet and two stories high. There is one firing room for each of the four high bay areas in the VAB. Thus, theoretically, four moon rockets could be worked on at the same time by four different launch crews, although to date only three of the rooms and three high bays in the VAB have been outfitted.

Each firing room serves all the same purposes as the blockhouses across the Banana River at Cape Kennedy. Flight preparations from the time rocket stages arrive at KSC, through checkout, testing, transportation from the VAB to the pad, countdown and liftoff, are controlled in the firing rooms, three and a half miles from where the vehicles are launched.

The location of the LCC at such a distance from the pad area was made possible by rapid developments in automated checkout systems. Over the years, as man and machine progressed with each launch, there has been a gradual switchover to computer techniques rather than manual operations. This cuts down the human error element somewhat, though engineers must still program the computers. But, more important, as the rockets and their missions became larger and more complex, so did the preflight preparations. With Saturn V, the evolution from manual to automatic operations becomes virtually complete. This was made necessary by the great numbers of functions which must be verified and measured simultaneously.

Checkout data is transmitted from the LCC to the bird either in the VAB or on the pad via a high-speed digital data link system over coaxial cable. This is made possible through the use of two RCA

110-A computers. The master unit is located in a specially air-conditioned area at the rear of each firing room. Slave units are housed wherever the assembled rocket is—VAB or pad—on a Mobile Launcher tower. Through a data link, the computer at the rear of the firing room controls the operations of the slave unit. It stores Saturn V test programs in its memory unit and relays these routines to the second computer, which, in turn, stores the diagnostic and maintenance routines for the rocket, and relays the test stimuli through electrical support equipment to the appropriate stage system.

The imput response to the computer from the tested item is compared against a predetermined value. If it is OK, the computer goes on to the next checkout item. If the data received does not meet predescribed standards, however, the slave unit relays this to the master computer and asks for instructions. If the malfunction is a common one, one that can be anticipated, the 110-A in the firing room sends back a corrective command.

The computers are used for preflight checkout of the launch vehicle's multiple stages. The firing room unit sends messages to the slave unit, commanding the opening or closing of switches and valves. Readings of temperatures, voltages, and pressures are made on board the vehicle and transmitted back to the proper display console via the computer route. A separate system, to be discussed later, is used for the Apollo spacecraft.

Man is still very much involved, however, in the overall checkout process. Automation gives the technicians, engineers, test conductors and launch directors the information they need at their consoles in the control center about conditions on board the rocket, whether it is in the VAB or on the pad. But it is still the men, not the computers, who make the final decisions during the countdown.

The system is designed to "keep man in the loop" at all important decision points. In the event of computer system failure for any reason, alternative command links are available to place rocket systems in "safe" configurations until the computers can be restored to service.

Also, many test procedures do not lend themselves readily to automation. For these, the console operators control the test progress through operation of switches on the firing room consoles. Other test procedures can be completely automated in such a way that men need only start the test and leave the rest to the computer.

Basically, three things are achieved with automation: repeatability, complete predefinition of test procedures, and economy of test time.

Once the computer is told what to do, it will perform complex tests in exactly the same way every time the tests are made. The computer also runs these tests in a fraction of the time required to conduct them using former methods. Hundreds of test programs are used, some requiring only a few seconds to complete, others lasting as long as 20 or 30 minutes.

Many Spaceport engineers remember the "good old days" when hard wire was used for every function and measurement conducted between the blockhouse and vehicle. Unfortunately, this becomes impractical in a bird as large and complex as Saturn V, because there are so many different functions that have to be monitored and controlled over such a long distance.

There were about 50 engineers and technicians shoehorned in the small blockhouse at Complex 26 the night Explorer I was launched in January, 1958. Each man had a specific job to do, but he also had to be versatile, and often performed tasks far outside his specialization as prelaunch conditions dictated. For Apollo/Saturn V flights, the firing room in use is packed with more than 450 men, and none of them is a jack-of-all-trades. Each one is a skilled specialist—in propulsion, guidance, radio frequency, etc.

There are, by actual count, 218 individual console positions and 238 separate measurement racks in each firing room. Each individual console is a literal maze of lights, buttons, dials, switches, gauges, panels, and phones. Some are equipped with tiny TV monitors. At the head of each firing room are four rows of consoles rising on elevated tiers. There are 10 consoles on the top row which overlooks, with a commanding view, the entire room. Here, the Center director, the launch director, launch vehicle director, and spacecraft director sit, along with the KSC director of technical support, program manager, an Air Force Eastern Test Range representative, and a public information officer. These men include the Center's top decision makers. If a major problem develops leading up to a launch, they are the final level of authority. They are the policy makers. Behind them are hard decades of experience. Some of these men have been in rocketry for more than a quarter of a century. There are virtually no problems involving launching a rocket that they have not, at some point in their careers, been faced with and solved.

The next line of consoles down is the major operational one. Here, the space vehicle test supervisor and launch operations manager, the men who direct the countdown, are flanked by rocket and spacecraft test conductors. In front of them are consoles occupied by the test conductors of the companies who built each stage of the rocket. When men are aboard the Apollo/Saturn V, additional positions in the firing room will be manned by the astronaut communicator and by aeromedical personnel.

On the fourth row from the top are positions for pad safety, range safety, flight dynamics, technical commentary, data display controls, and instrumentation controller personnel. Consoles on the main floor have been designed for first, second, and third stage and instrument unit propulsion and networks; stability and guidance; umbilical swing arms; flight control and mechanical ground support equipment; measurement and radio frequency; and propellants.

The eight rows of instrumentation or measurement racks that extend to the end of the firing room record various ground functions, such as liquid oxygen line pressure, flow rate, pump bearing temperature, and other items for each stage of the space vehicle.

High over the fifth row of consoles are four large visual displays. Test supervisors, test conductors, and systems engineers can see many kinds of data displayed on these. This data can come from the rocket and ground support equipment during prelaunch tests and launch. Trajectory and vehicle data can be displayed in the postlaunch period.

The information can be shown in alpha numeric listings, graphs, realtime plots, and many other forms. It is also possible to flash closed circuit television scenes from any of the dozens of TV cameras throughout Complex 39. To the left of these screens is a large Functional Event Display, tied in through electrical networks. This lists 47 key countdown milestones and major post-liftoff events.

When such items as "instrument unit ready" and "first stage fuel tank pressurized" are passed in the count, a green light will flash in the appropriate place on this board. There is a similar board and system on the right side of the firing room for additional milestones and events.

Scattered throughout the room are large countdown clocks, which tick off seconds in Eastern Standard and Greenwich Mean Time. There are also clocks for indicating the precise liftoff time and for recording hold time.

If steel and concrete form the skeleton and muscle of Launch Complex 39, then the communications and electronics systems are the eyes, ears, and nerves. Every imaginable sort of telephone and instrumentation cable, wave guide, and coaxial and video cable crisscrosses the length and breadth of the complex to form the communications network.

Launch team personnel use two critical communications and control systems throughout the checkout cycle of a rocket and spacecraft. One is the operational intercom system, and the other is the operational television system. There are 2,000 dual operator stations throughout the area on the intercom setup, including ones at each of the two pads, on each Mobile Launcher, and in each equipped firing room of the LCC and high bay area of the VAB.

There are 112 different communications channels available to key personnel during major tests. This is nearly triple the number used on Saturn I launches at Cape Kennedy. The need for additional channels stems from the fact there are more people in "the loop," more stages on the vehicle, and more support personnel. Each station has a capability of operating on two of the 112 channels, and thus communicating with all other stations on the channel in the same area and mission.

The operational television system provides remote viewing of launch activities from virtually any point on the complex, between the VAB and the pad. During a mission, 50 cameras in the pad area supply pictures to 80 monitor screens in the firing room. Overall, there are 114 cameras and 255 monitors throughout the complex, complete with highly complicated switching, signal transmission and distribution, and synchronization systems.

At the southwest corner of each firing room is a large glass-paneled viewing area. Distinguished guests sit here during launch countdowns. Opposite this is an operations management room. At the east end of each firing room are laminated glass windows, measuring 80 feet long by 22 feet high. They are protected by center-pivoted power operated louvers, and they reduce sound transmission into the room to normal audible levels during rocket blastoffs.

It was an ironic fact of life in the past that launch team members could never see the bird they had labored over so carefully when it lifted off. The closeness of blockhouses to the pad precluded this. But with the LCC three and a half miles away, the men can now view the fruition of their efforts—through the firing room windows.

This, then, is the Vehicle Assembly Building and the Launch Control Center at Complex 39. The VAB is the home of the rockets during their months of preflight inspection, assembly, checkout, and testing. The LCC is the brain center of the entire cycle. From the time Saturn V stages arrive at the Kennedy Space Center until they are launched, all their operations are controlled from one of the four firing rooms.

Chapter 14

TOWERS AND TRANSPORTERS

The second, or slave, computer that connects with the master unit in the firing room is located in a 445-foot-tall red tower of steel called the Mobile Launcher. It is one of the essential keys to the mobile launch concept at the Kennedy Space Center, replacing the service structures and umbilical towers used at the Cape. Under the new concept, Saturn V rocket stages are placed, one atop another, onto the base of a Mobile Launcher in one of the VAB's high bay areas. Then, when the vehicle is ready to be taken to the pad, it moves out still mounted. At the pad, this entire package remains intact, and the rocket lifts off the launcher, which is then refurbished and readied to go back to the Vehicle Assembly Building for another load. Exhaust is funneled down through a large hole in the launcher and is dispersed by a flame deflector.

NASA authorized the construction of three of these versatile towers. Work began on the first in December, 1963. Ingalls Ironworks of Birmingham, Alabama, was the prime contractor for steel erection. As with other facts of the lunar complex, the Mobile Launchers' statistics are impressive. At more than 11.5 million pounds each, they are the heaviest portable steel structures in the Free World. Picture three Washington Monuments standing side by side, and you have a fair idea of how they look when parked outside the VAB.

Work on the towers was done in three phases. Erection of the structural steel began in 1963, and the three launchers were topped out, respectively, in September, 1964, December, 1964, and March, 1965. The second phase of the work, the installation of mechanical and electrical systems, began in December, 1963, and was completed in May, 1966. The installation of ground support and miscellaneous equipment, including swing arms that would connect to the rocket, began in June, 1965, and was finished in 1967.

Each launch platform measures 135 feet by 160 feet and is 25 feet high. There are two levels inside them, containing rooms and five compartments, including a mechanical equipment room, an operations support area, communications and television equipment, the slave computer, system test sets, propellant loading equipment, electrical equipment racks, and engine hydraulic service units.

Actually, the three structures serve both as launch platforms, and as the umbilical towers to the Apollo/Saturn V. Each tower, based on the platform, rises 398 feet and is topped by a hammerhead crane. Two elevators transport technicians and equipment to 16 work platforms and the swing arms.

Nine swing arms extend from the umbilical tower to the rocket, allowing technicians entrance to the vehicle at various levels. Astronauts board the Apollo spacecraft from the topmost arm, 320 feet above the launch platform. The arms also support propellant lines used in fueling the rocket and carry electrical and pneumatic feeds from the ground into the bird. Two of the arms are for the booster, three for the second stage, two for the third stage, including the instrument unit and lunar module, and two for the Apollo. These arms, which breathe life support into the rocket through propellant, pneumatic, and electrical lines, vary in length from 45 to 60 feet and weigh between 35,000 and 52,000 pounds. Hydraulic systems pull them back against the tower when ignition of the rocket engines occurs. Five of the nine swing arms disengage and pull free of the vehicle against the tower some time before liftoff. The other four swing back upon first vertical motion of the rocket after ignition.

Design of the arms was a feat worthy of mention in itself. They were much larger and heavier than the swing arms which have been used at Launch Complexes 34 and 37 on the Saturn I series of vehicles. Their retraction must occur from two to five seconds after first motion to avoid deflecting the giant space vehicle as it thunders upward. Extensive tests had to be run before this key part of the liftoff sequence was perfected.

There were other design problems of an unusual nature. The Mobile Launchers are used time and again and are often moved between the VAB and the pad area. And they are exposed to tremendous heat, shock, and vibration pressures when 7.5 million pounds of

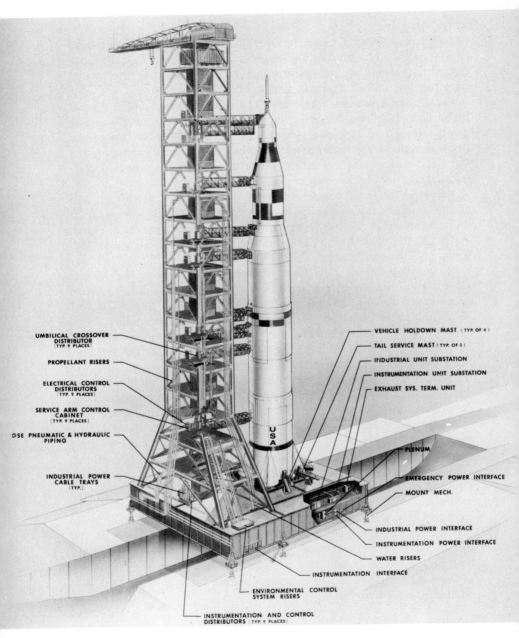

UMBILICAL CROSSOVER
DISTRIBUTOR
(TYP. 9 PLACES)

PROPELLANT RISERS

ELECTRICAL CONTROL
DISTRIBUTORS
(TYP. 9 PLACES)

SERVICE ARM CONTROL
CABINET
(TYP. 9 PLACES)

GSE PNEUMATIC & HYDRAULIC
PIPING

INDUSTRIAL POWER
CABLE TRAYS
(TYP.)

VEHICLE HOLDOWN MAST (TYP. OF 4)

TAIL SERVICE MAST (TYP. OF 3)

INDUSTRIAL UNIT SUBSTATION

INSTRUMENTATION UNIT SUBSTATION

EXHAUST SYS. TERM. UNIT

PLENUM

EMERGENCY POWER INTERFACE

MOUNT MECH.

INDUSTRIAL POWER INTERFACE

INSTRUMENTATION POWER INTERFACE

WATER RISERS

INSTRUMENTATION INTERFACE

ENVIRONMENTAL CONTROL
SYSTEM RISERS

INSTRUMENTATION AND CONTROL
DISTRIBUTORS (TYP. 9 PLACES)

USA

Mobile launcher for Apollo/Saturn V at Complex 39, Pad A ("Typ."
—Typical). (Courtesy of NASA)

rocket thrust roar to life. These factors had to be considered in their creation, for sensitive electronic and electrical equipment mounted in the base of each tower had to be protected against damage during movement or launch and during the months of checkout and servicing operations in between.

One of the few fixed features of the mobile launch concept is the concrete pad area. There are two virtually identical octagonal-shaped pads at Complex 39, A and B, 8,716 feet apart. Each covers about one quarter square mile. Pad A is three and a half miles from the Vehicle Assembly Building; Pad B is about four miles from it.

Pad A construction began in November, 1963. The area lies so close to the Atlantic Ocean, and the land is so marshy, that thousands of tons of dredged fill had to be pumped onto the site from the Banana River, resulting in an 80-foot-high pyramid of sand weighing 1.5 billion pounds. This settled the pad site about four feet. The fill was then removed, and the building started. Pad A was constructed by the Blount Brothers Corporation and the M. M. Sundt Company

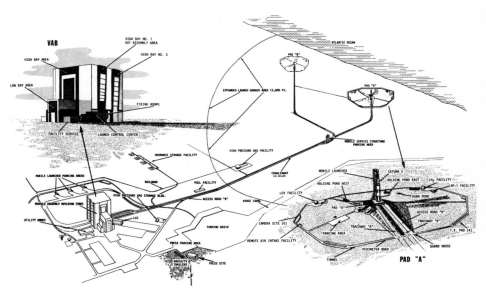

Map of Launch Complex 39, John F. Kennedy Space Center. (Courtesy of NASA)

of Montgomery, Alabama. Pad B's contractor was the George A. Fuller Company, Los Angeles.

The design differed drastically from that of conventional launch pads at the Cape. Two semicircular concrete structures were built, rising to a point 42 feet above the ground. They are 400 feet long and 40 feet wide and are divided down the center of the pad by an open flame trench. Beneath the cellular structure and the flame trench is a concrete mat 11 feet thick, 150 feet wide, and 450 feet long.

Major facilities at each pad include the concrete hardstand, a pad terminal connection room, environmental control system room, high pressure gas storage area, flame trench and apron, and an emergency egress system. Surrounding the pad are various other supporting structures, such as liquid oxygen, liquid hydrogen and RP-1 fuel storage sites, propellant holding ponds, and camera pads.

On the hardstand are service towers to provide connections between pad facilities and the Mobile Launcher for liquid oxygen, liquid hydrogen, RP-1 fuel, electrical power and communications, compressed air and environmental control systems. Also at the hardstand are support pedestals for the Mobile Launcher. During a Saturn V liftoff, the launcher is supported by six permanent legs and four additional extendable arms that are temporarily fastened to the bottom of the launcher platform and the pad to take the dynamic loads and the rebound at liftoff.

Considerable effort was put into the design for the dispersion of Saturn V's tremendous fire created at launch. The 450-foot-long flame trench, which bisects the center of the pad, has floors and walls protected with a refractory brick surface that can withstand temperatures up to 3,000 degrees F. Just before each flight a rail system brings the 1.3-million-pound flame deflector into place at the base of the trench and directly beneath the rocket's five massive F-1 booster engines. It is down the inverted V of the deflector that the long fire streamers of Saturn V shoot.

The pad terminal connection room houses electronic equipment providing a connecting link for communication and digital data link transmission lines from the Launch Control Center to the Mobile Launcher when it is on the pad. The Environmental Control Systems Room serves as a distribution point for conditioning and purge gases. Nitrogen and helium, used for pressurizing electrical and water systems, are stored in the high pressure gas storage facility, under the top of the pad on the east side of the flame trench.

Liquid oxygen (lox) is stored in a 900,000-gallon tank, 1,450 feet from the pad. Pumps transfer this oxidizer to the vehicle at a maximum rate of 10,000 gallons per minute. A similar 850,000-gallon tank is used for liquid hydrogen storage. RP-1, the Saturn V's basic first-stage fuel, is kept in a 258,000-gallon tank. Its maximum pump rate is 2,000 gpm. All propellant loading operations are remotely controlled from the LCC.

A Saturn V launch pad at liftoff of a moon rocket resembles a miniature Niagara Falls. Up to 45,000 gallons of water per minute are poured onto the facility by a special deluge system, even as the bird's flames are still beating down upon the flame deflector. This cooling action helps hold down fire damage.

One of the most interesting features of the pad area, and in fact, of the entire lunar launch complex, is the emergency egress system. Astronauts have two modes of escape should there be trouble on the pad while they are in the Apollo spacecraft, atop the Saturn V rocket. If a problem develops without warning that might endanger their lives, the launch escape tower will fire, yanking the manned capsule up and away from the bird. Parachutes will float it gently back to earth, where the astronauts will be quickly recovered by specialized teams that began training before the first Mercury flight in May, 1961.

On a hazardous condition where launch directors feel there is sufficient time, perhaps a slow propellant leak, or an automatic shutdown of the booster stage after ignition, as happened to Wally Schirra and Tom Stafford on Gemini 6, the built-in emergency egress system may be used.

The astronauts would leave their spacecraft, cross over to the Mobile Launcher on a swing arm, and then ride a high-speed elevator 30 stories down. They then would jump into the opening of a 170-foot-long, sliding boardlike chute, down which they would skid at 30 miles an hour, like logs in a lumber flue. The chute ends in a thickly padded rubber wall far below the concrete pad. There, they would enter a blast-proof room, designed to withstand an on-the-pad explosion of the entire space vehicle, and to keep astronauts alive for 24 hours or more to allow rescue crews time to dig them out should such a catastrophic event occur. Entry to the room is through a six-inch-thick door of steel much like that of a bank vault.

The sealed-off room, surrounded by reinforced concrete, has thickly padded seats and balances on a cushion of springs which would help absorb blast forces up to 56 times the pull of gravity. The emergency egress system may also be used by spacecraft technicians who tuck the astronauts into Apollo. They are among the last men to clear the pad before liftoff. It takes only three or four minutes to reach the sanctuary of the explosion-proof room from the top of the rocket.

The entire system—elevator, chute, and room—will be one of the least used facilities at the complex. Officials hope it will never be used. Still, with human life involved, no chance can be taken, no expense spared. Should the need arise, a fast escape route is available.

When the fully assembled Apollo/Saturn V space vehicle, mounted atop its Mobile Launcher, is on the pad at Complex 39, a mountainous scaffold of steel, 402 feet high and weighing 9.8 million pounds, is brought up to wrap immense work platform "arms" around the spacecraft. This is the Mobile Service Structure. It is another key element of the new launch concept used at NASA's Spaceport.

Fabrication of the MSS steel framework began in October, 1964, and construction by Morrison-Knudsen, Perini, and Hardeman was completed in July, 1966. This huge, derricklike structure was originally designed for workmen to install potentially hazardous ordnance items on the rocket and spacecraft at the pad. Later, it was decided most such installations could be safely made inside the Vehicle Assembly Building. The main purpose of the Mobile Service Structure today is to provide virtually complete working access to the top levels of the Saturn V and Apollo at the pad via its five work platforms, which are cantilevered from the forward plane of the tower. These are opened as the MSS approaches the pad, and then embrace the space vehicle once the structure is in place.

Most of the work performed from these air-conditioned platforms involves the spacecraft and launch escape tower. The MSS carries the great bulk of Apollo's propellant, pneumatic, and electrical lines from ground systems to spacecraft level. Hypergolic and cryogenic propellants for the capsule, for instance, are loaded through MSS facilities. They also allow technicians external access to a few items on the launch vehicle that are not reachable from the Mobile Launcher's swing arms.

A variety of buildings are provided on the base working level of the MSS for electrical, mechanical, elevator, communications and television equipment, and operations support. Once its job at the pad has been completed, the Mobile Service Structure is carried back to a park position a safe distance from the pad.

One of the thorniest problems design engineers tackled in creating the mobile launch concept was to find the actual means of transportation that would take the fully assembled moon rocket and its Mobile Launcher from the VAB to the pad. The problem was compounded by the sheer size and weight of the load to be carried, roughly 12 million pounds! Also, it would have to move in an upright position.

Many ideas were considered. One that received a lot of attention was a barge and canal system, where the rocket and launcher would be floated to the pad. Merritt Island's water table is only six feet, and at one point it looked as though NASA might choose this mode of conveyance. But tests were run and proved negative. They revealed that a barge carrying the Saturn V would be unstable.

Rails were also given serious consideration. The Air Force later was to prove this a feasible idea when they successfully employed it in their Titan III-C program. But Titan nowhere nearly approached the immense size of the Saturn V or the Mobile Launcher. To haul such a load by rail, studies showed, would be prohibitively expensive. Another way would have to be found.

Some thoughts were perhaps more imaginative than practical, yet bold ventures often call for bold new concepts. Among other methods discussed were such things as a transporter with pneumatic tires, and a ground effect machine, such as a hovercraft.

Then someone brought up the possibility of using a machine similar to the huge vehicles employed in Kentucky surface coal mining operations. These used huge, tanklike treads, much like those of a bulldozer. At first, this appeared "far out," but as other types of transporting were ruled against, one by one, this crawler-transporter began to look more and more promising. Studies proved that it could be modified and developed to carry the Saturn V at a reasonably low rate.

Engineers finally decided to choose this huge land vehicle as the means of movement on July 25, 1962, and contracts for two of the monsters were soon after awarded to the Marion Power Shovel Company of Marion, Ohio. Each transporter was so big it had to be assembled at the plant and then taken apart in movable sections before being shipped to the Spaceport, and reassembled there.

Certainly, these are two of the strangest-looking creations of the space age. Each weighs about six million pounds, is 131 feet long, 114 feet wide, and has an adjustable height of from 20 to 26 feet. Each is powered by two 2,750 horsepower diesel engines, which drive four 1,000-kilowatt generators, providing electrical power to 16 traction motors. Through gears, these motors turn the four double-tracked crawlers, spaced 90 feet apart at each corner of the trans-

One of the two cabs from which the huge transporter for Apollo/Saturn V is controlled. (NASA Photo)

porter. Each of the eight treads is seven feet six inches wide and 41 feet three inches long, and each link in the tread weighs about one ton.

A separate power system provides AC power for the load leveling, jacking, steering, ventilating, and electronic systems aboard. This system has two diesel engines of 1,065 horsepower each and two generators of 750 kilowatts each. There are two driver cabs on opposite corners of each machine so they can be driven in each direction. Inside the cabs are the most unusual speedometers in the world. They have only two numbers on them—one mile per hour and two mph. Maximum speed of the transporters is two mph when empty, half that when carrying the rocket and launcher. Steering is done by means of electronically controlled hydraulic systems. Minimum turning radius is 500 feet.

In motion, two cab operators, working as part of a team of six engineers, steer the transporter. It cannot be operated by one man alone. The "drivers," who work with ground observers, besides controlling the speed, steering, and braking, cannot see anything behind them or anything on the opposite side of the vehicle. They have to rely on the ground crew, who communicate with the cab operators via walkie-talkies and intercom systems. Reliance on other members of the team is also critical for engineers in the control room, inside, who jack and level the launch towers, rockets and the Mobile Service Structure on top of the transporter. In addition to carrying the Saturn V and launcher, the transporter also moves the MSS into position on the pad.

Balancing a 12-million-pound load calls for precise engineering. The motion of the transporter, the sheer height and weight of the load, variances in the level of the roadway, wind, and other factors combine to throw the cargo off balance. To maintain stability, an elaborate leveling system was designed into the transporter. It is keyed on two manometers, or pressure-measuring devices, located just under the topside deck. The manometers are mercury-filled tubes, each about 135 feet long, which stretch diagonally from corner to corner, crisscrossing like a large X.

Changes in the level of the vehicle's load create a pressure which is sensed by the manometers. An engineer notes these changes in pressure and keeps the load level by raising or lowering any of the transporter's four corners. If the chassis is out of level by as little as one-half inch, the engineer takes corrective action. This may happen hundreds of times during the three-and-a-half-mile trip from the Vehicle Assembly Building to the pad. A level platform within 10 minutes of arc must be maintained at all times. The leveling system is particularly critical when the transporter moves its load up the five degree incline at the pad.

When the rocket and Mobile Launcher are ready to be picked up inside the VAB for the trip to the pad, the transporter slips under the launcher's platform and raises it from pedestals with 16 hydraulic jacks. It is capable of positioning its load on similar pedestals at the pad within a maximum deviation of two inches.

Like the family car, the transporter needs fuel, oil, grease, and coolant. Its fuel tank holds 5,000 gallons. A complete oil change requires 3,600 gallons of high grade oil. The vehicle's six radiators need over 500 gallons of water to keep the half dozen large diesel engines operating satisfactorily, and an automatic lubrication system continuously pumps grease into each of the 176 bearings that support the great weight it carries. On the road, the transporter burns 150 gallons of diesel fuel per mile. There are six mufflers on the vehicle, weighing 3,000 pounds each.

The first transporter was ready to move by the summer of 1965. Technicians started and warmed up six diesel engines, energized several dozen electrical circuits, started up three hydraulic systems, one pneumatic system, a fuel system, and two lubricating systems, and made several dozen checks called for in the 39-page start-up procedure manual. Tapered-pin roller bearings on the shafts of the unit's drive trucks cracked, however, and there were difficulties with the load leveling system. Many became skeptical of the entire concept. But with any new development, especially one as radically different and untested as this, such problems were anticipated. Engineers soon substituted new sleeve bearings and worked out all of the other bugs.

The transporter, along with the Saturn V and Mobile Launcher, makes a complete package weighing about 18 million pounds. Such a tremendous load would sink deeply into the marshy terrain at Launch Complex 39. Thus, a fortified roadbed, called the crawlerway, had to be built. It had to withstand loads in excess of 12,000 pounds per square foot. Actually, there was a variety of land conditions over the selected three-and-a-half-mile route from VAB to pad, including dry land, swamp, and sloughs. Preliminary borings made on dry land showed generally satisfactory subsurface material consisting mostly of fine sands extending down to 45 feet below sea level. In watery areas, soft silty sands and clays were found above the fine sands. From minus 40 feet to bedrock at 160 feet, the material was more or less compressible.

Thus began, in November, 1963, a colossal excavation job. The softer, unsuitable material was replaced with more than three million cubic yards of hydraulic sand fill. This was compacted with vibratory rollers and then proof-rolled with a 100-ton roller. Nearly seven feet of graded crushed aggregate base course and selected subbase material was added. This was topped with asphalt.

Work was completed in August, 1965. The crawlerway is 130 feet wide—two 40-foot lanes separated by a 50-foot grass median strip—about the same overall width as the New Jersey Turnpike. It is about 10 times stronger than the average big city jet airport runway. One major design change occurred following initial test runs. The smooth asphalt surface prevented the transporter's drive-trucks from finding their natural level, which placed extremely unequal loads on the shafts. This was solved by adding a layer of river rock imported from Alabama. Ironically, a simple farm machine, a spring-tooth harrow used in cultivating crops, has been found to be the best means of smoothing the rocks after the transporter has passed over them.

Paralleling the crawlerway on both sides are utility and pipe lines linking the VAB and LCC with the pads. Communication and instrumentation lines are placed in ductbanks buried along the north side of the road.

As the Spaceport was being built, so, too, were the Apollo spacecraft and Saturn V stages being fashioned at plant sites across the country, from Bethpage, New York, to Downey, California, and at many points in between. Coordination of the construction efforts and of the planned shipments and arrivals of stages at KSC was a monumental job in itself. Facilities would have to be ready on time to receive the stages. If one contractor fell behind on the job, the entire project could be delayed. And there were so many contractors, doing so many things at one time, there was obvious need for a master coordination center. NASA provided this with its Site Activation Board.

A management system called PERT (Program Evaluation Review Technique) was used. It had also been employed during development of the Navy's Polaris Fleet Ballistic Missile program. Under it, computer analyses were updated every two weeks to direct proper management attention to those areas spotlighted as presenting potential problems, such as faulty planning, delays in completion of contracts, and scheduling conflicts. At the program peak, the PERT system was handling about 40,000 individual packages of significant work activities.

An Equipment Record System that kept track of 63,000 contract end items was set up in conjunction with PERT. ERS provided up-to-date information on delivery schedules of all equipment required to outfit Launch Complex 39. Anticipated delivery dates were compared by computer with the "need date" defined in the PERT system. The computer printed out an exception list of all equipment not expected to be delivered by the date needed, and it also compared progress on the actual work schedules to the master plan and printed out a list of trouble areas that required special attention.

The Site Activation Board reviewed these problems, and its 32 members, NASA and contractor employees, developed "workarounds" where possible—engineering deviations from the original plan that would permit other work to continue. Through these efforts, the major components of Launch Complex 39 were readied essentially in time to begin handling Apollo and Saturn V. The board supervised the work of a tremendous task force of people and a large amount of equipment, and saw to it the job was properly coordinated and carried out on time.

The Vehicle Assembly Building, Launch Control Center, Mobile Launchers, Mobile Service Structure, Transporters, Crawlerway, Pads A and B, and the various outlying support facilities—these are the key elements that make up the mobile launch concept. This is the heart and nerve center of America's only Spaceport.

The entire system was put to the test on May 25, 1966, appropriately enough, five years to the day from the late President John F. Kennedy's pronouncement of a manned lunar landing national goal. Before the first flight version of the Saturn V rocket was shipped to the Spaceport, a full-scale model vehicle, called 500F, was first sent. Its purpose was to check the proper fitting of all components at Launch Complex 39, from the VAB's checkout cells to the Mobile Launcher and the pad. After assembly of the model's multiple stages in High Bay One, a transporter picked up the entire load for the trip to Pad A. It was a milestone event of major significance, and many of the nation's top space officials were at the Kennedy Space Center for the ceremonies, including Wernher von Braun and Dr. George E. Mueller, NASA Associate Administrator for Manned Space Flight.

Slowly, majestically, the transporter backed out of the VAB and began moving down the crawlerway, over a route that has been described as the first three and a half miles to the moon. It was a sight unseen before by mankind. It was like moving a 44-story building down the street. The successful trip took about nine hours from first motion until lockdown at the pad. Next came a series of fit checks to make sure the various propellant, pneumatic, and electrical lines, which run from the hardstand to connections on the Mobile Launcher, matched. Mechanical and electrical compatibility tests between the vehicle, launcher and ground support equipment and checkout systems were also run.

A major problem occurred during a propellant-loading test, when a liquid oxygen line broke and 800,000 gallons of lox poured out, causing damage to the storage tank. Repairs were made, more lox was ordered, and the loading tests continued during the several weeks the 500F was on the pad. The Mobile Service Structure was also brought up by the transporter for more fit checks and tests.

There was one unscheduled test, held under operational conditions, during the time 500F was on site. Launch team members had often worried about what would happen if a hurricane threatened when a Saturn V was three and a half miles from the security of the Vehicle Assembly Building, which was built to withstand winds up to 125 miles per hour. The plan called for moving the bird back into the VAB. It could not ride out a full-scale tropical storm on the pad.

Hurricane Alma, the first tropical storm of the 1966 season, put the plan to a realistic test, when it began hammering the south Florida coastline early in June. Center Director Kurt Debus decided it would be a good time to see how fast his crews could secure the rocket. Without warning, he ordered the move on June 8.

It took two hours to disconnect cables at the pad and secure the transporter, Mobile Launcher and 500F vehicle for the trip. By first motion, winds were blowing steadily at 32 mph with gusts to 57 mph. It took an hour to get down the pad's ramp, but then the transporter "revved up" to top-loaded speed of one mph down the crawlerway. Winds gusted to a peak 68 mph en route, and rain came down in horizontal sheets, but the move was made without any major problems. Debus' order had gone out at 1 P.M. At 12:37 A.M. the next morning, everything was tied down in the VAB's High Bay One. It had taken just over 11½ hours. The operational plan said the move had to be made in 12 hours.

After the storm passed, 500F was taken back to Pad A, and the exhaustive tests continued. When they were completed several weeks later, the Spaceport had gained complete confidence in all aspects of the mobile launch concept. Every element of it had now been tried under fire and declared workable. All doubts had been dispelled, all questions answered.

The Center was now ready to receive and launch its first Saturn V flight vehicle.

Today, there are about 23,000 employees at NASA's Spaceport on Merritt Island. Only about 12 percent are federal workers. The rest are on the payrolls of industrial companies which build the various rockets and spacecraft that are flown, and operate, under NASA supervision, the Center. As did the Air Force at Cape Kennedy, NASA has contracted out much of its support services to major aerospace companies. There are simply not enough civil service employees to perform all the tasks. Some of the prime contractors and their missions are:

—Trans World Airlines: general operations and maintenance of the Spaceport, including shops and field services, mail and postal service, roads and grounds, heavy equipment, mechanical and electrical utilities, supply operations, and janitorial services, among others. TWA was also first to conduct the daily escorted bus tours at KSC.

—The Wackenhut Corporation, under a subcontract to TWA, provides fire and security protection.

—Bendix Corporation: launch support services for Complex 39, ordnance storage, technical shop operations, propellant systems components laboratory, and other services.

—Federal Electric Corporation: planning, maintenance and operation of communications and electronic maintenance shops. FEC also supports the Center in prototype tracking, operating a central recorder station, mobile receiving stations, a transmitter information facility, launch control information centers, central timing station, calibration, and scientific computer operations.

—General Electric Company: services and materials for checkout, reliability and integration of launch equipment, including pneumatic, electrical, water, and propellant systems, vehicle ground support equipment, vehicle measurements, firing systems, and environmental control systems at Saturn Launch Complexes 34, 37 and 39.

—Ling-Temco-Vought: technical services, including technical information. Launch photography is subcontracted to the Technicolor Corporation, and reproduction services are performed under a subcontract to McGregor & Werner.

—Dow Chemical Company and Catalytic Construction Company: engineering services, including planning estimating, and preparation of design criteria; documenting design programs, and preparing reports on facility concepts and layouts.

In a move to strengthen Apollo/Saturn V system integration at Launch Complex 39, the Boeing Company, manufacturers of the rocket's booster, are also under contract for support of assembly and system integration of the Saturn V's stages.

In addition to the support personnel named, there are dozens of other companies represented among the stage contractors who manufacture the various components of rockets, spacecraft and ground support equipment used at the Center.

The NASA staff at the Spaceport has the job of integrating these multiple government and contractor organizations into a single team responsible for supporting and carrying out the major launch missions of America's space programs.

Chapter 15

TOWARD A LUNAR LANDING

Apollo is perhaps the most intrepid single project ever undertaken by man. It is doubtless the most adventurous step since Columbus set sail for the New World nearly five centuries ago, and signals the greatest technological advance since the beginning of civilization. When two American astronauts step out of the lunar module and down upon the surface of the moon, the combined teamwork of 300,000 highly skilled people will have reached its culmination; the dividends of more than $20 billion will have been received. Seldom if ever in world history has one country set itself such a demanding, and at times seemingly unreachable national goal. Seldom if ever have a nation's people responded with such enthusiasm and dedication in peacetime.

When John Fitzgerald Kennedy announced the target of landing Americans on the moon and returning them safely to earth, he set in motion probably the greatest engineering-scientific mission ever attempted.

In Greek mythology, Apollo was the god of light, and the twin brother of Artemis, goddess of the moon. Apollo was also known as the god of prophecy and the god of the embarker and disembarker—an appropriate name for America's boldest venture.

In the manned flight program of the United States, Apollo is the third and most advanced step. The first was Mercury, followed by Gemini. These were the training grounds for astronauts, leading to the effort to conquer the moon. By the books, Apollo has a triple objective, as announced by NASA in July, 1960:

1. To land American explorers on the moon and bring them safely back to earth.

2. To establish the technology required to meet other national interests in space.

3. To achieve for the United States preeminence in space.

Though man has dreamed about going to the moon for as long as he has roamed the earth, it has only been in the past decade that serious planning for such an epic voyage has been carried on. First, NASA had to decide the most feasible way to get there and back, keeping in mind at the time the state of rocket and spacecraft development, then and projected.

Basically, three concepts were seriously considered. The first called for direct flight of a full-size spaceship from earth to the moon and back. The second included the launching of two separate sections of a craft from earth into orbit, joining them together, and sending them as a single unit to land on and take off from the moon. The third approach was to launch the whole spacecraft from earth into a lunar orbit, and land a section of the craft on the moon while the other part waited in orbit for the landing craft to return.

The third method, called lunar orbit rendezvous, was finally chosen, after months of careful study, for many complex technical reasons. Principally, a direct flight to the moon was ruled out because the launch vehicle would have to be so immense and expensive as to make it impractical. In early 1959, planners believed there would be need for a titantic-type booster which could develop 12 million pounds' thrust with eight engines. The project was called Nova. With its potential of great power, however, were equally sizeable problems of handling and launching due to its bulk alone. Nova soon died on the drawing boards.

A craft using the earth orbital rendezvous method would have to weigh more than twice as much as the one using the lunar orbit rendezvous, mainly because of the additional fuel that would be needed. The selected plan seemed safer and less complicated, and represented an important saving in payload weight. Moreover, it provided a higher probability of mission success, and promised fulfillment some months earlier than other modes. It was also estimated this way to the moon would cost American taxpayers 10 to 15 percent less—a significant difference, since the entire manned space flight program, including the lunar landing, had been budgeted at about $20 billion. Also, lunar orbit rendezvous (LOR) required the least amount of new technical development beyond existing commitments while advancing the national technology.

Once the course which astronauts would take to reach the moon had been chosen, the next logical steps in the program were to design a spacecraft and launch vehicle to carry out the project. Designers had to work with the fact that a spacecraft capable of housing three astronauts to fly the LOR mission would weigh about 45 tons.

The entire Apollo spacecraft is 82 feet tall, weighs 90,000 pounds, and is composed of three modules (separate units or blocks), plus an adapter and a launch escape system (LES) very similar to the one used on Mercury capsules. Apollo, including its command and service modules and the adapter which houses the lunar module, is taller than the entire Mercury-Redstone launch vehicles used by astronauts Alan Shepard and Gus Grissom in 1961.

The three major units are the command, service, and lunar modules. Astronauts fly in the command module (CM). It is the spacecraft's control center for all flights and is, as we have seen, the only unit that will return from the lunar mission. The CM, twice the size of Gemini, is cone shaped, 12.8 feet in diameter, and 11.7 feet high. Fully loaded, it weighs 9,500 pounds. It has two shells: a pressurized inner crew compartment and an outer heat shield coated with special ablative materials to protect the module against the fiery 4,500- to 5,000-degree temperature generated by the friction of re-entry. There are five windows through which astronauts make navigational sightings and observe flight progress and moon orbit rendezvous operations.

Inside, the CM is a compact but efficiently arranged combination cockpit, office, laboratory, radio station, kitchen, bedroom, bathroom, and den. It is home for three men flying missions up to two weeks and longer, far from their native planet. There is more room for astronauts to move around in Apollo than there was in Mercury or Gemini. They may switch stations or stretch their legs. The CM offers 73 cubic feet per man compared to 55 cubit feet in Mercury and 40 cubic feet in Gemini. The average compact car affords 68 cubic feet per passenger. Pilots spend most of their time in space, however, reclining in special couches, contoured to their body size and shape. Control devices are attached to the arm rests of each couch.

While in space, the Environment Control System (ECS) supplies pure oxygen in the cabin, which is also air conditioned to a comfortable, shirt-sleeve temperature of 75 degrees. The system, overall, performs 23 functions, compared to five for the average home conditioner, including air cooling, heating, humidity control, ventilation of space suits, ventilation of cabin, air filtration, carbon dioxide removal, odor removal, and waste management functions, among others.

Actually, the command module is built somewhat like a Thermos bottle, with an inner compartment made of aluminum honeycomb and an outer shell of stainless steel. It is completely covered by an ablative material of reinforced plastic, which burns off during reentry into the earth's atmosphere, to protect the astronauts from searing heat.

Each CM is equipped with controls to enable the pilots to guide it during flight. Television, telemetry and tracking equipment, and two-way radio provide communications with earth. Communication between the astronauts during the moon exploration and moon-orbit rendezvous is also provided. These and other systems, such as the reaction control earth landing, parts of the ECS, stabilization and control, and parts of the electrical power systems, occupy virtually every inch of available space in the module. In fact, there are nearly two million wires and skeletal components in the CM. The family car, by comparison, has about 2,500 functional parts. The command module panel display includes 24 instruments, 566 switches, 40 event indicators, 71 lights and 15 miles of wiring—enough to wire 50 two-bedroom apartments.

Directly beneath the command module at launch is the service module (SM). It is a cylindrical unit, 12.8 feet in diameter, 22 feet tall, and weighing 55,000 pounds. It contains the spacecraft's electrical power supply equipment and its primary propulsion system, which produces 22,000 pounds' thrust. Its stop and restart engine will be used for several important maneuvers while Apollo is moonbound. It will also be used to slow the craft to go into lunar orbit and to make midcourse corrections while it is earthbound. The entire service module will be jettisoned in space before the command module reenters the earth's atmosphere on the homeward leg of a lunar mission.

An adapter section connects the Apollo spacecraft to the third stage of the Saturn V launch vehicle and houses the lunar module (LM), the actual moon landing vehicle. The adapter is just under the service module at launch. It is a 28-foot-tall fairing, the same width as the CM and SM, and weighs two tons. It flares out at the bottom to a diameter of 22 feet, to match the width of the rocket's third stage.

The strangest-looking part of the entire Apollo/Saturn V space vehicle is the lunar module. It resembles the cab of a two-man helicopter, mounted on spiderlike metal legs, and has, in fact, won the nickname of "the bug." With two large windows as eyes, a tubular mouth for entry and exit of the pilots, and four spindly legs, the LM has the appearance of something overly developed from the insect world.

Mock-up of the Apollo Lunar Module in the Pyrotechnic Installation Building at the Kennedy Space Center. (NASA Photo)

It is 19 feet tall, about 19 feet in diameter, and weighs roughly 35,000 pounds. It has its own complete guidance, propulsion, computer, control communications, and environmental control systems, with at least one and sometimes two backup systems. This was built-in reliability, for once the astronauts begin their descent to the moon's face from lunar orbit in the LM, they are pretty much on their own. Everything must function perfectly from that point on.

LM is a two-stage vehicle. The bottom half contains the rocket engine and legs for lunar landing. It also serves as the launch platform for the upper stage, which includes the cabin for the astronauts and the ascent engine. LM's descent propulsion system has a throttle control; its rocket engine's thrust power can be varied considerably to control the touchdown on the moon with great precision. This engine provides the braking thrust for the landing. Final descent can be slowed to three miles per hour at an altitude of 15 feet, but the LM can land at a faster speed and absorb the shock without harm to the crew or equipment. The ascent engine propels the upper stage from the lunar surface, for rendezvous and docking with the combined command and service modules (CSM), which remain in lunar orbit during the landing phase of the operation. The LM's bottom half stays on the moon.

The launch escape tower, 33 feet tall and 8,200 pounds heavy, rides atop the command module at launch. It is designed to separate the CM from the rest of the rocket and spacecraft should an emergency occur on the launch pad or shortly after liftoff. It would rocket the command module a safe distance away from the bird, and to an altitude high enough for parachutes in the module to deploy for descent to earth. If the launch goes off OK, the tower is jettisoned about 35 seconds after ignition of the Saturn V's second stage.

Major contractors for the spacecraft are North American Rockwell's Space Division, command and service modules; and Grumman Aircraft for the lunar module.

While Saturn V is checked out automatically by computers (the main one in the Launch Control Center, and the slave unit in the Mobile Launcher), the Apollo spacecraft preflight test program is handled separately by an altogether different system. It is called ACE —Acceptance Checkout Equipment. Engineers at the Kennedy Space Center began designing it in 1961. They were looking for a system that could automatically test thousands of different parameters, computer instructions, while permitting technicians to switch to manual or semiautomatic testing at any time.

Terminal equipment that connects to Apollo is located at each test site in the Manned Spacecraft Operations Building, in the high bays of the VAB, on the Mobile Launchers and Mobile Service Structure, Pads A and B of Complex 39, and at Complexes 34 and 37. The 2,000 measurements that tell what's going on aboard the spacecraft are encoded, mutiplexed, and transmitted to an ACE station by PCM —Pulse Code Modulation.

At the ACE station, the data passes through a decommutator, a decoding device, and is fed into a computer. The computer room processes the information and displays the results on meters, charts, and readout screens for the engineers and technicians in the control room. If any of the key parameters checked by ACE exceed the tolerance established for nominal operation, the problem is signalled in the control room. On cathode ray tubes, much like small television screens, the computer sets up a flashing display of the particular readout line, while other lines on display are unaffected.

If an engineer wishes to command the operation of a particular device or system on board the spacecraft, he can press the proper button on his console. The computer will transmit the order and monitor the result without disrupting the preplanned test procedures. NASA systems engineers manning the ACE stations during tests of Apollo command and service modules work with their counterparts with Apollo contractors North American and Grumman.

At least 15 to 20 different test runs are made on each spacecraft, beginning with tests of individual systems, proceeding to integrated systems checks, and continuing to the final prelaunch checkout. General Electric participated in the initial design, packaged all of the ACE stations for NASA, and is responsible for their operation and maintenance. There are a dozen stations across the country, four at KSC and others at NASA's Manned Spacecraft Center in Houston, and at Apollo contractor plants in New York and California.

While the spacecraft checkout operations were revolutionized for Apollo, NASA's Manned Space Flight Network was also rebuilt and refurbished. Before it was declared ready to support a mission, it was thoroughly tested. The network demonstrated:

—Around-the-clock station tracking and telemetry at lunar distance.

—Engineering crews trained and ready for continuous communications with the spacecraft.

—Test and checkout of the Real Time Computer Complex in Houston by demonstrating data processing, receiving and complex orbital calculations.

New equipment was also put to the test. The Apollo Unified S-

Band System combines in a single transmission five communications functions previously requiring separate systems for Mercury and Gemini. They include: (1) Tracking and determining flight path and velocity; (2) commanding the spacecraft; (3) voice communication with the astronauts; (4) receiving telemetry on astronaut health and mission research; and (5) receiving telemetry on the condition of the spacecraft and its batteries, fuel, systems, and performance. Television monitoring of activities inside the spacecraft was added as a sixth function for Apollo.

By using the latest electronic techniques, all this and other information exchanged between Apollo and ground stations can be carried on one wide-band frequency, which operates in the 2100 to 2300 megacycle band. This communications system is designed to support Apollo missions in earth orbit or on a lunar journey, providing real-time data for mission control.

The Unified S-Band System uses two kinds of antennas: parabaloidal 30-foot diameter "dishes" for vehicle support primarily during launch and earth orbit, and larger, 85-foot dishes to handle the more complex tracking and telemetry in regions a quarter of a million miles from earth. Three new 85-foot antennas were added to the network—at Goldstone, California; Canberra, Australia; and near Madrid, Spain. Thirty-foot antennas (dishes) were installed at Hawaii, Guaymas, Mexico, Merritt Island, Carnarvon, Australia, Ascension Island, Canary Islands, Grand Bahama Island, and Antigua. With such global coverage, one or more of the sites will be able to communicate continuously with the astronauts, despite the earth's rotation. Engineering teams manning the stations around the world gained much invaluable practice tracking experience during the unmanned Lunar Orbiter program.

To cover the vast stretches of ocean between land stations, five super instrumentation ships have been added to the network. Three of them, *Vanguard, Mercury,* and *Redstone,* follow earth orbital insertion and translunar injection portions of the Apollo mission. The other two vessels, the *Watertown* and the *Huntsville,* are used for the reentry phase of the flights.

Each of these ships has an instrumentation complex capable of target acquisition, tracking, communication, command and control, and telemetry reception. They are larger, swifter, and more durable than the ocean range vessels used to support Mercury and Gemini shots. *Vanguard, Mercury,* and *Redstone,* for instance, are each nearly 600 feet long, and have a full load displacement of

23,310 tons. They can remain on station for more than 100 days, and have a maximum range of 20,000 nautical miles. During missions they are manned by 17 officers, 71 crewmen, and 100 technical specialists, including flight controllers. The two reentry ships are just over 455 feet in length and have a full load displacement of 12,199 tons. Their complement is 14 officers, 56 crewmen, and 70 technicians each.

One of the more recent additions to the Air Force Eastern Test Range's inventory of aircraft is the revamped C-135 jet transport and cargo carrier. It has been modified to support the Apollo program. These planes hold the biggest steerable antennas ever flown in their peculiar, bulbous, 10-foot-long noses, nicknamed "droop snoots." Support includes reception, recording, and retransmission of telemetry information from the Apollo space vehicles.

With the announcement by JFK in May, 1961, of the manned lunar landing goal, NASA also began work on developing a rocket large enough to do the job. Once the Lunar Orbit Rendezvous flight sequence had been chosen as the best way of reaching the moon, there were some basic guidelines set for designers to keep in mind. Using this approach, the launch vehicle would be required to hoist 280,000 pounds into earth orbit and close to 100,000 pounds into a lunar trajectory; by far the heaviest weight-lifting job ever imposed on a rocket.

Saturn I was ruled out as a possibility because, even with its 1.5 million pounds' thrust, it was not strong enough. To use it, about six rockets would have been required for each mission, with a complicated assembly of their combined payloads in earth orbit to form a moonship.

A number of vehicles were considered. Solid-propellant rockets were never really seriously discussed, however. Such a stage would have been too large to handle, and, at the same time, there was no propellant available that could match the high performance characteristics of liquid hydrogen, which had been proven on Atlas-Centaur and Saturn I flights. It provides 40 percent more thrust per pound than any other liquid propellant in use today.

NASA finally settled on what has become known as the Saturn V. Its drawing board dimensions were awesome: 363 feet tall; six million pounds heavy when fueled; three stages plus an instrument unit and the Apollo spacecraft. Its potential power was equally impressive. One rocket would be able to orbit the equivalent of 1,500

Sputniks, or 9,000 Explorer I satellites, or the combined payload weights of all previously launched U.S. spacecraft!

There were many advantages to the final design concept. The S-IVB third stage and instrument unit, for instance, would be nearly identical to the second stage and IU (instrument unit) already developed for the Saturn I program. Only the first and second stages would have to be built from scratch. Boeing was selected in December, 1961, to manufacture the booster; North American, second stage, September, 1961; Douglas Aircraft (now McDonnell-Douglas), third stage, December, 1961; and IBM, instrument unit, August, 1964. NASA's Marshall Space Flight Center had overall design and supervision of the Saturn V's development.

The lunar rocket came into being approximately four years after the beginning of the Saturn program, and all its huge components were essentially flight ready by the end of 1966. The S-IC booster stage is a massive structure, 138 feet long and 33 feet in diameter. Its interior is spacious enough to accommodate three large moving vans side by side. The cylindrical booster has separate propellant tanks which hold 203,000 gallons of RP-1 and 331,000 gallons of liquid oxygen. It is powered by five F-1 engines, built by the Rocketdyne Division of North American. The engines are clustered in the tail of the rocket, four mounted on a ring so they can be gimballed (swivelled) for control proposes, and the fifth rigidly mounted in the center. Each engine generates 1.5 million pounds' thrust at liftoff; they are the most powerful liquid propellant rocket engines ever made in the western hemisphere, if not the world. The F-1 has the most reliable start system in operation today.

The S-11 second stage also has a 33 foot diameter. It is 81½ feet high and its one million pounds of thrust are developed by five J-2 engines, also manufactured by Rocketdyne. They are the most powerful hydrogen-fueled engines ever fashioned for flight and represent many new advances in rocket technology, including the ability to meet requirements for starting and restarting them at various altitudes with long coast times between ignitions. The S-II liquid hydrogen tank holds 288,750 gallons, and the liquid oxygen tank, 93,750 gallons.

Apollo/Saturn V Lunar Flight Configuration, showing measurements from base of Saturn V in inches and meters. (Courtesy of NASA)

SATURN V APOLLO FLIGHT CONFIGURATION

VEHICLE STATION IN:	INCHES METERS

SPACECRAFT (NORTH AMERICAN AVIATION)

LES JETTISON MOTOR & LAUNCH ESCAPE SYSTEM

LAUNCH ESCAPE TOWER

COMMAND MODULE

COMMAND PILOT
SENIOR PILOT
PILOT

	INCHES METERS
SERVICE MODULE	
CARRY ON UMBILICAL	3757.17 95.432
FLY AWAY UMBILICAL	3760.92 95.527
FUEL SUMP TANK	
H_2 CRYOGENIC STORAGE TANK	

RCS THRUSTER ASSEMBLY 4 PLACES

LEM UPPER DOCKING TUNNEL

LEM LANDING GEAR 4 PLACES

INSTRUMENT UNIT (IBM)

S-IVB (DOUGLAS)

	S-IVB INCHES	S-IVB METERS
LH_2 TANK VENT	3203.56 81.370	657.70 .17.198
ACCESS PLATFORM SUPPORT FITTING	3161.56 80.303	
ANTENNAS CENTERLINE	3983.56 81.196	
COLD HELIUM SPHERES (4)		
LOX TANK		
LINE FAIRING LH_2 FILL & DRAIN		
TOP OF AFT SKIRT	2832.00 71.933	296.15 7.268
LOX LH_2 FILL AND DRAIN	2760.04 70.105	214.19 5.440
RETRO ROCKET (4 PLACES)		
BOTTOM OF AFT SKIRT	2746.50 69.701	200.05 5.096
ACCESS PLATFORM SUPPORT FITTING	2664.33 67.674	

S-II (NORTH AMERICAN AVIATION)

	INCHES METERS	XB STA INCHES	XB STA METERS
SYSTEMS TUNNEL		938.50	23.837
LH_2 VENT		942.00	23.926
S-II TOP FORWARD SKIRT	2519.00 63.982	955.00	24.257
RADIO COMMAND ANTENNA 4 PLACES		929.00	23.464
TELEMETRY ANTENNA 4 PLACES		902.00	22.910
LOX TANK			
LOX PROPELLANT MANAGEMENT PROBE			
RING SLOSH BAFFLE		357.00	9.067
LH_2 RECIRCULATION SYSTEM 5 PLACES		366.60	9.311
LH_2 FILL & DRAIN		341.00	8.661
DIVISION OF AFT SKIRT	1890.00 48.006	283.00	7.188
TOP OF AFT SKIRT		326.00	8.280
BOTTOM OF SLOSH BAFFLE		284.00	7.213
TOP ULLAGE ROCKET FAIRING MOTOR		176.69	3.725
TOP OF THRUST CONE		223.00	5.664
BOTTOM OF THRUST CONE		112.00	2.844

S-IC (BOEING)

	INCHES METERS
TOP FORWARD SKIRT	1541.00 39.141 -23.00 -0.584
LOWER SECTION OF FORWARD SKIRT	1420.30 36.075
RING SLOSH BAFFLES	
LOWER SECTION OF HELIUM BOTTLES (4)	946.50 24.041
TOP OF INTERTANK ASSEMBLY	885.20 22.484
FUEL VENT LINE	696.00 17.678
ACCESS DOOR 4 PLACES	
LOX FILL & DRAIN (FAR SIDE)	794.16 20.172
LOX FILL & DRAIN (FAR SIDE)	776.18 19.715
BOTTOM OF INTERTANK ASSEMBLY	628.80 15.971
SLOSH BAFFLES	
FUEL FILL & DRAIN	130.00 3.302
RETRO ROCKETS (2 EACH 4 PLACES)	
BOTTOM OF FUEL TANK	225.00 5.715
TOP OF HEAT SHIELD	112.00 2.844
BOTTOM OF F-1 ENGINE	-115.30 -2.920

VEHICLE STATIONS IN:	INCHES METERS

SPACECRAFT

	INCHES METERS
VEHICLE STATION	4240.79 107.716
BASE OF CONARD NOSE CONE	4201.73 106.724
CENTERLINE LAUNCH ESCAPE MOTOR	4185.53 106.305
BOTTOM OF LES SKIRT	3860.03 98.005
TOP OF BOOST COVER	3890.92 98.527
VEHICLE SEPARATION	3840.92 97.526
AFT HEAT SHIELD	3749.96 95.239
REACTION CONTROL SYSTEM MODULE	3715.45 94.372
VEHICLE STATION FLIGHT SEPARATION	3594.55 91.301
VEHICLE SEPARATION	3593.50 91.275
PROPULSION MOTOR	
RENDEZVOUS RADAR ANTENNA	
LUNAR EXCURSION MODULE	
LEM FORWARD DOCKING TUNNEL	
VEHICLE SEPARATION	3340.45 84.837
VEHICLE STATION	3285.18 83.443

INSTRUMENT UNIT

	INCHES METERS
INSTRUMENT UNIT TOP	3258.56 82.767
INSTRUMENT UNIT BOTTOM	3222.56 81.853

S-IVB

	S-IVB INCHES	S-IVB METERS
TOP FORWARD SKIRT	678.70	17.459
BOTTOM OF FORWARD SKIRT	3100.36 78.754	584.70 14.899
FUEL MASS SENSOR PROBE		
INSTRUMENTATION PROBE		
LOX TANK PROBE		
AUXILIARY PROPULSION SYSTEM (APS) (2)		
LOX VENT (FAR SIDE)	2759.00 70.078 213.18 5.414	
HELIUM SPHERES (9 PLACES)		
TOP J-2 ENGINE	2645.65 67.204 100.00 2.540	
J-2 ENGINE		
BOTTOM S-IVB TOP S-II	2519.00 63.982 -26.99 -.682	

S-II

	INCHES METERS	XB STA INCHES	XB STA METERS
BOTTOM OF FORWARD SKIRT		823.00	20.904
LH_2 PROPELLANT MANAGEMENT PROBE			
PRESSURIZATION MAST			
LOX VENT LINE			
TOP OF LH_2 FEED FAIRING 5 PLACES		451.73	11.474
LOX TANK EQUATOR	1848		46.939
LOX FILL & DRAIN (FAR SIDE)		207.00	5.257
CRUCIFORM BAFFLE		173.00	4.394
BOTTOM LH_2 FEED FAIRING		158.00	4.013
FLIGHT SEPARATION	1760.00 44.704 196.00 4.978		
GIMBAL PLANE		100.00	2.540
BOTTOM ULLAGE R M FAIRING		-0.44	-.011

S-IC

	INCHES METERS	XB STA INCHES	XB STA METERS
FLIGHT SEPARATION		0.00	0.000
S-II INTERSTAGE BOTTOM	1541.00 39.141 -23.00 -0.584		
LOX VENT	1523.00 38.635		
GOX LINE	1511.75 38.398		
Y RING	1404.00 35.661		
PRESSURIZATION TUNNEL (2 PLACES)			
LOX FEED LINE TUNNEL (5 PLACES)			
Y RING	909.00 23.088		
BOTTOM OF LOX TANK	772.00 19.600		
TOP OF FUEL TANK	742.00 18.846		
FUEL PRESSURE LINE	692.90 17.570		
Y RING	605.00 15.367		
TOP OF ENGINE FAIRING	362.00 9.194		
TOP OF THRUST STRUCTURE	345.70 8.780		
INTERCONNECT LOX DRAIN	130.00 3.302		
BOTTOM OF ENGINE FAIRING	48.50 1.231		
BOTTOM OF THRUST STRUCTURE	100.00 2.540		
GIMBAL	100.00 2.540		

POS II   POS III

ISOMETRIC SCALE

0   100   200   300   400   500 INCHES
0 1 2 3 4 5 6 7 8 9 10 11 12 13 METERS
196.85   393.70   511.81

The third stage of the Saturn V, the S-IVB, is much like that of the second stage of the Saturn I. Its measurements are 58 feet tall by 21 feet eight inches around, and it has a single 200,000-pound thrust J-2 engine which also burns liquid hydrogen and liquid oxygen. It is much different from the first two stages, however, for it operates both as a booster rocket and as a space vehicle. First, it must shove the payload the last leg of the way into an earth orbit velocity; then it must provide attitude control for itself and the spacecraft, and must restart its engine in space for the final kick toward the moon, achieving a translunar trajectory.

The instrument unit for the moon rocket is a three-foot-high "wafer" which originates in-flight commands for engine gimballing, sequencing of engine propulsion systems, staging operations, and all primary timing signals. It, too, is very similar to the IU developed for Saturn I. It has the same diameter as the S-IVB stage and weighs 4,000 pounds. Structural, environmental control, guidance and control, measuring and telemetry, radio frequency, and electrical systems are fastened on panels mounted to the inside perimeter of the wafer.

There are something like two million different parts in an Apollo/Saturn V space vehicle, including a vast range of materials running from gold to polyurethane tile. The sheer size of some of the components opened up entire new horizons of manufacturing techniques. Shaping and welding the immense fuel tanks, for example, rendered past processes obsolete. As with the spacecraft, legions of skilled employees at plants across the country—contractors and chains of subcontractors—built their individual parts, tested and retested them.

These components were then joined in subsystems and checked again. Eventually, entire stages were assembled. These were placed on static firing stands at the Marshall Space Flight Center and at other sites in Mississippi and California and "launched" on flights that never left the ground. While the stages were bolted down onto hardstands, their engines were revved up to full force, even beyond the strains they would be called upon to encounter during actual flights.

As assembly techniques were refined, production lines were set up to turn out the number of stages NASA would need in its quest to reach the moon. By early 1967, the major units for the first Apollo/Saturn V launch at the Spaceport were ready. They had each been tested and retested, inspected and reinspected. Everything humanly possible to prepare them for flight had been done. They were set for the ultimate test: launch. Some parts were shipped by barge, others were loaded onto aircraft. All had the same destination: John F. Kennedy Space Center, Florida.

Chapter 16

TRAGEDY ON THE PAD

Before the astronauts could go to the moon, it was decided to first check them out, to train them in the Apollo spacecraft during earth orbital missions. There, they could perfect techniques of rendezvous and docking the lunar module with their command and service modules, as well as get used to the new spacecraft.

An intermediate launch vehicle, between Saturn I and Saturn V, was developed to boost three men in Apollo into earth orbit. It is called Saturn IB. By continuing with known rocket stages, NASA would be assured of a high degree of performance reliability. Planners also envisioned multiple uses of Saturn IB on a variety of space missions, manned and unmanned, beyond Apollo.

Like its baby brother, Saturn IB is a two-stage vehicle. It stands 225 feet tall and weighs about 640 tons when fueled. Its booster (S-IB) is a modified Saturn I stage, which has a liftoff trust of 1.6 million pounds, 100,000 pounds more than its predecessor. Its S-IVB second stage generates 200,000 pounds thrust, more than twice as much as the second stage of Saturn I. With this extra kick, the rocket's payload capability increased 50 percent, without the cost of a new development program. It can place 18 tons of payload into low earth orbit, compared to the 11 tons that was Saturn I's maximum weight capacity. The intermediate rocket also uses an instrument unit ("brain") similar to the ones flown on Saturn I. It carries electrical, guidance and control, instrumentation, measuring, telemetry, radio frequency, environmental control, and emergency detection systems. It controls first- and second-stage powered flight, stage separation, injection into earth orbit, and earth orbital stabilization.

Saturn I contractors—Chrysler Corporation for the booster, Douglas Aircraft for the second stage, and IBM for the IU—were also employed for the new, uprated version of the rocket.

The first of this family of birds was ready for flight from Launch Complex 34, site of the first four Saturn I shoots, in late February, 1966, after two scrubs for bad weather. Atop it was the initial flight version of the Apollo spacecraft. Though no men would be inside the command module, and there was no lunar module aboard, it was still a major test for the space vehicle.

The mission plan was full. Objectives included: ,

—Verify the rocket and spacecraft during actual flight, and confirm their compatibility.

—Demonstrate separation of the rocket's stages and segments of Apollo.

—Verify operation of Saturn IB's propulsion, guidance and control, and electrical systems.

—Verify operation of the command module heat shield for reentry into the atmosphere from low earth orbit, through temperatures up to 4,000 degrees F. (Apollo's shield must resist heat twice as great as that encountered by Gemini, and four times as great as Mercury.)

—Verify operation of the service module propulsion system, including restart of the main engine in the weightless environment.

—Verify operation of the spacecraft environmental control system, reaction control system, launch escape system, and the recovery system.

—Evaluate the emergency detection system during unmanned flight.

—Demonstrate mission support facilities required for launch, mission operations and recovery.

Saturn IB vehicle number 201 lifted off from Cape Kennedy at 11:13 A.M., February 26, 1966. Thirty-nine minutes later the Apollo moonship rammed back into the atmosphere at more than 18,000 mph, splashed into the South Atlantic off Ascension Island, and was recovered. All major mission objectives were successfully met. The first Apollo shot, though unmanned, was a triumph of technology. The spacecraft's ablative heat shield withstood the searing temperatures of reentry, helping assure astronauts a safe return through the earth's atmosphere on their way back from the moon. Launch vehicle personnel were equally happy with the performance of the new 200,000 pound thrust J-2 engine of the second stage. This would be the workhorse engine for both the second and third stages of Saturn V.

The second Saturn IB flight, July 5, 1966, did not carry a space-craft. Rather, it had a primary purpose of further testing the second stage, this time in orbit. The powerful rocket boosted the world's heaviest satellite at the time—the S-IVB second stage, instrument unit, and a nose cone, totaling 58,500 pounds—into earth orbit. A camera was placed inside the stage's cavernous liquid hydrogen tank to send back photos to engineers to see if the propellant was settled in the tank or sloshing about. Such information was critical, for on manned lunar launches, the S-IVB engine would have to be restarted in space, and if the liquid hydrogen was not settled, there would be some problems to be resolved before this step could be taken. The only way to check this under realistic orbital conditions was to fly a camera inside the tank. The test proved what engineers had hoped for: there was no evidence of splashing or sloshing. Another test had been passed.

The first two flights of Saturn IB had been so successful, and tests on the Apollo spaceraft were shaping up so well, that officials decided that if the next shot in the program went as planned, astro-nauts might fly on the fourth mission. By August 25, 1966, both spacecraft and launch vehicle crews said they were ready for this key test, the final dress rehearsal before Apollo could become man-rated.

Trailing a brilliant orange spear of flame, the rocket, in a near flawless flight, shoved a fully instrumented Apollo three quarters of the way around the world and safely down a reentry path much like the one astronauts would have to follow. It was the 13th flight of a Saturn rocket and the 13th success. Again, all major mission objec-tives were fulfilled. The space vehicle was now ready for man to climb aboard.

Even as the third Saturn IB was lifting off at Launch Complex 37, the booster for the next flight was being erected on the pad at adjacent Complex 34. This one would carry a live cargo: three American astronauts. The rocket and spacecraft together received their designated number: Apollo/Saturn 204.

NASA selected two veterans of space flight and one rookie to man the 204 vehicle. Command pilot would be Virgil "Gus" Gris-som, the crusty old pro who had skippered Mercury's *Liberty Bell* 7 and Gemini's *Molly Brown*. Certainly, no one could question Gris-som's qualifications to lead off in the Apollo series of flights that would climax in a landing on the lunar surface. He had been through his share of tight spots, both in space and back on earth during recovery operations. He had proven his cool ability to meet whatever situation might arise with the best possible solution at hand.

The 40-year-old Grissom would fly on the left side of Apollo. In the middle, a senior pilot and second in command, would be Edward H. White, 37. He, too, had experienced space flight. He was the first American to participate in extra vehicular activity (EVA)—to walk in space. The right-hand couch in the capsule would be occupied by a 31-year-old rookie, Roger B. Chaffee, a member of the third group of astronauts, and the youngest American ever named to fly in space.

For nearly a year, the three spacemen followed the progress of their craft. They kept close tabs on it during the final phases of its manufacture in California. Fabrication was begun in August, 1964, and the basic structure was completed in September, 1965. They prepped for their coming mission several months before Apollo 4 arrived at the Kennedy Space Center for checkout, on August 26, 1966. Grissom, White and Chaffee took up residence on Merritt Island.

Because of the complexities of the new capsule, and because new crews were being broken in on it, there were a number of schedule delays. The launch date slipped from the last quarter of 1966 into 1967. On November 17, 1966, NASA announced some major changes in flight plans for the coming months.

Originally, Wally Schirra, Donn Eisele, and Walter Cunningham had been named to fly the second manned Apollo, number 205. Their mission was scrubbed, and they were appointed as the backup crew for 204. There had been some development problems in readying the first man-rated Apollo spacecraft for launch, and officials decided that if the Grissom-team flight was successful, a repeat mission, which 205 was to be, would not be necessary.

The Apollo service module for the first Saturn V shot suffered a structural failure in a test and was completely lost. The Schirra 205 SM was then reassigned to the Saturn V. There had also been a failure during qualification testing of the water boiler in the Apollo 204 spacecraft environmental control system (ECS). Parts had to be shipped across the country from Merritt Island to California for work. More troubles came up when the capsule was placed in the altitude test chamber in the Manned Spacecraft Operations Building for checkout at simulated high-altitude conditions.

Through the frustrating delays, which seemed to plague the first manned flight in any new series of craft, the patient astronauts continued to bone up on their mission plan. Purpose of their flight was to check out the manned operation and performance of Apollo, ground tracking and control facilities. Grissom was given the OK to fly an "open end" mission, which meant he had no hard-set limitation to the amount of time the astronauts could stay in orbit. They could fly up to 14 days, depending on how well things went.

One of the key elements of the flight plan called for eight separate burns of the service propulsion system's 21,500-pound thrust engine in the service module. This would be given a thorough examination, for in future flights to and from the moon, it would provide critical thrust for midcourse guidance corrections and for lunar orbit entry and exit. Final ignition of the engine on the 204 flight would set up reentry and splashdown, planned in the Atlantic Ocean about 350 miles southeast of Bermuda.

Finally, the launch date was set. Apollo 4 would fly February 21, 1967. And, once it got into orbit, Grissom was determined to keep it there the full 14 days he had been granted, unless the craft was virtually coming to pieces. Though each of the three pilots, by this time, knew their flight plans inside out, there was still much work to do at the pad. There were a number of vital ground tests to be run with the mated spacecraft and rocket. The astronauts were to participate in several of these.

On the night of January 26, less than four weeks to liftoff, the prime and backup crews pored over mission plans. One of the last major checkpoints was to be run the next day. This would be, in Cape engineering jargon, the "plugs out" test. A simulated countdown would be picked up shortly before T minus zero, the instant of liftoff, and then the test would be carried through three hours into plus, or flight time. There would be no fuel in the bird and no ordnance items hooked up to the Saturn or spacecraft. Still, Grissom, White, and Chaffee would don their full spacesuits and be sealed inside the Apollo, breathing pure oxygen, to approximate orbital conditions as closely as they could on the ground. Apollo Control at the Manned Spacecraft Center in Houston would "pick up" the flight after liftoff, and the astronauts would be checked on their performances.

By the books, a plugs out test is to demonstrate all space vehicle systems and operational procedures in as near a flight configuration as is practical and to verify their capability in a simulated launch. All communications and instrumentation systems are activated, and measurements are monitored by ground stations. At the start of sim-

(Left to right) *Astronauts Edward H. White, senior pilot; Roger B. Chaffee, pilot; and Virgil I. Grissom, command pilot, practicing in the Apollo Mission Simulator shortly before the tragic fire in the spacecraft that took their lives.* (NASA Photo)

ulated flight, umbilical lines are disconnected, thus the "plugs out" tag, the spacecraft is on simulated fuel cell power, and the launch vehicle is on its flight batteries.

The test began at 7:55 A.M., Friday, January 27, 1967. The three astronauts did not have to take part until later. They entered Apollo at 1 P.M. Communications problems stopped the countdown at 5:40 P.M. By 6:20, all final functions up to the transfer to simulated fuel cell power were completed, and the count was still holding. Ground stations were having trouble getting through to each other and to the crew in the spacecraft. To Grissom, it was an annoying delay.

"Hey," he barked into the intercom. "How do you expect to get us to the moon if you people can't even hook us up with a ground station?"

Biomedical sensors were attached to Ed White in the capsule, and at this time data indicated he was resting. Communications people were trying to clear up the trouble and get on with the test.

At 6:31 P.M. the count was about to be picked up again, when ground instruments showed an unexplained rise in the oxygen flow into the spacesuits. There also was indication of movement by one of the pilots, perhaps Grissom.

Four seconds later an astronaut announced, almost in a casual voice over the intercom, "Fire . . . I smell fire." Two seconds later Ed White's voice was more insistent: "Fire in the cockpit," he said. In the blockhouse, engineers and technicians looked up from their consoles to the television monitor trained at the spacecraft. They were horrified at the picture being flashed. Flames were licking furiously inside Apollo, and smoke blurred the reception. No one spoke. The men were stunned, shocked into disbelief. Their eyes saw what was happening, but their minds refused to absorb it.

There was another wait of three seconds. And then came a near hysterical shout: "There's a bad fire in the spacecraft!" Sensitive equipment in the blockhouse indicated the astronauts were scrambling about in the cockpit during the next few seconds. The emergency procedure for escaping called for White to reach over his left shoulder to turn a rachet handle to unlock six lugs. He and Grissom would then lower the inner door to the cabin floor. A press of a plunger would send the outer hatch flying, and the three astronauts would exit in order, White, Chaffee, and Grissom. This maneuver was timed for 90 seconds, but in practice the crew had never accomplished it in the minimum time. Indications were White was now trying to turn the rachet. Several more seconds passed and then Chaffee screamed something that sounded like, "We're on fire; get us out of here!"

Mated atop the Saturn IB rocket, the Apollo capsule was 218 feet above the ground, surrounded by the service structure's specially built "white room." This was an enclosed, super-clean work access site that surrounded the spacecraft in an environmentally controlled area.

At the first report of fire, the pad leader in the white room ordered emergency egress procedures. Spacecraft technicians ran toward the sealed Apollo, but before they could reach it, the command module ruptured. Bursts of flame and thick black clouds of smoke funneled out, filling the room. One or two men got close to Apollo's outer hatch, but when it cracked, the intense white-hot heat drove them back. It was like walking into an oven. Technicians now feared two things: the command module might explode; and the fire might set off the launch escape system atop Apollo. This could set the entire service structure on fire. Natural instinct told the men to evacuate, but as they gulped in breaths of fresh air just outside the white room, they knew they had to go back inside. No matter how grim things looked, they had to try to get the astronauts out.

About 90 seconds after the first report of fire, pad personnel tried to get into the white room to open the escape hatch from the outside. Visibility was absolute zero. Smoke completely clouded the once pure-white room. A special tool had to be fitted into the hatch to open it. The heat was searing, and the smoke bit hard into the eyes of the technicians. They had to work in shifts. One man would feel his way toward the spacecraft and work the tool for a few seconds before being driven back. Then a second man would go in and repeat the process. Six men participated in the heroic effort. At last, more than five minutes after the report of fire, the hatches (actually there were three of them, outer, middle and inner) were opened. Again, the men were driven back as more heat and smoke poured forth from inside the command module. Firemen arrived within three minutes of the hatch openings, and doctors came soon after them. It was too late. There was nothing that could be done. The three astronauts had died within seconds of the fire's ignition. In the pure-oxygen atmosphere of the command module, flames had spread rapidly and uncontrollably. It had been a thermal holocaust inside the cabin. Humans were helpless, no matter how courageous their efforts inside or outside the spacecraft. Twenty-seven pad crewmen were treated for smoke inhalation; two had to be hospitalized.

It was this nation's worst space disaster. Black banner headlines announced the tragedy to a shocked world. The astronauts were international heroes, and their sudden and unexpected deaths caused international grief and mourning.

"Three valiant young men have given their lives in the nation's service," President Lyndon B. Johnson said in Washington. "We mourn this great loss and our hearts go out to their families." Vice President Hubert H. Humphrey added, "The United States will push ever forward in space and the memory of these men will be an inspiration to all future spacefarers."

"We in NASA," said Administrator James E. Webb, "know that

Interior of the Apollo spacecraft following the fire that killed Astronauts Virgil I. Grissom, Edward H. White, and Roger B. Chaffee on January 27, 1967. (NASA Photo)

their greatest desire was that this nation press forward with manned space flight exploration, despite the outcome of any one flight. With renewed dedication and purpose we intend to do just that."

Gus Grissom, like all American astronauts, knew the risks of his profession. He was also well aware of the unlimited potential of space exploration. "If we die," he had once said in an interview, "we want people to accept it. We are in a risky business, and we hope that if anything happens to us, it will not delay the program. The conquest of space is worth the risk of life."

Even before the bodies of the astronauts were removed from the charred, furnacelike interior of the command module, plans were set in motion to investigate the accident. NASA named some of the top aerospace experts in the country to the Apollo 204 Review Board, including some of the world's outstanding authorities on fires.

Only the astronauts' bodies were removed, for autopsy. Everything else at Launch Complex 34 was immediately impounded for analysis. Grissom, White, and Chaffee, accordingly, were given full military burial honors. Hundreds lined the Cape's skid strip as the three men were flown out, not by rocket as planned, but by aircraft. To the launch teams, their deaths were still difficult to believe. No one had expected tragedy to strike on the ground. In space, dangers could be anticipated, but in a space vehicle bolted to the pad, it was almost inconceivable that such a catastrophic event could occur. The plugs out test, in fact, was not even classified as hazardous. Similar tests had been run throughout the Mercury and Gemini programs without incident.

Perhaps never before in history has a review board conducted such a thorough and documented examination into the cause of an accident. Every ash in the command module was sifted; every angle photographed; every wire checked and rechecked; and every man even remotely related to the fire questioned in exhausting detail. Every component in the cockpit was carefully dismantled and inspected.

The board was in session at the Kennedy Space Center for months. Its final, formal report was submitted to Administrator Webb on April 5, 1967. Following are excerpts:

"It is most likely that the fire began in the lower forward portion of the left-hand equipment bay. This would place the origin to the left of the command pilot (Grissom), and considerably below the level of his couch. The first stage of the fire, with its associated rapid temperature rise and increase in cabin pressure, terminated approximately 15 seconds after the verbal report of fire. At this time, the pressure vessel, which constitutes the command module cabin, ruptured. This marked the beginning of the brief second stage of the fire, characterized by the period of greatest conflagration due to the forced convection that resulted from the outrush of gases through the rupture in the pressure vessel. The swirling flow scattered firebrands throughout the crew compartment, spreading the fire.

"The fire in Apollo 4 was most probably brought about by some minor malfunction or failure of equipment or wire insulation. This failure, which most likely will never be positively identified, initiated a sequence of events that culminated in the conflagration."

It was generally considered, however, that faulty wiring ignited flammable cockpit materials, and then combustible coolant and high pressure oxygen fed the flame. The official death certificates for all three crew members listed the cause of death as asphyxiation due to smoke inhalation due to the fire.

Following the board's release of the detailed report, Congress conducted its own investigation. It was also thorough. Hundreds of witnesses testified at hearings, and thousands of pages of testimony were taken. Both the 204 Review Board and subcommittee members of Congress came to many of the same conclusions. Basically, it was felt, the potential hazards of ground testing had been underestimated; NASA had been lulled into a false sense of underestimating these hazards through six years of successful spacecraft testing without incident. There were some specific charges too. Hardware wiring procedures were critized, as was the practice of having highly flammable objects, not absolutely necessary to the flight, inside the cabin. These had helped spread the fire so rapidly.

Astronaut Frank Borman, a member of the 204 board, summed up the fact that the ground testing had been taken for granted. "The crew has the right not to enter the spacecraft if they think it is unsafe," he said. "But we did not identify this portion of the spacecraft procedure as being a real hazard."

Even so, both the board and members of Congress were particularly critical of the fact that there were no quick means of escape for the astronauts. Ninety seconds to open the hatches from the inside was considered much too long. From the board's lengthy review and the following Congressional probe, a number of recommendations for major Apollo changes were made. A redesigned hatch that could be opened in two or three seconds was at the top of the list. Right below it was the recommendation that the amount and location of combustible materials be severely restricted and controlled.

There were a number of other proposed changes too, that were quickly implemented into the program. On the spacecraft:

—Fire breaks were built in to prevent spread of flames.

—A fire extinguishing system, using flexible hose and nozzle working off Apollo's water supply, was introduced into the command module interior.

—Wire bundles and harness routings were redesigned.

For the spacesuits, a flameproof material called Beta Cloth replaced nylon. At Complex 34 new and larger connection points to the hatch were made, and a fan was installed in the white room to ventilate smoke. More water hoses and fire extinguishers were added, as was an escape slide wire, down which astronauts and crew workers could ride during emergencies. They could reach ground from over 200 feet up in seconds. The Apollo Review Board also recommended regular training practice for emergencies, improvements in communications, and that full scale mock-ups in flight configuration be tested for fire risk and fire safety. KSC Director Kurt Debus said, "Fire is something that will not be underestimated again as long as we are around to look at it."

There is no question that the horrible fire that snuffed out the lives of astronauts Grissom, White, and Chaffee had a profound impact on the space program in general, and Apollo in particular. The late President Kennedy had issued the goal of landing Americans on the lunar surface before the end of the decade. Up to the time of the fire, it appeared that NASA was well on the way to meeting that binding challenge. Had the 204 flight gone on schedule, in February, 1967, other flights would have followed, possibly at three-month intervals. Pilots would have prepped for the moon shot in earth orbit, getting acquanted with their new spacecraft and practicing rendezvous and docking with lunar modules until they were ready for the ultimate mission. But the fire changed a lot of things and a lot of thinking.

To meet the before-1970 deadline, everything had to work well. There was room for delays, even failures. But no one had anticipated a national disaster. The 204 accident was as severe a blow to Apollo plans as could be rendered to the young project. There were many, in fact, including ranking congressmen and other well-known leaders, who felt the entire Apollo program should be called off. Critics of space exploration decried the waste of money, and, now, the sacrifice of human life. Others felt the scheduling for the lunar flight had been too tight, the pressures of meeting target dates too great. They adopted a "what's the rush" attitude. What difference did it make if we got there in December, 1969, or January, 1970? To some, the hurried-up attitude, the rush and bustle of getting the program moving, had been a contributing factor to the catastrophe.

But space officials, backed by the President and his administration, felt a national target, such as the lunar landing this decade, was needed to keep Apollo moving forward with a definite purpose. Without such a goal, the technological drive of progress would be acutely handicapped. NASA argued that the schedules set were not unrealistic, and that the pressures of maintaining these schedules had not been a cause of the fire. Astronauts' safety, they reiterated, was the overriding factor on all missions, and it would continue to be so in the future.

The space agency reshuffled its master plans, and still aimed for a lunar landing before the decade was out. How much 204 delayed achievement of the goal can only be answered by time. Certainly, it had a devastating effect on the program. The first manned Apollo flight was to have taken place in February, 1967. It would be well over a year before this mission could be rescheduled and carried out.

Redesign of the spacecraft, principally of the escape hatch, was the major cause of delay. Apollo engineers were sent back to the drawing boards, and capsules already on the manufacturing production line had to be pulled off and modified to incorporate the changes in the system. Morale had to be rebolstered, faith restored. Scheduled shortcuts were made. NASA contended the national goal could still be met—if everything went well from this point on. Any sort of a failure following 204 would in all probability cross out the final hopes of getting to the moon with men before 1970. Everything would have to work perfectly. There was no time cushion left. The schedule, if anything, was even more imposing, tighter than ever before. But no step would be taken, no test made, no rocket ignited if there was even a whisper of doubt of success. Astronaut safety would override every other concern. Nothing within human limitations would be left to chance. If this meant missing the goal, so be it. The goal would be missed.

With this attitude, and under these conditions, NASA began picking up the Apollo pieces to get the program back on the tracks. The 204 fire had been a costly lesson. Never again could any step in the project, no matter how seemingly insignificant, be underestimated. A repeat of 204 could conceivably kill the entire program and endanger America's chances of preeminence in space.

Craftsmen began modifications to the Apollo spacecraft, and a new flight crew was named May 9, 1967. As many had suspected, it was the 204 backup team: Wally Schirra, Donn Eisele, and Walter Cunningham. Schirra, of course, was the gritty, hell-for-leather pilot of *Sigma 7,* the Mercury capsule which orbited earth six times in October, 1962. He also served as command pilot for Gemini 6, which scored the historic rendezvous in space with Frank Borman and Jim Lovell in Gemini 7 as Christmas of 1965 neared. No astronaut at the Manned Spacecraft Center, with the lone exception of Gordon Cooper, could match Schirra's experience. He is the dean of the active corps.

In fact, at the time he was named to command the Apollo 101 flight, only two of the original seven Mercury astronauts were still on flying status. Deke Slayton had been grounded for a heart murmur, and is now Chief of Flight Crew Training. Alan Shepard has a bad ear, and now heads the astronaut office in Houston. John Glenn and Scott Carpenter have left the program to follow business and oceanographic careers, respectively. And Gus Grissom is dead. That leaves only Schirra and Cooper.

Eisele, an Air Force major, was one of the third group of astronauts chosen by NASA in October, 1963. He has over 3,200 hours' flying time, and flew experimental and developmental test flights in jet aircraft in support of special weapons programs. Cunningham, a civilian, was also among the third group of spacemen. He has logged more than 2,500 hours in flight, and has a master of arts degree in physics from the University of California at Los Angeles. Backup crew named for the first manned Apollo flight were Tom Stafford, John Young, and Gene Cernan, all experienced space pilots. Stafford and Young flew twice in the Gemini program and Cernan once, including a space walk.

"We will fly the spacecraft when we, the crew, think it is ready," the veteran Schirra announced at a press conference at the North American Apollo plant in Downey, California. "So far, to my knowledge, not one pilot has ever been pushed inside a spacecraft; he's always been helped, and we're here to work with the people that are helping us prepare a spacecraft. It's sort of refreshing to know that attitudes have changed considerably as a result of the accident we all suffered. People have changed, their personalities have changed, and the can-do atmosphere is permeating everyone that comes into the plant these days."

The 204 spacecraft that Grissom, White and Chaffee were to fly was known as a Block I Apollo. The capsule Schirra, Eisele and Cunningham would climb into is a Block II, differing basically from the first version by having an upper docking hatch for rendezvous with the lunar module.

At first it had been hoped to transport the Apollo 101 spacecraft to the Kennedy Space Center in late 1967, and ready it for flight by March, 1968. But modifications took longer than planned, and there were additional problems. The schedule lagged, and the mission had to be put off until later in 1968.

Fourteen months after the accident, following intensive studies, NASA announced an important change in the Apollo cabin atmosphere during ground operations. From 100 percent oxygen, it was decided to switch to a mixture of 60 percent oxygen and 40 percent nitrogen. More than 140 flammability tests were run, and they proved such a change would drastically reduce the hazard of a spacecraft fire during critical prelaunch work. In space, the atmosphere inside the command module is still oxygen only, but once astronauts have reached orbit, the chances of flames breaking out are greatly diminished.

As a footnote to the Apollo 204 tragedy, the six spacecraft technicians who had risked their lives to save the astronauts were presented the NASA Medal for Exceptional Bravery, in Washington, October 24, 1967. They were Henry H. Rogers, Jr., of NASA, and Donald O. Babbitt, James D. Gleaves, Jerry W. Hawkins, Stephen B. Clemmons and L. D. Reece, all of North American Rockwell.

Chapter 17

TO LAUNCH A GIANT

Moon rocket stages come to the Kennedy Space Center by sea and by air from sites across the United States. In some instances, the transportation industry has actually been revolutionized to meet space age requirements. The S-IC booster stage of Saturn V has such outlandish dimensions—140 feet tall and 33 feet around—that it can be carried to the Spaceport by only one means of conveyance—barge. If it moved by rail, the stage would cover two flatcars, riding side by side on parallel tracks. If moved by truck, it would cover four lanes of highway. By air, it would fill more cargo space than is available in any aircraft now flying or under construction.

Early versions of the S-IC were put together at the Marshall Space Flight Center in Huntsville, and like the Saturn I rockets had to be barged 2,200 miles to reach the Cape area. Today, boosters are shipped from NASA's Michoud facility near New Orleans, where the stages are fashioned by the Boeing Company. Giant dredges moved into the Banana River in November, 1962, to open a new barge canal to connect the Spaceport with the open access lock at Port Canaveral.

A crew of specialists accompany the stage on each trip. They must maintain a continuous record of all events affecting the rocket booster during transportation. These include temperature, relative humidity, vibration and shocks, internal tank pressure, and barge pitch and roll. Measurements are taken by sensors located on the stage and are recorded automatically on a moving tracer chart. One of the prime reasons for all the concern is that pressure inside the fuel tank and the liquid oxygen tank must be maintained slightly above atmospheric pressure. Temperature changes during the day keep the pressure rising and falling as the gas inside the stage heats or cools. Tanks are pressurized by nitrogen to keep out dust and to prevent decompression.

A 260-foot barge, the *Poseidon*, carries the S-IC from Michoud to KSC. It has an enclosed hangar 40 feet wide, 44 feet high, and 190 feet long. The trip takes about nine days, winding up with delivery of the stage in the turn basin on Merritt Island, just south of the Vehicle Assembly Building.

The special barge Poseidon, *carrying the huge S-IC booster stage of Saturn V, coming through the bridge at Port Canaveral.* (NASA Photo)

NASA's space programs are a matter of public record. There are no classified launches, and it is, perhaps, just as well. Otherwise, how would the agency keep deliveries of moon rocket stages a secret? Tens of thousands of people line bridges and shorelines all along the barge route. Each shipment becomes a news event to every local community the *Poseidon* passes through, and the word that the rocket barge is coming inevitably travels faster than the booster. Ironically, the barge moves the S-IC at a top speed of seven knots. In flight, the stage propels the Saturn V to speeds of 6,000 mph and more.

The S-II second stage has much further to go to reach the Spaceport. It, too, is so oversized (81 feet long and 33 feet around) that it must also be shipped. Its point of departure is the North American Rockwell plant in Seal Beach, California. It moves 4,000 miles, down the coasts of California, Mexico, and Central America, through the Panama Canal, and then north to NASA's Mississippi Test Facility for static firing of its engines, before final delivery to the Spaceport in Florida. A seagoing vessel, the *Point Barrow,* carries the second stage.

A bizarre new type of aircraft, the world's largest, was designed to transport the S-IVB third stage of Saturn V, and the F-1 booster engines, from the west coast across the country. It is called the Super Pregnant Guppy, and it is a converted Boeing 377 Stratocruiser that was modified to enclose the 58-foot-long, 21-foot-in-diameter third stage. The Super Guppy looks as if it would never get off the ground. In flight, it is the most ungainly-looking craft in the skies. But it has proven aerodynamically stable, and cuts delivery time of the S-IVB from three weeks to 12 hours flying time.

Earlier, a smaller plane, the Pregnant Guppy, was built to ferry spacecraft and rocket components across the states. This stratocruiser was lengthened 16 feet. Inside, seats, galley, and the original fuselage were stripped, and the top of the cabin was raised from eight to 21 feet. The diameter of the Guppy was expanded by 12 feet, more than tripling the original volume to 29,187 cubic feet, making it the largest plane in the world in terms of cubic capacity (until the Super Pregnant Guppy was built).

To load and unload its cargo, the original Guppy was rebuilt to separate at the middle of the fuselage into two parts. For flight, the tail end is bolted to the forward section. Despite the bulky midsection, the 45-ton Guppy has a cruising speed of 250 mph, only 15 mph less than the standard stratocruiser.

The S-IVB second stage of the Saturn IB AS-204 vehicle arriving at the Cape Kennedy skid strip in August, 1966, via the world's largest airplane, the Super Guppy, *seen in background.* (NASA Photo)

The Super Pregnant Guppy has an even more phenomenal waist-line. It is 25 feet in diameter. It consumes 49,790 feet of cargo space, dwarfing its record-setting predecessor. It was built, primarily, to haul the S-IVB third stage of Saturn V, which was expanded somewhat from the version that flew on the Saturn I.

The Saturn V's instrument unit and components of the Apollo spacecraft are all flown to Cape Kennedy. The IU comes from Huntsville, the command and service modules of Apollo from Downey, California, and the lunar module from Bethpage, New York.

Stages for the maiden flight of Saturn V began arriving on Merritt Island in August, 1966. The third stage came first, followed a month later by the booster. The second stage was delayed a few months, so technicians in the Vehicle Assembly Building placed a metallic "spacer," simulating the length of the S-II, between the first and third stages, in order that some preliminary tests could be run while engineers waited for the S-II, which arrived in January, 1967.

The second and third stages were placed in low bay checkout cells of the VAB. These cells are on both sides of the transfer aisle. Here, their engines were inspected, and minor leak checks of propellant plumbing lines and of the tanks were made. The booster was

The first stage of the Apollo/Saturn V launch vehicle being hoisted by an overhead crane into High Bay One of the Vehicle Assembly Building. (NASA Photo)

hoisted by a 250-ton crane into High Bay One, and placed gently upon a Mobile Launcher. When individual checks on the second and third stages and the instrument unit had been completed, they were placed in order on top of the booster.

A month later all stages were electrically mated in "the stack." Overall integration tests of the launch vehicle then began—of guidance and control, preflight malfunction sequential, in-flight emergency detection, and power transfer. Meanwhile, the command and service modules for Apollo arrived in December, 1966, and were taken to the Manned Spacecraft Operations Building for preliminary checkout work.

A month later the spacecraft was trucked to the VAB and mated with its launch vehicle. The first Apollo/Saturn V flight was to be an "all-up" mission. That is, all stages were live. This makes it a much more difficult task than, say, if only the first stage were live, as was the case on the initial Saturn I launching in October, 1961. The all-up concept speeds development considerably, but it compounds the preparations at the Spaceport. Every stage, every component, has to work for the flight to be a success. The concept was not new. One of the most notable missiles tested at Cape Kennedy to employ it was the Air Force's Minuteman I. But with Saturn V, it was a story of a larger, more complex rocket *and* a spacecraft. Consequently, problems were expected and encountered as crews readied the huge bird for flight. Test conductors and engineers of each stage of the vehicle met daily to anticipate these trouble areas and resolve them as quickly as possible.

There was a new launch team for the flight of Apollo 4. In the early days at Cape Canaveral, there were as few as 50 engineers and technicians in a blockhouse. They were versatile men, who, through experience of working on hundreds of past flights, could cope with virtually any area of concern that might come up during the countdown. They could "jury rig" or improvise quick fixes if a line broke or a signal faltered.

The evolution of launch crews from that period to the present has been nearly as dramatic as the change in Spaceport facilities. The rockets have grown too large, more complex, and too expensive. There must be specialists for every key individual segment of the operation, be it guidance, propulsion, tracking, or ground support equipment. Instead of a handful of old pros who could handle a variety of jobs under pressure if necessary, there are, now, hundreds

Engineers and technicians examine the upper stage of the Apollo/Saturn V launch vehicle in High Bay One prior to its mating with an Apollo spacecraft, top. (NASA Photo)

Top-to-bottom view of the 36-story-tall Apollo/Saturn V space vehicle was provided when work platforms surrounding the Saturn V rocket and spacecraft were retracted during tests in High Bay One of the Vehicle Assembly Building. (NASA Photo)

of skilled specialists, each with a specific task to complete, fitting into the overall scheme.

The role of NASA personnel in launch operations has changed somewhat, too. The veterans who "did it all" years ago now do more supervising and monitoring of operations. Each stage of the rocket is manufactured by a different company, and contractor engineers and technicians from that company are responsible for the direct checkout operations involving their stage, under overall NASA supervision.

Dr. Hans F. Gruene, KSC's long-time Director of Launch Vehicle Operations, summed up this evolution of launch team personnel:

"I think the NASA engineer's role today is just as important as it ever was if not more so. I can't overemphasize the importance of experience. By applying this, we can actually predict or anticipate problems and thus eliminate them before they develop. Although we don't get our hands dirty during launch preparations, as we once did, I believe there is still a strong feeling of accomplishment, or participation when we can advise the contractors on the best way to do this or that, relying on experience."

There were two particular problem areas during the checkout of the first Apollo/Saturn V in the Vehicle Assembly Building. In February, the spacecraft had to be taken down from the stack and removed to the MSOB so the electrical wiring system could be reverified. Part of this became necessary as a result of the 204 accident and the following report of change recommendations by the Review Board.

In June, 1967, the S-II second stage had to be demated when some hairline cracks were discovered in the seams of another S-II stage. Launch crews wanted to make sure the stage at Kennedy didn't have the same cracks. A series of X-ray and dye penetrant tests proved negative, and the Saturn V was put back together.

The rewired spacecraft was again placed atop the three-stage rocket and was electrically mated on July 24. Next came checks of the overall emergency detection system, and a series of simulated countdown and flight operations. This was followed by tests of the Mobile Launcher's nine swing arms, and then installation of retro and ullage rockets and the launch escape tower.

When the final ordnance items were fitted onto the rocket, its months of preliminary testing and checkout in the VAB were completed. The first flight version of the Saturn V, designated Apollo 4, was now ready to go to the pad. Early on the morning of August 28, the 456-foot-high doors of High Bay One began opening, and, shortly after 6 A.M., an hour before sunrise, the giant rocket and its Mobile Launcher—a 12.2-million-pound load—began the three-and-a-half-mile trip to Pad A on the back of the squat transporter. The 12.2 million pounds carried was considerably heavier than the 500F facilities model that had made the same trip in 1966. Final outfitting and activation of the launcher, plus the flight hardware, added about 1.7 million pounds.

Scores of reporters and photographers, representing network television, the major wire services, and newspapers across the country, recorded the event. The trip was made without incident, and by the middle of the afternoon, the Apollo/Saturn V space vehicle was secured on the pad. The Mobile Service Structure was later brought up from its park position to encircle the rocket and spacecraft.

Once communications circuitry, pneumatic and propellant lines, environmental controls, and electrical power supply lines were connected, power was applied to the vehicle. Propellant loading tests and spacecraft systems verification checks were completed, running into late Sepember, and leading to the Countdown Demonstration Test (CDDT): a full-scale dress rehearsal of the actual count, including propellant loading, where everything is done except igniting the rocket's engines.

The original CDDT was planned to run 83 hours. According to plan, during the first half of it, spacecraft subsystem checks are made, pyrotechnic hookups and mechanical work is performed, and propulsion checks and ordnance connections are made on the rocket. From T minus 41.5 hours to T minus 13 hours, spacecraft servicing operations, such as helium loading, fuel cell activation, and fuel cell cryogenic loading are completed. Batteries are installed in the Saturn V, and final preparations are begun with the propellant-loading facilities at the pad. RP-1 fuel is pumped aboard the booster about two days before launch.

From T minus 13 hours to T minus 0 in the CDDT, the launch vehicle is powered up and the spacecraft is closed out after a last inspection. Destruct packages are installed and checked out with the Air Force Eastern Test Range Safety Officer. This is done to make sure, should the bird wobble off course, it can be blown up by the RSO when he triggers a signal to the destruct package.

Final propellant loading and pressurization of the stages are finished, the Mobile Service Structure is moved back to a safe position, power is transferred internally to the rocket and spacecraft, and, at T minus three minutes and 10 seconds, the automatic sequencer firing command is triggered.

The CDDT is an all-important test. For the first flight of the Saturn V, which cost well over $100 million per rocket, it carried added significance. Both Dr. Debus and Dr. von Braun closely followed the test from their consoles on the top row of firing room one in the Launch Control Center.

Though the test was to last 83 hours, it actually ran several days beyond this. There were computer failures and problems with equipment. A helium pressure regulator went out. Much of this was to be expected. It is, in fact, one of the main purposes of such a test to ferret out, to trouble shoot, potential problems before the actual countdown is begun. There were also human errors. At one point in the practice count the clock went down to T minus 17 seconds and was automatically halted there when pressure dropped unexplainedly in the booster stage. Investigation revealed that a manual valve had simply not been fully turned. This was, however, a new launch team working on a completely new vehicle. The CDDT was rescheduled and recycled several times, but finally reached T minus 0 on October 13. It had been a rough test, but a vital one. The launch teams learned a lot. Many of the mistakes would not be repeated. Most of the problem areas would either be cleaned up or worked around on succeeding runs.

As a direct result of CDDT experience, the final count was shortened from 83 to 49 hours, with two built-in holds added—cushion time to allow launch crews to catch up on items that fell behind during the countdown.

A few days after completion of the CDDT, the Flight Readiness Test (FRT) was held. This was the last major checkpoint before actually setting the launch date and beginning the final countdown. It was a final look at all systems.

Apollo 4 was equipped with everything except a lunar module. It was decided to test the first flight LM on a Saturn IB launch that would follow, in sequence, the maiden Saturn V, which itself would carry only a dummy LM. The mission was scheduled to last less than nine hours. Its major objectives were to test the three stages of the rocket in flight, and to subject the Apollo spacecraft's heat shield to reentry temperatures that would approximate those which astronauts could expect upon their return home from the lunar mission.

Every nut and bolt of the entire space vehicle, over two million individual parts in all, had been tested, retested, and tested again on the ground, but the moment of truth is always on the launch pads of the Spaceport. There were 780 full duration firings on F-1 engines alone, and over 2,000 tests. There were 3,605 tests on the J-2 engines, totaling 314,959 seconds of firing time. Still, regardless of how well engines have performed in static tests, no matter how reliable guidance systems are during prelaunch checks, there is no substitutte for the actual flight.

"For six years we've been testing the subsystems, the systems and the stages," said Dr. George E. Mueller, the Associate NASA Administrator for Manned Space Flight. "More than 200,000 people have been working on the bird, with another 100,000 in support. We're looking to this mission to give us verification of all that has gone before. It is being flown to verify correctness of design."

Mueller continued: "It is the first time we've flight tested the entire vehicle. It's the first flight of the booster stage with the F-1 engines; the first flight of the second stage with the J-2 liquid hydrogen engines. There are so many 'firsts' I can't mention them all. The heat shield alone—it's the first time we've been able to test it at lunar reentry velocities. The heat shield is a crucial test—just as they all are. But we've got to get this data before we move on to manned flights.

"This mission," he emphasized, "is the culmination of effort of a lot of people. We've done everything humanly possible as far as ground testing goes. We depend on people to do things properly. The integrity of their work is the basis of the integrity of the space vehicle.

"All the blood, sweat, and anguish that went into the building of the Pyramids, all the hurry-up scientific genius that went into the Manhattan atomic bomb development project, all the 60 years of preparatory aircraft work that went into the supersonic transport— those three combined just begin to equal what Americans have accomplished in the past six years leading to this launch."

By the end of the first week in November, Apollo 4 had gone through everything man could do for it to achieve launch readiness. Thousands of tons of propellants were pumped into its cavernous tanks, and the final countdown got under way. Liftoff time was set for 7 A.M., November 9, 1967.

Beginning the day before, all roads leading into Brevard County, Florida, were jammed. Thousands of people from all over the state drove toward the Spaceport to see the launch of the mightiest machine man had ever made. Motels had been crammed for days, and all along the roads leading into Cape Kennedy and Merritt Island campers parked and tents blossomed.

At the newly constructed press site, 500 newsmen, photographers, and television commentators and technicians relayed in word and picture what was happening at Launch Complex 39. In the darkness, searchlights deluged Saturn V in a brilliant white that could be seen for 100 miles up and down the coastline.

Unlike the dress rehearsal, where there were innumerable problems, the countdown progressed with an unexpected smoothness. In fact, the one big worry in the predawn hours before launch was the weather. Gusty winds had whipped the Spaceport for three days, and there was a final weather briefing at midnight. Officials would keep a close look at the winds, but decided Apollo 4 could be flown if there were no further changes.

The hours slipped by and the countdown continued to run on time. Still, many felt there would be numerous holds, as there had always been in the past on the first flight of any new vehicle. But Saturn V was to set precedents in this respect too. There were no holds.

At T minus five minutes, the green clocks in firing room one were still winking off the seconds, but now there was at least a hint of a problem. A computer at a site on Bermuda, part of the manned space flight tracking network, was down. It was critical to the mission. Status reports were "go" down the line until the flight controller in Houston was asked. He answered "no go." Launch personnel decided to carry the count on down, hoping the computer would come up in the final minutes before zero.

At T minus three minutes and 10 seconds, the automatic sequencing system went into effect. At the press site, and to millions of people watching on television, there was no indication of any trouble. Only the launch crews were sweating out the situation. Finally, at about T minus 90 seconds, the flight director came over the main communications channel and said the Bermuda station was now okay. The flight was on.

At T minus 8.9 seconds, the ignition sequence for the rocket's mighty booster engines was begun. In an instant, all five F-1 engines were screaming at full thrust, straining to be unleashed. Each one consumed 1,000 gallons of propellants a second. Fuel was fed by turbo-pumps equal in power to 30 diesel locomotives.

Enormous funnels of flame completely engulfed the rocket, poured

Saturn V brilliantly illuminated by searchlights as it stands on the pad at Launch Complex 39. (NASA Photo)

over the launch platform, and ran along the ground for hundreds of feet north and south of the flame deflector. To observers looking to the east, it was as if there were a second sunrise on this morning. At T minus 0, the commit signal was flashed. Massive hold down arms retracted, and Saturn V began to climb.

"Liftoff! We have liftoff at one second after the hour," came an excited voice from the Launch Control Center.

The great bird rose slowly, under its 6.2 million pounds of bulk. It took 10 or more seconds just to clear the launcher tower, as the fireball from the five booster engines continued to beat down. Then the sound caught up with the fury. The earth rumbled for miles around. Plaster dust shook loose in the LCC, coating engineers. Flocks of birds took wing. Thunder rattled off the grandstand roof at the press site. The noise level hit 130 decibels, and many onlookers instinctively put hands to their ears.

As the propellants were burned, the rocket's rise accelerated. At T plus 12 seconds, the vehicle began a change of attitude to alter its course to the proper flight azimuth: 72 degrees east of north. Now it

Liftoff for the Apollo/Saturn V lunar vehicle on its successful first flight test, at 7:00 A.M., November 9, 1967. (NASA Photo)

began soaring, burning a hole through low-level clouds. In two and a half minutes the first stage had propelled Apollo 4 about 38 miles up and 100 miles down range. Two thousand one hundred fifty tons of fuel had been expended. The booster separated and fell back into the ocean in broken pieces, and the S-II second stage took over. Its five J-2 engines ignited and burned for over six minutes, increasing speed from 6,000 mph to more than 15,000 mph. It then burned out and separated, and the single S-IVB third stage fired, with enough kick to insert the S-IVB and spacecraft into orbit at 17,500 mph.

On the second pass across the United States, Apollo 4 was re-aligned for a second burn of the S-IVB. The engine fired again, for more than five minutes, setting another precedent. After coasting for 10 minutes, the third stage and Apollo command and service modules parted. The spacecraft reached an apogee of 11,234 miles. At this point, earth's gravity overcame Apollo's speed and began to pull it back. The service propulsion system was then ignited for four and a half minutes, to push the spacecraft's speed to almost 25,000 mph. Ninety seconds before ramming back into the atmosphere, the command and service modules were separated, and the CM was turned so its heat shield could take the brunt of temperatures over 4,500 degrees F.

The heat shield survived in good condition, and, at 10,000 feet, Apollo's three main parachutes deployed perfectly. Less than nine hours after liftoff, the spacecraft splashed down in the Pacific Ocean, about 630 miles north of Hawaii, and a scant six miles from the prime recovery ship. Not only did Saturn V perform beyond all expectations, but the Apollo craft soared 11 times higher, reentered the earth's atmosphere 7,000 miles an hour faster and more than 2,000 degrees hotter than Mercury or Gemini. Both the rocket and capsule earned flight honors under the severest of tests.

More than 2,800 measurements were taken on the launch vehicle alone, over three times the number recorded on Saturn I flights. Only 75 were taken on Redstone shots. Measurements included acceleration, acoustic, temperature, pressure, vibration, flow rate, position, guidance and control, radio frequency and telemetry, electric power, and others. Apollo 4 also carried 22 telemetry systems, two tracking systems, and two motion picture cameras. The cameras were mounted on the second stage of the rocket and were ejected after booster separation. Recovery crews picked them up in the Atlantic about 100 miles off shore, and engineers gained much information by viewing staging operations at the unique angles covered.

Surprisingly, despite the searing blast from the five F-1 booster engines, pad damage was relatively minor; in fact, less than officials had expected. Several small fires broke out on the Mobile Launcher tower and in the pad area, but they were soon extinguished by the deluge system. More than 25,000 gallons of water were pumped onto the smoking launcher platform through 29 nozzles during the first 30 seconds after ignition. Additional nozzles were directed to cool the flame deflector. Primary structures on the launcher, the nine swing arms and the rocket hold-down arms were scorched, but undamaged. Three tail service masts, several winches, the ground level elevator shaft, and six cameras were lost in the fiery blastoff, but this had been anticipated. Refurbishment of the Mobile Launcher and pad area began within hours of liftoff.

Congratulatory telegrams poured into the Spaceport following the successful flight. Vice President Hubert H. Humphrey called Dr. Debus to commend the launch crews personally. From the White House, President Johnson lauded the mission as proof that "we can launch and bring back safely to earth the spaceship that will take men to the moon."

At a postlaunch press conference on Merritt Island, Air Force Major General Samuel Phillips, NASA's Apollo Program Manager, said, "This has demonstrated the power of a good group of people. You could almost feel the power of the launch team during the night and on through the early morning hours in the last minutes and seconds of the countdown. I was tremendously impressed with the smooth teamwork that this combined government-multi-industry team put together. It was smooth. It was professional. It was perfect in every respect. It was a powerful operation. You could almost feel the will with which it was being carried out."

Apollo 4's magnificent accomplishments were almost too numerous to list. Man had taken a long stride nearer the moon. All stages worked as planned, and an all-time record 285,000 pounds had been placed in earth orbit, giving the United States a booster power unmatched anywhere. The flight also inaugurated a new complex of facilities, and proved beyond doubt the practicality of the mobile launch concept.

Many benefits were less tangible. Dr. Robert C. Seamans, then-Deputy NASA Administrator, spoke on one of these at a postflight press conference in Houston:

"The morale of those involved in the Apollo program following the accident we had last January was low, in a sense that everyone involved felt that it must have been something that he or she could have done to have avoided the fire. We have to recognize when we have accidents that they are not acts of God, they are human mistakes. In that particular case, after a very careful review, we uncovered a large number of areas where we felt that we should and could make improvements.

"The group of people involved have moved ahead, I think, in a remarkable fashion following that accident. At times, it has not been easy because of outside pressures and outside concerns about the capability of the team. I am sure the team itself has wondered whether they really were up to the job and up to the responsibility.

"I believe that the results achieved today clearly demonstrate that this team, made up of NASA people and other government and industrial people, truly have the competence to not only take on the manned lunar landing program, but any other space objective that this country feels is important, and to which we should dedicate our efforts."

Chapter 18

PLANS AND SCHEDULES

Flexibility is perhaps the most important word to manned space flight scheduling. There must be plans and alternate plans to cover every possible contingency on each flight in the Apollo program. *If* a launch is successful, then Plan A is followed. *If* the rocket blows up on the pad, Plan B must be used. *If* there are delays that have not been anticipated, then an alternate to the alternate plan must be devised. Everything is done with the ultimate objective in mind: to land American astronauts on the lunar surface and return them safely to earth.

Since the space program is borne of technologies that are rapidly advancing, and because NASA's financing is dependent upon Congressional approval and the ranking of national priorities, planners must be able to shift into high gear in any number of directions. Apollo scheduling has been sharply affected both by technical progress and governmental budget restrictions.

The war in Vietnam has put a severe drain on America's resources. Cuts have been felt across the board among the federal agencies, NASA included. The fiscal 1968 space budget, for instance, was sliced several hundred million dollars and caused planners to rechart many key programs. Though moneys to carry out Apollo's basic goals had been committed, it was still necessary to remap projects.

Originally, several manned Saturn IB's had been listed for astronaut training in earth orbit leading to the Saturn V lunar mission. At one point, dual Saturn IB launches were planned on successive days from Complexes 34 and 37. One would carry three men in the Apollo command and service modules, and the bird from 37 would boost a lunar module. Then the astronauts would rendezvous in earth orbit with the LM. Officials decided, however, that it would be more economically feasible, both in dollars and time, to shoot the command and service modules *and* the lunar module all on one Saturn V rocket. Thus, the emphasis in thinking shifted from multiple uses of the Saturn IB to the larger vehicle.

Again, everything was based on the *if* factor. Such planning shifts could successfully come off only if the moon rocket performed well on its first few flights. If it didn't, the schedules would have to be reworked again, bringing the smaller bird back into play.

NASA's launch schedules, particularly those involving manned flights, or missions leading up to them, have always been involved in such a juggling game, and of necessity. It's fine to say, for example, that men would fly on the third or fourth Saturn V rocket. But what if the first two had blown up? Thus, like the baseball manager in the midst of a tight pennant race, flight planners must call them one at a time, with each launch somewhat dependent on how well or badly the preceding mission went.

Following the Apollo 4 shot, launch crews prepared two vehicles at the same time: one to go from Complex 37 aboard a Saturn IB, and the second, a Saturn V which would essentially repeat the maiden flight of the moon rocket. The booster that was to have propelled Grissom, White, and Chaffee into orbit in the Apollo 204 spacecraft was taken down from Complex 34 after the fire, and re-erected in April at 37. It had not been damaged.

This booster was given a new job: to hurl the first flight-ready version of the lunar module into earth orbit. It was to be an unmanned mission with the fundamental objective of verifying operation of the LM's propulsion and staging systems, both the ascent and descent engines. This was necessary before man could be committed to fly the lunar module in space.

Again, as with practically all first flights at the Spaceport, there were many problem areas to be worked out before this space vehicle, Apollo 5, could be flown. The booster, of course, had been ready to go for more than a year. The lunar module developed troubles in the guidance-navigation system, with some engine valves, and had a leaky ascent engine. The launch was pushed back several months from its original schedule to January 23, 1968.

The flight, unlike the lengthy, problem-plagued checkout cycle and a countdown cluttered with technical troubles, went remarkably smooth. In fact, 32 of 33 primary and secondary objectives were achieved.

As the giant Apollo 4 thundered off its pad November 9, 1967, launch crews were already far along in their testing and checkout of the second Saturn V rocket (502, or Apollo 6) in the Vehicle Assembly Building. The three stages of the bird and the instrument unit had all arrived, been through individual examinations, and placed in the stack on a Mobile Launcher in High Bay Three. All that was missing was the spacecraft, sister ship of number 017, which had flown on Apollo 4 and plunged back into the earth's atmosphere at lunar reentry speed. Spacecraft 020 arrived at the Center late in the year.

The second Saturn V rocket, designated Apollo 6, lifted off, again right on the dot of 7 A.M., April 4, 1968. Once more, the giant booster performed flawlessly, and a record 132-ton payload was shoved into earth orbit. The shot fell short of the remarkable performance of the first moon vehicle the previous November, however. Two second-stage engines shut down a couple of minutes before they should have, and the third-stage engine failed to restart after two orbits. Consequently, the spacecraft was not subjected to the roasting reentry temperatures that had been hoped for. Nevertheless, the rocket further proved its structural soundness, and many other mission objectives were achieved.

Though Apollo 6 created some schedule concern, as officials pondered possible causes of the engine shutdowns, there was optimism that overall program goals could be met on time. While flight data was still being sifted, planners began to seriously consider two innovative approaches: (1) to man the third Saturn V vehicle, if satisfactory solutions to Apollo 6's shortcomings could be found; and (2) to precede the moon landing with a circumlunar mission early in 1969. Both steps would considerably advance the Apollo timetable.

Following a total assessment of the engine irregularities on the Apollo 6 flight, NASA officials decided proper corrections could be made through ground tests, and announced the third Apollo/Saturn V vehicle would be manned. The shot was scheduled for late 1968 or early 1969.

As this book went to press, final preparations were being made for the first manned Apollo flight, to be piloted on an earth orbital training mission by astronauts Wally Schirra, Donn Eisele, and

Walter Cunningham. The crushing impact of the tragic 204 fire hit
full force on the scheduling for this critical mission. Originally, it
had been hoped the spacecraft could be ready in time for a late
1967 flight date. But the many major changes that had to be incorporated into Apollo as a result of the 204 Review Board's recommendations caused continuing delays. The launch was reset for the
spring of 1968, but had to be postponed again when modification
work fell behind. As Schirra had said, "We will fly the spacecraft
when it is ready."

Apollo 101 is the first of the Block II series of capsules. It differs
from the one in which the astronauts were burned in a number of
ways. The major distinction of the Block II series is the addition of
an airlock through which astronauts will crawl from the command
module to the lunar module. There is also more instrumentation on
the "second generation" of Apollo spacecraft.

At publication time, this first manned flight, with a Saturn IB
booster, had still not been officially scheduled, though planners
were sure it would go sometime in late summer, fall, or winter
of 1968, well over a year after the 204 fire. It was to be an open-
ended shot of up to 10 days, to check out performance of spacecraft
systems and crew operations. Eight operations of the service module
main propulsion engine were planned. Orbital attitudes were to range
from 104 nautical miles at insertion, to approximately 230 nautical
miles. Recovery area is in the western Atlantic Ocean, about 800
miles southeast of Bermuda.

The second manned Apollo launch will include the full Saturn V,
a block II Apollo command and service module, and a fully instrumented lunar module. It or a following shoot will be, if all goes well,
a training mission, practice for the actual lunar flight, as described
in Chapter One. The astronauts will not go further however, than
earth orbit.

The spacecraft will be injected into a 100-nautical-mile parking
orbit, and after two passes around the earth, the S-IVB third stage
will be ignited to simulate ejection to the moon. The burn of the
stage's J-2 engine, however, will not be as long as it would be in a
lunar run; thus Apollo will be put into an ellipse which will carry it
to a distance of about 4,000 nautical miles from the earth. During the
four or more such passes around the earth, the spacecraft will be
transposed for docking.

After these revolutions through the Van Allen radiation belt,
which could be dangerous, the spacecraft will recircularize at 200

miles in order to avoid passing again. The rest of the maneuvers will be performed in this parking orbit to simulate the burns that will be encountered on the lunar flight. This includes the lunar orbit insertion, the lunar module braking when it goes down for its landing, the LM ascent, and, finally, the transearth injection on the way home.

Objectives of such a mission are to:

—Qualify the launch vehicle in a simulated lunar landing profile.

—Qualify the spacecraft. Demonstrate that Apollo and the crew can fly the lunar landing mission.

—Verify that the thermal conditions during the engine burns, throughout the maneuvers, are as anticipated.

The spacecraft for this all-important tune-up will be the same as that for a lunar landing, with one exception: the lunar module will have more research and development instrumentation aboard to make sure its temperatures and pressures are within limits.

On November 20, 1967, NASA announced that James McDivitt, David Scott, and Russell Schickart would pilot the first manned Saturn V shot, and Frank Borman, Michael Collins, and William Anders would fly the next one. A later rocket, possibly the fifth in the series, will be the one to make history. If all goes well on all previous flights leading up to this vehicle, it probably will be ticketed as the one for the lunar landing mission. But this will be an open-ended flight. If everything goes as planned, astronauts will land on the moon. If anything goes wrong, the flight will be cut short, or some sort of alternate plan will go into effect. A successful shot would closely follow that described in the opening chapter.

NASA Administrator James E. Webb said in September, 1967, "We should be able to get off as many as nine Saturn V's before the end of the decade if necessary." Two months later, he spelled out the schedule in more detail. Three Saturn V's were listed for 1968 launches. Either the third or fourth one would be manned. There would also be three Saturn IB flights: two unmanned tests of the lunar module, and the mission of astronauts Schirra, Eisele, and Cunningham.

Webb also forecast five manned Saturn V shots for 1969. Four of these, vehicles 505 through 508, are programmed as lunar mission development flights or lunar mission simulations. "It is possible," the Administrator said, "that the lunar landing could be made on Apollo/Saturn V 509, but it is more likely that it will not occur until later, on one of the remaining six Saturn V flights in the program."

Months later these predictions were updated. Conceivably, if all goes well, the fifth Saturn V flight (the third manned one) could be the man-to-the-moon mission. However, most NASA officials feel that several earth orbit flights might be necessary to qualify all the hardware. It is also possible astronauts will fly into orbit around the moon. The lunar landing would then be attempted on the next flight. There are a number of options open, and the actual schedule will slide forward or backward with the individual success or failure of each mission along the way.

The quicker the conquest of the moon takes place, the more rockets NASA will be able to save for follow-on projects. A second lunar landing, giving the astronauts more time to examine the moon's features, may be scheduled. But the initial mission is the key one. With its achievement, America will have accomplished man's greatest technological feat. The entire planning of the Saturn V series of rocket is dependent upon when the lunar landing is carried out. NASA will spend as many vehicles as required. Overall, the agency has bought 27 large Saturn rockets; 12 Saturn IB's, and 15 Saturn V's.

What are the odds of a successful manned lunar landing and safe return this decade? Are they 50-50, 40-60, 10-90? There is no measurable way to calculate such chances. Each launch in the step by step progression leading to the moon shot is dependent upon the other. Any failure or slippage, certainly, cuts into the percentages, and the Apollo 204 accident was especially damaging to the time-table. Just before 204 was to fly, in February, 1967, optimistic officials held hope the actual lunar flight could be made in late 1968. The fire eliminated any possibility of that. The impact of 204 has been to reduce the probability of hitting the moon in this decade, not eliminate it. To the gambler, it is a parlay. If the first manned Apollo launch on Saturn IB goes well, and if there are no problems in the Saturn V series, than it is conceivable that the deadline can be met, the calendar can be beaten. Time and the sequence of events will be the deciding factors.

In a very real sense, the future of the nation's space programs depends largely on the attitude of the American public. If the people feel it is a wasted effort, or if they don't thoroughly understand it, their attitudes are reflected among congressmen who vote the appropriations that keep NASA in business.

Vice President Hubert H. Humphrey summed up the importance of public understanding when he said: "Not as many people as we would wish understand the full impact of this aerospace revolution, with its new methods and awesome productivity. Particularly, there is too little understanding of how this technological change can improve man's lot with better education, increased chances for world peace and higher standards of living. I believe that each of us has a responsibility to help improve the dissemination of such information, since realization of the practical advantages of the space program, rather than blind faith, will best assure healthy growth for this technology. With clear understanding, we shall maintain the momentum of our progress."

It is thus incumbent upon the space agency to promote its programs. One of the most effective and simplest ways to do this is to show the public exactly what is being done at the Spaceport. Consequently there are no secret launches, no hidden operations. There are still today some military missile and satellite systems that, for reasons of national security, are not open to the public. But at Cape Kennedy and on Merritt Island, this is not true for the most part. The majority of NASA shoots are announced 30 days in advance, and are covered by the press. Only a few Air Force launches remain classified. In the early days of testing at the Cape, however, the story was different. Missile weapons systems were being developed, and many of the results were classified.

Newsmen had a hard time covering these launches. It would be obvious to anyone within 50 miles that a rocket was being fired, but which one was it, how did it do, and what was its objective? Reporters and photographers were barred from the launch sites in the early and mid-1950's, so they covered the shoots from the neighboring beaches. It was a hit or miss operation at best, and as often as not the information that reached newsprint was misleading or inaccurate.

With the creation of NASA in 1958, and with a general loosening of security restrictions on Air Force, Army, and Navy missiles, the policy began to change in the late 1950's. Reporters were allowed on the Cape to cover launches. And in turn, the public began to get a better understanding of what the people at the Spaceport were trying to do.

It is written in the National Space Act of 1958 that all NASA programs will be open. And so it is today. Accredited newsmen from all over the world cover the big flights, including journalists from countries behind the Iron Curtain. More than 500 newsmen reported the launch of Apollo 4, and 1,000 were on site when John Glenn went into orbit. Not only are the launches open today, but preflight press conferences are held for most major space shoots, with experts presenting detailed briefings of what the mission goals are, and how the rocket and spacecraft preparations are going. In many instances, a postlaunch briefing is also held.

Without such open coverage, the public would not have as clear an understanding of the space program and its overall objectives. There are drawbacks to such a policy, of course. When the Vanguard exploded on the pad December 6, 1957, it did so before the eyes and ears of the world, and the United States suffered a dreadful black eye in prestige. On the other hand, reportage of the many great triumphs that have been achieved through the years has more than countered news of the infrequent disasters.

Today, any person on earth can drive into the Kennedy Space Center and onto the Cape to see the sites where American space history has been recorded. This open access began in December, 1963, when the Air Force allowed motorists to follow a marked route through the Cape. Less than a year later, NASA opened the Spaceport to drive-through tours.

More than 400,000 people took the Sunday tours in 1964, but this was only a trickle of what was to come. The National Park Service was called upon in 1965 to make detailed studies of the visitor potential in the area and suggest means of satisfying the increasing public demand for information. Results of the study were incredible. The Park Service estimated the Spaceport would draw two to three million visitors a year by 1970! They recommended that NASA build a Visitor Information Center on Merritt Island and provide escorted bus tours for the public.

By July, 1966, NASA began the bus tours. They received enthusiastic initial response, far beyond expectations. Several thousand people a day came to a temporary exhibit site to take the tours, which included a drive past all major launch sites and stops at key points, such as the old Mercury Control Center on Cape Kennedy, in the Vehicle Assembly Building at Launch Complex 39, and inside the Flight Crew Training Building, where astronauts prep for coming flights. Another main attraction is the Air Force space museum at Cape Kennedy, where flight versions and full-size models of most missiles launched since 1950 are on display. Nearby are the actual pads used for the flights of Explorer I, America's first satellite, and the Mercury Redstone shots of Alan Shepard and Gus Grissom.

Nearly half a million people from all 50 states and more than 60 foreign countries took the Spaceport tours during their first year of operation. Meanwhile, Congress authorized just over one million dollars for the construction of a Visitor Information Center at the Spaceport. It was formally opened August 1, 1967. America's space programs are explained in detail via films, slides, paintings, photographs, full-scale spacecraft models, panels, exhibits, and displays. There is everything from a working model of the VAB to a fully suited astronaut dummy, and the actual Gemini 9 spacecraft flown by Tom Stafford and Gene Cernan. The attractions are unique, and the public response has been warmly receptive. And people are becoming better informed as shareholders in the nation's space programs. As taxpayers, they have a significant stake in the activities!

In addition to the public, a number of world dignitaries, including many heads of state, have visited the Spaceport. Three United States Presidents, Dwight Eisenhower, John Kennedy, and Lyndon Johnson, have made several trips to the Center during their administrations. Other distinguished guests have included the King and Queen of Afghanistan, the President of India, the Shah of Iran, the King of Jordan, the Grand Duchess of Luxembourg, and the King and Queen of Nepal among others.

Public response to the Space Center is not limited to adults or dignitaries, however. The age of space has, in fact, created a new breed of all-American hero: the astronaut. His unparalleled popularity is bolstered each time a postman empties his bag at the Spaceport. Fan mail averages several hundred letters a month year-round, but when an astronaut soars into space, the volume of correspondence overflows the KSC post office. The vast majority of mail, of course, is penned by starry-eyed youngsters who ask for autographs, offer advice, pose questions, denounce failures, and volunteer—by the hundreds—for space flight. Some of the letters are priceless in their unintended humor.

—"I read where you launched an artificial satellite. Does this mean it really isn't up there?"

—"I just heard a newsman on the television say that the space program is costing every American 20 cents. Enclosed are my two dimes."

—"Why don't you put giant fans to one side of the launching pad? Then, when you shoot your rockets off, the smoke would be blown away so you could see what's going on!"

—"Dear astronaut Gordon Cooper: Good luck on your way around the earth. I'll blink my flashlight on and off so as to say hello."

All letters mailed to the Spaceport requesting information are answered. NASA and the Air Force, in fact, are delighted in the interest in rocketry shown by the nation's youngsters. Officials know tomorrow's astronauts, engineers, and technicians will come from the ranks of today's youthful letter writers, and they encourage them through a number of national space education projects. In fact, special space lecture demonstrations are held at KSC on a regular basis for visiting schoolchildren.

Some of the letter requests have to be turned down, however, such as the following from a lad in New Jersey:

"Dear Sirs: I am offering my little sister as a replacement for your satellite's radio. This would be much better, because, as you know, a radio's battery eventually wears out, but my little sister *never* stops talking. I feel she is specially qualified for this job because she is small (four years old) and willing to travel."

Just as the Spaceport has become an international attraction of first magnitude, so, too, has the community surrounding the Center grown. In 1950, Brevard County was a quiet area known only for its citrus, fishing, and fine strips of beach. It was mostly undeveloped, and had a population of 23,000. Then the missile boom hit. By 1960, Brevard had become the fastest growing county in the United States, with a population of more than 111,000. By January 1, 1968, the growth had swelled to a quarter million. Property on the ocean that sold for $48 a front foot now commands $1,000 and more. Personal income increased proportionately—from $24 million in 1950 to nearly $600 million 15 years later.

To be expected, there were tremendous growing pains. It took housing years to catch up to the demands. Schools, roads, public utilities, and business services also had a difficult time maintaining the rapid pace of expansion. To help meet the problem, state and federal governments joined forces. By mid-1967, the federal government had contributed $90 million in grants or loans to develop or support essential facilities and services, including housing, public schools, roads and bridges, harbors and waterways, hospitals, health centers, and airports.

There are still areas of concern: water supply, pollution control, cultural activities, urban shopping and traffic. But Brevard County has made remarkable developmental strides over the years to grow with the Space Center, and, in time. solutions will be found to the remaining problems.

Chapter 19

APOLLO APPLICATIONS

Apollo has received and will continue to elicit more news coverage than perhaps any other single project ever undertaken by man. It has so overshadowed all other aspects of the nation's space program, in fact, that to many, it is *the* program, the end all. Such a notion, of course, is far from correct. Today, while one massive team marshals its resources and personnel to complete the far-reaching Apollo program, other teams are at work on other projects, perhaps not as glamorous as landing astronauts on the moon, but equally as important in the development of an overall in-space capability.

Apollo Applications is one such program. Its birth and development, as a carry-on of Apollo itself, not only assures continued expansion of the U.S. manned space flight program without any appreciable hiatus, but also allows additional goals to be set and striven for, while achieving maximum economy. Apollo Applications, or AAP, will assure the American taxpayer of more for his money, because it will use hardware and technology already developed for Apollo.

Each AAP mission, in fact, is designed to take full advantage of Apollo's flight experience, ground facilities, and trained manpower. Specifically, Saturn IB and Saturn V launch vehicles will be used. For the manned lunar landing program 12 Saturn IB vehicles and 15 Saturn V's were purchased. It is probable that not all of them will be needed to accomplish Apollo's basic objective of landing astronauts on the moon and returning them safely to earth. NASA planners thus decided that when this goal was accomplished, the launch vehicles still in the stable could be turned over to AAP. The same applies to the Saturn IB. When it is felt the necessary training missions have been successfully completed, the rest of these rockets can likewise be switched to AAP.

One of the most important objectives of AAP is to determine man's capability in space over long periods of time. To date, the two-week flight of astronauts James Lovell and Frank Borman is the longest on American logbooks. Early development of long-duration flight capability is clearly one of the most important goals to be pursued for man to continue his exploration further into space.

Astronauts will take the first step toward setting up a home away from home in an orbital workshop. They will use the 10,000-cubic-foot volume of the Saturn's S-IVB upper stage, converting the inside of its hydrogen tank into two-story living and working quarters for flights of 28 or 56 days or longer. The S-IVB tank is 58 feet long and 21½ feet in diameter. In it, astronauts will be able to work and live in a shirt-sleeve, zero gravity environment. Electrical power will be provided by fuel cells, solar cells and batteries.

The orbital workshop may be the second of the first four planned AAP flights launched by Saturn IB's. Other payloads in the series included a lunar mapping and survey system and an Apollo telescope mount. These are to be clustered in orbit to form a stabilized space station.

The projected first flight will place a manned spacecraft and a lunar mapping and survey system into a circular orbit 140 miles above earth. After Apollo is turned around and docked with the mapping and survey system, experiments will be conducted for about five days. The orbital workshop will be launched on the sixth day of the mission. This package will include the spent S-IVB stage, an airlock module, and a multiple docking adapter—all of which will be directly injected into a circular orbit 300 miles up.

Using rendezvous and docking technology gained from Gemini and Apollo flights, astronauts will then maneuver their spacecraft for a linkup with the huge workshop. Crew members will enter the empty S-IVB through an airlock module which has a 65-inch tunnel connecting to the workshop. Then they will set up housekeeping. The mission is planned to be open-ended, with a duration of 28 days. This means that if anything goes wrong at any point, the rest of the flight can be scrubbed and the astronauts called back to earth.

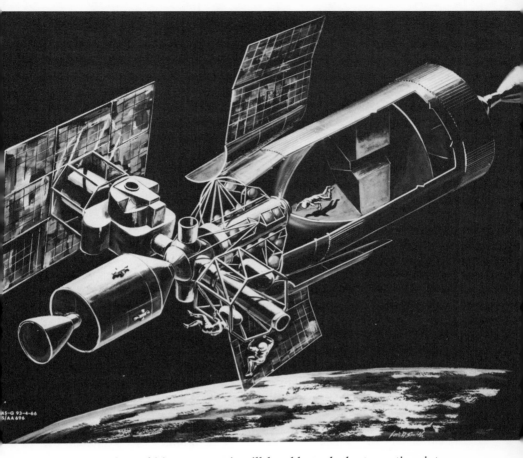

As many as five orbiting spacecraft will be able to dock at one time into the Multiple Docking Adapter. In this artist's conception, the adapter is attached to the S-IVB spent stage, which has been converted into an orbital workshop. Also docked to the adapter are Apollo command and service modules (left), *the Apollo telescope mount* (upper left), *and the mapping and survey system module.* (Courtesy of NASA)

While the first AAP crew will come down after four weeks in space, most of the hardware will remain in orbit for further use. From three to six months later, another team of astronauts will go back up to the original clustered space station. A day after their launch, an unmanned payload will be sent up after them, aboard a fourth Saturn rocket. This will be an Apollo telescope mount and equipment for experiments. Again, rendezvous and docking with the workshop will be carried out, and this time the crew may stay up to eight weeks, depending on how things go. When they come down, the cluster will once more be prepared for extended storage.

The telescope will make this the first manned solar observatory, and observations will be made in orbit, where the sun and stars can be clearly studied without being obscured by distortions of the earth's atmosphere. Scientists hope to obtain measurements of the sun in the extreme ultraviolet and X-ray portions of the electro-magnetic spectrum, which cannot penetrate the earth's atmosphere, and to get pictures of the sun's corona in the white light portion of the spectrum. When the telescope is in operation, the astronauts will gather information on film, tape, and by means of television and other special instruments. A TV system will enable them to view images of sun recorded by the telescope.

Later in the AAP program, depending on funding appropriations, Saturn V rockets may be used to follow up the first Apollo landings on the moon. Scientist-astronauts may explore the lunar surface for up to 14 days at a time. Their findings would help determine whether it will be worthwhile to continue such explorations, or perhaps to colonize the moon.

Also, lunar orbital missions may be planned for high-quality mapping and survey photography from polar lunar orbits. This will permit detailed study of the geological features of the entire moon.

As this book went to press, the final outcome of the Apollo Applications Program had not been fully determined. Everyone at the Spaceport, however, feels strongly that only if this country has such a key, long-range goal can the space effort continue with the impetus it has had over the past two decades. The potential is too great and the investment already made too heavy to curtail operations once the moon mission has been accomplished. NASA and the Air Force have invested more than $2 billion in the Spaceport installation, and it would be a shameful waste should these facilities not be used in the future for the benefit of mankind.

Apollo's momentum began with JFK's May, 1961, pronounce-ment of a manned lunar landing as a national goal. The program will continue at high speed perhaps into 1970 or so. Beyond that, a specific and challenging new goal must be set to keep our space tech-nological progress moving forward. Congressman Olin Teague of Texas, Chairman of the House Sub-Committee on Manned Space

Flight, has summed up the importance of declaring specific, ambitious goals in space:

"Merely landing on the moon is *not* our end objective. If we expect to continue the rapid progress made to date in this country, to compete in the world marketplace in the years to come, and to help other peoples improve their standards of living, we will need still more technological progress. And this is what the space program is providing us—a technology on a large scale so vast and varied that we can barely keep up with it. There is hardly a single field of scientific endeavor that is not touched by the space program.

"If I could sum up the reasons, I would say that the national space program is an integral part of our national well-being, not only for today, but for the future as well—intellectually, materially, and spiritually."

The great question is, which should be the next step? There is no easy answer. In fact, several steps may be chosen, both for military security purposes and for the continuing peaceful exploration of outer space.

Almost everyone agrees that one logical follow-on to Apollo would be more detailed exploration of the moon, perhaps even the establishment of a colony there. The chief reason for placing men on the lunar surface—a fact that is sometimes overshadowed by the dramatics of getting them there—is for man to carry out a scientific investigation of that body. Much can be learned from such an investigation, possibly answers to the origins of our solar system. The moon's chief resource may well turn out to be knowledge. We know it was formed about 4.5 billion years ago, but we do not know how, and this has been the subject of much speculation and thought for centuries. The moon may hold some invaluable answers to this, or at least some leading clues. The moon is a body whose surface has preserved the record of its history for a much longer period than has the face of the earth, and probably longer than the surfaces of Mars or Venus. Examination of the moon's origin may well carry man far back into the early history of the solar system, perhaps billions of years.

Kurt Debus says the best thing about the moon is not that we may find what we expect there, but the surprises, the unknowns that may be uncovered. "We may find water there," Debus says, "not water as we generally recognize it, but crystallized water. This can be processed, and with water we can support colonies."

There are other reasons for making lunar flights a cornerstone of future space operations. Once manned landings there have been mastered, the moon can be used as a stepping-stone for deeper penetrations in space. Dr. Debus calls the moon only a beacon in space, a marker for even bolder efforts.

A semipermanent colony on the lunar surface would condition man for the alien atmospheres he will have to survive on other planets. It will prepare him for other hostile environments. If it can be proven that man can sustain life on the lunar surface, then this will be a big step toward manned landings and the establishment of bases on neighboring planets such as Mars and Venus.

The moon's surface gravity is just one sixth that of earth's. To a man landing there for the first time, the mere act of walking will require careful adjustment. There will be less friction each time he presses his foot down. There are many other questions of adjustment that can only be answered once the astronauts have explored the lunar face. How, for instance, will the low gravity affect the heart, kidneys, and chemical balance? Only experience can tell. Yet, such knowledge will be essential to plan realistically for more distant ventures into space and for landings on other worlds.

To support life on the moon, we must also develop and master logistical problems. Supplies and crew replacements must be shuttled via rockets. Again, the development of this capability will aid our first interplanetary explorers.

For these and other reasons, total conquest of the moon seems a likely target following Apollo's intital landing there. The President's Science Advisory Committee, in their February, 1967, report, "The Space Program in the Post Apollo Period," recommended a sustained program of lunar exploration after the first Apollo landings, with one or two manned expeditions a year. Wernher von Braun has said, "To make a one-night stand on the moon and go there no more would be as senseless as building a railroad and then making only one trip from New York to Los Angeles."

Why go to the moon? Why colonize it? Undoubtedly, Columbus was asked the same questions about the New World as he set sail in the 15th century.

Chapter   *20*

ON TO INFINITY

While NASA's Saturn IB and Saturn V launch crews will be busy for some time to come at the Spaceport with Apollo and Apollo Applications, the unmanned launch operations team will also continue to be active in the immediate future. With the phasing out of the Atlas-Agena early in 1968, booster emphasis was concentrated on the ever-reliable Delta for lightweight projects, and Atlas-Centaur for larger payloads.

For the next two years at least, there will be about two unmanned spacecraft flights a month, but more and more will go from the Western Test Range in California, where a polar orbit can be more easily obtained. There will be Orbiting Solar Observatories, Pioneer-type Explorers, ESSA weather watchers, and Interplanetary Monitoring Platforms, among others. More business is expected from such organizations as the Communications Satellite Corporation, and ESRO— European Space Research Organization. NASA will direct the launches for such payloads, with the satellite owning agency acting as the customer.

Beyond these missions, it becomes obvious that a more powerful space booster will be needed for flights in the 1970's. Several serious studies have surveyed the field, and the most probable answer would be either a Titan III-C or a Saturn IB booster with a Centaur upper stage. There are pros and cons for either concept. Both vehicles could do the job. Titan would be less expensive, but there are counter-arguments for using Saturn, such as keeping a production line going for unmanned projects as well as for Apollo and AAP uses.

Drawing of an Interplanetary Monitoring Platform, designed to extend knowledge of solar-terrestrial relationships by means of a continuing study of radiation in interplanetary space. (Courtesy of NASA)

If Saturn is chosen, Centaur would be the third stage, atop the S-I and S-IVB stages. On Titan, Centaur would fit above the liquid-fueled core, and the solid booster strap-ons would also be employed. Either way, the cost of such a vehicle placing medium-weight payloads on target would be minimal compared to Saturn V.

NASA Administrator James E. Webb may have settled the question in September, 1967, when he said, "I think we will be working closely with the military services to determine the most effective use of the Titan III for NASA programs, with the Saturn IB to be completely phased out."

At present, the exact mission uses of such an uprated unmanned spacecraft launcher are somewhat hazy. But long-time lead planning is not the necessity it was with the larger Saturn V program. As one veteran NASA manager put it, "We can whip up a program and fly it in three years."

Satellites of the future that will be launched from the Spaceport will revolutionize our way of life. Already, great progressive strides are being made in the fields of communications, meteorology, navigation, astronomy, geophysics, and many others. More sophisticated communications satellites will one day make global television possible. Home TV sets will be tuned to programs originating in London, Bombay, or Manila. Satellites, acting as electronic ambassadors, will also provide service to areas not reached by other means of communication because of their isolation.

Kennedy Space Center Director Kurt Debus is fascinated by the rich fruits of space technology that are to be reaped. "Communications satellites have already proven their worth economically," he says. "But I think there is more far-reaching potential available—a means to end war, to end ignorance of peoples; to wipe out hostility and hatred. In the very near future, satellites will make it possible for everyone on earth to look into our backyard. The peoples of Africa, Asia, America and Europe will all be neighbors. Each of us will have a visual knowledge of the other's environment and society. The politics and religion of the other fellow will be better appreciated. Animosities will have a hard time to survive, and the future of earth and its civilizations will be assured."

Inexpensive transatlantic and transpacific telephone calls in unlimited number, day or night, are another benefit to be derived from future spacecraft. Educational television will guarantee that all the world's culture will be available to everyone. Medical men in remote regions will be able to keep in constant touch with their colleagues in more up-to-date centers. For example, a heart specialist in London may review, via satellite, an Australian patient's cardiograms and quickly diagnose the case and offer expert advice.

It is estimated there are 20,000 surface craft at all times on the Atlantic Ocean alone, and thousands of aircraft crowd the skies over much of the world. Navigation spacecraft circling the earth from orbit will greatly reduce the possibility of plane and ship collisions. By providing accurate position fixes, a system of such satellites could lower the separation distances between aircraft; automatically steer ships across oceans; warn high-flying supersonic jets of radiation dangers; guide craft around bad weather; monitor airplane systems for possible trouble; and pinpoint ditched planes or ships in distress.

Orbital photography, too, has great potential for useful exploitation. Color pictures taken by Gemini 4 astronauts Jim McDivitt and Ed White in 1965 showed possible undiscovered oil and mineral deposits in the United Arab Republic. Chromium, iron, manganese, phosphates, and other elements might be spotted by such future satellite prospecting.

The United States Department of the Interior has plans for an advanced series of Earth Resources Observation Satellites (EROS) that will help prevent natural disasters, provide knowledge valuable in agricultural planning, and help raise underdeveloped nations from poverty by locating unknown oil or valuable minerals. Secretary of Agriculture Orville Freeman has expressed keen interest in the feasibility of measuring forest growth, crop production, and water storage reserves to provide a sounder basis for forecasting food supply.

Urban problems of traffic and housing congestion, air and water pollution, and inadequate water supplies might also be overcome by EROS. The satellite would, in effect, provide a continuing surveillance of the earth's resources. Dr. Debus adds that a fleet of reconnaissance spacecraft could provide instantaneous data on the status of crops, crop diseases, inventories, and water supplies. He feels that eventually man will be able, for the first time, to plan and manage the feeding of the world's peoples.

Perhaps nowhere are the immediate benefit of unmanned satellites more quickly realized than in the science of meteorology. Weather, more than any other force of nature, has a direct, day-to-day influence on life on earth. An operational system of meteorological satellites can provide the world with daily observations of global weather conditions. "Such a system," said John F. Kennedy, "would be of inestimable commercial and scientific value, and the information it provides will be made freely available to all the nations of the earth."

It has been estimated that an improvement of only 10 percent in the accuracy of weather forecasting might result in the annual saving of billions of dollars for farmers, builders, airlines, shipping, the tourist trade, and many other enterprises the world over. Already, satellites have warned of the birth and direction of tornadoes, floods, blizzards, hurricanes and typhoons, and other forms of catastropic

In a striking photo taken by the crew of the Gemini 11 spacecraft, India and Ceylon are seen from a distance of 540 nautical miles above the earth's surface, looking northward, with the Bay of Bengal to the right and the Arabian Sea to the left. (NASA Photo)

weather. Preparations made following these early detections have saved billions of dollars and thousands of lives.

Scientific satellites and space probing craft will provide us with many long-range, though less easily measured advantages. They will help man unlock ageless mysteries of the universe, and in so doing, show him ways to improve his well-being on earth. With such missions, our knowledge of geoscience, physics, astronomy, and bioscience, among others, will be greatly enhanced.

With satellites, physicists, for instance, can better study the earth, its atmosphere and its magnetic field. They can also study the sun and its strange characteristics, and obtain a greater understanding of cosmic and other forms of radiation. Generally, scientists are offered a vast new laboratory in space, one that provides them an entire new perspective. Space research may also reveal answers to long-puzzling questions about the origin and composition of life.

Direct application of these research flights for material gain will not always be possible. Nevertheless, basic space research has a significance closely paralleling the missions that do bear more immediate fruition in measurable benefits. The fundamental storehouse of research information we acquire through scientific spacecraft will have a profound effect on the life of man in the future.

There are bright horizons in the future of aerospace medicine, too. Important studies have already been made on astronauts' behavior and performance under conditions of great stress, emotion, and fatigue. Discoveries have been made as to what type of man can best endure long periods of isolation and removal from his ordinary environment. The studies promise new developments in the treatment of heart and blood ailments, among others. Much of what doctors learn about men in space will have direct application, also, to man on earth.

Not to be overlooked in any discussion of potential returns from space programs to come are the advantages that can be gained by joining launch forces and sharing technologies here on earth. Today, the United States conducts a broad program of international cooperation in space research. Some 70 foreign countries, including Russia, participate with NASA in joint satellite projects, launching sounding rockets, ground based support of scientific spacecraft, participation in worldwide tracking networks, and programs of technical training, education, and visitor exchange. Such sharing of knowledge, equipment, and manpower can only help strengthen relationships. There are no international boundaries in space.

It is obvious today, even to shortsighted pessimists, that man is destined to explore the planets. It may not come for five years, maybe not for 10 years or more, but with the great on-rushing technological progress being made, such a goal is now inevitable.

Already, we have sent electronic eyes sweeping past the earth's two neighbors in the vast solar system: Venus and Mars. Much was learned from the Mariner interplanetary flyby series. Before man can venture to the planets, however, more must be learned about the characteristics and environment of foreign surfaces, and more studies must be made on how astronaut-explorers can hold up during extra long periods of space flight, perhaps up to two years or longer.

Some of the answers could come from the first flight of Voyager. This advanced scientific, 5,000-pound capsule may be launched atop a Saturn V in the 1970's. It would land on Mars several months later. It is hoped Voyager, or a similar unmanned project, will answer some of the following questions:

What does Mars look like?

What is its structure and composition?

What makes up its atmosphere?

What is its weather like?

How was the planet formed and what has been its evolution?

How does it relate to earth, and to other planets,

Is life present? If not, was it ever present, or might life be sustained there in the future?

Voyager would be the heaviest and most sophisticated unmanned spacecraft ever to be launched. It was based on sound technical knowledge gained from previous flight systems, namely Mariner (first successful planetary spacecraft); Lunar Orbiter (which pioneered in orbiting a distant celestial object); and the Orbiting Geophysical Observatory (which provided experience in space platforms designed to make sensitive scientific measurements from orbit). It will also use knowledge of the techniques of soft landing on a planet that were developed originally by Surveyor.

Some of the most elaborate and difficult prelaunch preparations ever would have to be made for Voyager, or whatever spacecraft is chosen for the interplanetary flight. This is due, essentially, to the fact that scientists are concerned about contaminating Mars with earthian germs. To solve this problem, the entire flight package will be sterilized before launch.

After launch from the Spaceport, Voyager would eventually reach an orbit around Mars. From this, suitable landing sites will be surveyed, possibly for several weeks. Then it will descend to the surface, all the while transmitting back to earth measurements of the atmospheric environment and television pictures of the Martian terrain.

Voyager's future became clouded, however, when Congress chopped it from NASA's 1968 budget request. It may be reprogrammed at a later date, when other governmental expenses are eased.

Preceding a landing on Mars will be another Mariner flyby mission, scheduled for 1969, similar to the successful one completed in 1965, that sent back the first close-up photos of the planet's surface.

A natural follow-on to sending robot spacecraft to Mars would be to have astronaut-scientists make the flight. The first manned interplanetary venture would probably not include a landing. Rather, it would be a flyby mission that would give the travelers from earth a close look at the planet's face.

When could such a fantastic voyage be made? "By the 1980's, we should be able to launch manned flybys of Mars and Venus," Kurt Debus has said. Mars is 150 times as far away from earth as the moon—35 million miles at its closest approach to us. A round trip to the moon, including a 24-hour stay on the surface, takes about seven or eight days. The Martian flight, without a landing, would keep astronauts in space for well over a year, perhaps closer to two years. This, of course, is based on present-day technologies. A major breakthrough, such as development and mastering of a nuclear rocket engine, which is entirely conceivable in the next decade or so, would reduce the flight time considerably.

Present planning hints the manned Mars expedition would not start from the Spaceport. Instead, the interplanetary spaceship would be assembled in earth orbit, from loads hauled up by shuttling cargo rockets. Following a successful flyby of the planet, a manned landing on Mars would be the next step. There are many scientific planners who believe this, too, can be accomplished in the 1980's, dependent upon technology advances and the priority such a mission would get as a national goal.

One of the most intriguing aspects of both unmanned and manned missions to Mars would be the search for evidence of life, past or present. Venus is closer to earth, but many scientists strongly believe its atmospheric conditions are too hostile to sustain life. If other extraterrestrial life exists in our solar system, it would probably be on Mars, and this is one of the overriding reasons for the presumed selection of that body as man's first target on interplanetary flights. No one is sure in what form life will be found, if, indeed, it will be found at all. There is also the very distinct possibility that man will not recognize life on Mars.

Venus may also be landed upon by man in the 1980's or later. And, after that, perhaps Jupiter, the solar system's largest body, will come within range. It is possible, in fact, NASA may send an unmanned spacecraft in the direction of the giant red planet sometime in the 1970's. It would be a 17- to 20-month journey.

Beyond that, it would be reasonable to assume man will explore all the planets within our solar system, and then, in decades or centuries to come, he will venture farther into other solar systems.

"From launch sites at the Spaceport, men will travel into the limitless region beyond earth's atmosphere where one day they will encounter other living things," Dr. Debus contends. "This prospect cannot be dismissed as metaphysical speculation. It is much more a mathematical certainty than were the early theories expounded by scientists and philosophers whose observations and discoveries made possible many of our activities today."

Debus quotes a theory about statistical speculation which states the earth is on the fringe of a galaxy of which we don't know the limits. We are way out in the suburbs. In the "metropolitan" area of our galaxy, there are millions of planets within the time span of human traveling distance from each other.

"The gist of this theory," he says, "is that Darwin's teachings are not unique to earth. That the same cell processes would occur on other planets. And, if so, given an inestimable number of galaxies, each with millions of planets, the chances of life evolving on some of them are pretty good. It may not be life as we know it, but it would probably be intelligent beings."

Dr. Debus is not alone in support of his views. Scientists increasingly are saying that life is probably not unique to earth, and that a superior order of it exists in star constellations elsewhere in the immensity of space. One prominent spokesman explained that a certain set of physical circumstances produced life on earth. Our galaxy, the Milky Way, has 100 billion stars like the sun. The number of earthlike planets in our galaxy alone could well be 100,000 by the most conservative estimate. And there are billions of galaxies in the universe besides ours. It is difficult to maintain a belief that earth's unique in supporting life, in the face of these numbers.

Debus believes our first contact with such life elsewhere in the universe will come through long-distance radio signals, perhaps traveling trillions of miles through space. He points out that there is a "dead" spot on the far side of the moon, a point where there is no radio or other signal interference from the earth or its ionosphere.

"I would like to set up sensitive radio receivers there to listen to the stars. Somebody . . . something . . . may be sending a message," he says.

There has been some debate—perhaps competition is a better word—over whether the emphasis in future space exploration should be on manned or unmanned flights. Certainly, both have their advantages. The biggest argument for sending machines into orbit and into the far reaches of our solar system is cost. Unmanned shots can be made for a small fraction of the expense it takes to send man into space. Less elaborate safety measures and savings in payload weight are two of the chief reasons for this. And, many scientists contend, the machines can be programmed to carry out virtually every function an astronaut could perform.

Debus disagrees. "I've been on the side of man since Day One. I know there are some very eminent people who say machines can do the job better and quicker and cheaper. But consider this: How do you program a machine to recognize the unknown? How does it test an unknown environment? Man has a unique quality for recognizing the unknown."

Proponents of manned flights agree. They claim that only man can effectively investigate the unknown, make correct decisions in unforseen circumstances, and use in full measure the opportunities which are opening up.

There is a strong case for both sides. Thus, it is a strong probability that the United States space programs will continue to maintain a broad balance of missions that will, as in the past, include both manned and unmanned flights. In many instances, machines will probe foreign surfaces on distant planets and report preliminary findings before man ventures forth.

Five, ten years from now, as far ahead as can be foreseen at this time, the Spaceport will be solidly engaged in the business of rocket launching of both men and machines to explore the universe and exploit the findings. The exact priority of missions—unmanned satellites on missions promising commercial benefits, unmanned probes into deep space, lunar colonies, earth orbital workshops, and manned interplanetary flights—has not been finally determined, nor has the level of operations. But wherever we go on this vast ocean of space, the main disembarking port in America for the foreseeable future will be the Kennedy Space Center.

There are enough programs now—current and planned ones that have been approved and are funded—to keep the Center operating until new long-range national goals are firmly established. These present programs include the military as well as NASA. Advanced versions of ballistic missiles are still actively tested at Cape Kennedy, and they will continue to be. The Air Force's Minuteman III, the Army's new Dragon minimissile, and the Navy's Poseidon, a sophisticated, next-generation Polaris, are but three such programs. Poseidon, incidentally, will have greater accuracy, double the warhead, and eight times the killing power of the Polaris A-3.

The Apollo program will carry into the next decade, and unmanned launch operations, both for NASA and for such other federal agencies as the Departments of the Interior and Commerce, are projected to continue for at least a few years into the future.

There will be, in the coming years, many new advances in rocketry. The Spaceport has been designed to facilitate them. Should gigantic rockets five and six times more powerful then Saturn V ever be needed, they could still be launched from the Florida site. Studies have shown that rockets on the order of 35 to 40 million pounds thrust could be safely accommodated at the Kennedy Center. Anything beyond that would have to be launched from an island, or from a Texas-tower-type rig at sea, primarily for safety reasons.

Chemically fueled rockets, however, are not ideally suited for manned flight beyond the moon. They use too much propellant, leaving little room for the spacecraft payload, including astronauts and their equipment, and scientific experiments.

The next likely major technological breakthrough will be the harnessing of nuclear power for a rocket's upper stage or stages. This, too, can be supported at KSC. Such a stage could double the thrust power of present-day chemically propelled systems. Thus payload weights could be doubled. The drawback here, again, is money. Development of nuclear powered rockets is expensive. How much and how fast do we want this technology for our space programs?

Far in the future are other, more exotic means of rocket propulsion, including the possibility of electrically powered vehicles, ion engines, and radioisotope electrostatic propulsion systems. Similar advances in spacecraft state-of-the-art can also be expected in years to come.

"We who are engaged in this business firmly believe it will bring rewards in knowledge and other dividends far exceeding the investment of money, materials, and brainpower," Kurt Debus says. "While no one can clearly foresee the implications, we can be certain of one thing. Space exploration will have profound effect upon life on earth. And if man is wise enough to apply his knowledge usefully, it will provide a technological structure to support a vastly improved social order. Man is embarking on a new, cosmic stage of existence of terrestrial civilization. The greater the area of outer space he conquers, the greater will be mankind's opportunities."

In future space ventures, man will be limited only by his own imagination. The onrush of technology will carry him in the years ahead as far and as fast as he wishes to travel. There will be delays, setbacks, and disasters. These are some of the expected side effects of progress. But man has a history of overcoming obstacles, of accomplishing the impossible. There are many goals that appear unreachable today. Time will disperse these illusions, and man will move forward on the ultimate frontier, which is ruled by vertical, not horizontal measurements. In the end, he will go as far as he wants to go. It will not be a lack of tools or techniques that halts him. That will only delay his march.

It will be man's own attitude that controls the pace of his space programs, not the temporary challenges imposed by the necessity of technical breakthroughs. The United States has a long heritage of ingenuity, daring, freedom, and the bold spirit of adventure. It would be contrary to our traditions not to continue forth.

"Space is the ocean of the future," John F. Kennedy said, "and as man sets forth on it, America can afford to be second to none."

No matter which specific goal we choose or what method we select to achieve it, the main point of departure from earth, the home harbor for this great new ocean, lies halfway down the Florida east coast, on a site that until 1950 was little more than virgin sand and scrubland. Many pages of history have already been written here at America's Spaceport. But the book is just beginning.

INDEX